AMAZING ADVENTURES

A SIEGE ENGINE PULP ROLEPLAYING GAME

BY: JASON VEY

EDITOR: Tim Burns

FRONT COVER: Peter Bradley **INTERIOR ART:** Peter Bradley, J.R. Flemming, Sarah "Dreamie" Walker, Jason Walton

SPECIAL THANKS TO Special thanks to Ross Thompson for outstanding suggestions and copy-editing, to Jason Alexander, for hooking me up in the first place, to Tim Stetzer for support and pointing out firearms errors, and to Robert Warren and Sonya Kirk for Latin translations, and to Juliette Gouirand-Vey for putting up with my crap every single day.

PLAYTESTERS: Ross Thompson, Juliette Gouirand-Vey, Ken Pittaway, Marya Pittaway, Bob Coligure, George Lurve, "Big" Tom Smith, Michael DeKlavon, Robert Warren, Michael Vogel, Eric Kiefer, Bill Charleroy, Tim Cooper, Taejas Kudva. This book is dedicated to the fans of Castles & Crusades, who kept the old-school spirit alive when there wasn't a lot of "new" going on in the old-school community, and to fans of pulp fiction everywhere.

1818 North Taylor, #143, Little Rock, AR, 72207
email: troll@trolllord.com
website: www.trolllord.com or
www.castlesandcrusades.com

Printed in the United States of America

TABLE OF CONTENTS

OGL

THE EYE OF THE GRAEAE:

AN ADVENTURE OF THE BROTHERHOOD OF WILLIAM ST. JOHN

Tennessee O'Malley was having a bad day.

In fact, 1938 was turning out to be the banner year of bad years. But today was especially bad.

He dove behind a platform supporting a gigantic statue in the ancient temple and crouched down as gunfire echoed its deafening roar throughout the chamber, bullets ricocheting off of the ancient statuary and walls. Chunks of stone and marble formed shrapnel as countless rounds of ammunition chipped the walls, and O'Malley gritted his teeth as he hunkered down.

"Damn!" he hissed, his heart sinking at the damage to the temple. "Someone is going to pay for this in spades."

The wall of gunfire lightened up, indicating that a few of his attackers had stopped to reload, and O'Malley risked a quick peek around the side of the huge, marble dais. A quick estimation revealed about a dozen goons, but Schwartzhofer was nowhere to be seen. One of the goons, he noted, held a Maschinenpistole 38 submachine gun. Two others were firing Mauser C98s, and the rest were using basic Mauser bolt-action rifles.

He slid back behind the pedestal, said a quick prayer (though he wasn't normally a religious man), and drew his Webley revolvers. Taking a deep breath, he leapt to his feet and leveled each pistol. Fire blazed from the barrels three times each, and all six rounds found their mark: the two with the automatic pistols went down, as did the submachine gunner. Then he dove into a forward roll as the remaining goons opened up again with their rifles, navigating the hail of bullets as though it were a gauntlet and holstering his pistols as he did so. He rolled three times through the deadly cloud of lead until his hands fell upon the sub machinegun. He came up to one knee and brought the weapon to bear.

His attackers were spread out, but he opened up, the weapon belching deadly fire like an angry dragon, and dropped four more in his first burst. As he spun to his left to take out the next group, he found himself facing down the barrels of their rifles. He pulled the trigger of his sub machinegun, and it clicked, the magazine expended.

O'Malley dropped the gun, closed his eyes and waited for the end, glad that at least he'd get to go out fighting with his boots on, like a man.

The rifles sounded their deadly report, but no searing pain ripped through his body. He opened one eye to see both men on their knees, their eyes wide with shock, smoke pouring from the barrels of their rifles, which were pointed up in the air. Each gushed blood from long, thin chest wounds. No further gunfire sounded, and he looked around to note the remaining goons were also dead.

Standing over the bodies of the two who had him dead to rights, was a woman with fiery red hair, a slender and athletic, but curvaceous, frame, and blazing blue eyes. She wore loose-fitting clothes of the kind favored by martial artists, dark blood red in color with a black belt, the scabbards for her swords hanging from her left hip, a Colt 1911 holstered at her right. He noted that she'd foregone her customary fur-trimmed cape due to the ungodly heat, though her knapsack full of such necessities as rope, lock picks, glass cutters, a grappling hook, and the like was still slung over her shoulders. Her face was hidden by a mask in the shape of a fox's head, but he knew all too well the beauty that mask hid.

She knelt down and wiped the blades of her matched saber and parrying dagger on the clothes of her victims, then re-sheathed the weapons. The blood of the two thugs pooled under them from the heart wounds she'd given each, straight through the back. A moment ago, there had been no sign of her, but years of training with Tibetan mystics had taught her certain useful tricks in that regard, and O'Malley knew that until she made her deadly strikes, she had clouded the minds of everyone in the room so that as far as they all were concerned, she simply wasn't there.

"Natalya," O'Malley said in a heavy Southern drawl. "Glad you could join the party, darlin'. I knew there was a reason I brought you along."

She lifted the mask to reveal a perfect oval of a face, with a small, rounded nose, softly shaped lips, and a slightly pointed chin, and regarded him with a stony gaze. When she spoke, her own Russian accent massaged the edges of her words. "You brought me along," she replied, "Because you needed someone adept in stealth and performance. You are uninjured?"

He nodded and grunted as he dragged himself to his feet. "Yeah, a few bumps and bruises, but I'll live. And as for your skills, don't forget burglary," he said. "I hadn't counted on that, but I reckon it looks like we'll need it."

She nodded. "Then Shwartzhofer has absconded with the gem?"

He stood and brushed off his khakis, then nodded. "German bastard ambushed me with his thugs, took the gem right out of my bag, then told them to kill me. Only by the grace of God I survived."

"I suggest," Natalya responded, "that when we find him, Shwartzhofer does not survive."

"Funny you should say that, darlin'," O'Malley said, "I was thinkin' the same thing."

He motioned to the temple's exit. "Probably best to get out of here before the authorities show up and we have to explain an illegal expedition to recover what could be one of the national treasures of Greece. At very least the diplomats would have a field day arguing whether it should be repatriated."

"Lead the way," Natalya said.

"Oh, no," O'Malley shot back. "You first. I don't want you at my back."

She shrugged. "I would point out that had I intended to betray you, I had a far better opportunity while you were under assault. But as you wish," she said, and sauntered out of the temple. O'Malley couldn't help but admire her figure and the lithe way in which she moved. With that grace and smoothness, and that flaming red hair, it was no wonder the papers had given her the moniker "The Fox." She'd even adopted the fox mask, which now hung from her belt, to play up the role. He wondered for a moment what her adoring public would do if they learned that the up-and-coming Hollywood starlet Natalya Abramova was the very high-class cat burglar that the Federal Bureau of Investigation had been tracking for three years.

He followed her out, and they began their descent along the rocky, rarely-traversed trails behind the temple rather than the tourist-designed road up. These trails led between jagged crags along tenuous footpaths and steep, loose ground. It was slow, dangerous going, but not nearly as dangerous as announcing their presence by going along the open route.

He looked at the sky; peeks of red were just starting to show on the horizon. The sun would be up, soon. His gaze then fell back to Natalya. Even after many adventures together, the archaeologist couldn't bring himself to trust her. When she'd been recruited to the Brotherhood of William St. John, it was on the idea that she was reformed and no longer in the crime game, but O'Malley wasn't so sure. The swords she carried, for example, looked an awful lot like a pair of weapons that were recently boosted from the Metropolitan Museum in New York—weapons that had once belonged to the Czar Nicholas I. He couldn't help but wonder why she'd continue on that path. She had a promising career in Hollywood, and the missions they went on for the Society should provide her plenty of opportunity to engage her lust for danger and excitement.

He shook his head. Perhaps she was just trying to keep her skills up. Or maybe she just couldn't resist taking what she wanted, if it wasn't available through legitimate channels. He resolved to have a talk with Mackie about Natalya's indiscretions later, but for now, he had to admit her skills had come in handy. More than that; she'd saved his life.

The two traveled in silence down the trail and stayed off of the main roads on their two-hour walk back to the Turkish town of Salihli. Since this expedition was to be kept quiet and O'Malley didn't anticipate the need for much digging, he'd thought it best to scout the place out with just him and the Fox before moving any further.

Of course, things never went as planned, and when they got there they'd found their adversaries already waiting for them. The only advantage O'Malley and Natalya had was that the ruins of Sardis were huge, and he and the Fox had split up to see if they couldn't locate the treasure before Schwartzhofer and his goons. O'Malley had managed to acquire the gem, only to lose it again when Schwartzhofer spotted and followed him.

This was definitely a bad day, and while he had his suspicions, without proper research he wasn't even really certain what the damn thing was, that Mackie had sent them to retrieve.

"Mackie," he grumbled.

Natalya turned to him and quirked an eyebrow. "Hmm?" she said.

"Nothin'," he replied, but reflected silently that when they got back to town, he and Mackie were going to have a sit down and she was going to get a piece of his mind.

O'Malley and Natalya rolled back into the boarding house in Ahmetli around mid-morning, to find Mackenzie "Mackie" Gleeson drinking coffee and waiting for them. She looked excited when they entered, her large, brown eyes sparkling. Somehow, even in this abominable heat and dust, she managed as always to look immaculate, her long, straight brown hair brushed through, her clothing neatly pressed and clean, her makeup perfectly applied. Her appearance was scandalous in this area of the world, but covering her face wasn't Mackie's style, and nor was combat, so she mostly stayed behind and flew the plane unless her contacts or money were needed. It was fortunate for them that they'd managed to find a boarding house in this town whose owner was open-minded to Western ways, though O'Malley figured they'd managed due to a combination of Mackie's silver-tongued ways and the fact that tourists likely came through here on a fairly regular basis.

"Is it there?" She asked. "Did you find it? Did you get it?"

Natalya walked past Mackie without a word and glided up the stairs to her room. O'Malley turned a chair around backwards and straddled it across the table from Mackie.

"No, fearless leader," he said, "We didn't."

Mackie clumped her mug down on the table and tilted her head, a look of disappointment and exasperation crossing her face. She motioned for their hostess to bring another cup of coffee for O'Malley and said, "What happened?"

The coffee arrived, steaming hot. O'Malley marveled at the irony of a hot drink when the temperature outside wasn't exactly what one would call "comfortable," but lifted the cup and took a drink of the strong liquid. He wiped the back of his hand across his mouth and said, "Schwartzhofer happened. I had it in my hand, and then," he shrugged, "then it was in his hand."

Mackie's mouth drew into a thin line. "He can't be allowed to have that," she said.

He sat back. "I figured you were going to say that. What the hell is that thing, Mackie? Why's it so important, aside from being more valuable than half the artifacts in the Met's collection?"

She shook her head. "Need to know, Ten. You know how it works." She took another drink of her coffee. "Truth be told, I'm not even sure myself. Marie just said it's powerful and we need to get it back to her in New Orleans so she can evaluate it for danger."

O'Malley lit up a cigarette. "You know, if you'd told me that six years ago I'd have dismissed you for a fool. But after what we fought in South America..." he shuddered.

Mackie nodded. "We've been through a lot."

O'Malley shot a glance at the stairs, leaned forward and lowered his voice. "Speaking of the Met," he said, "You notice the sword and dagger Natalya's sporting these days?"

Mackie's eyes widened. "You're not saying...?"

He nodded and took a draw on his smoke. "Not many as would notice that outside of an archaeologist or historian," he said. "Fortunately, I'm both."

Mackie looked past O'Malley for a moment, her eyes glazing over as they did when she was deep in thought. At length, she sighed and said, "We'll have to keep an eye on her, then. We need her skills, Ten, and I do believe that her heart is with us and what we do."

"And what happens when she decides that some treasure we recover to keep it out of the wrong hands, is better served with one of her fences and in her bank account? What then?"

Mackie shook her head. "It won't go that way. Trust me."

He took a drag on his smoke, and another swig of coffee. "You're the boss."

"So what next?" Mackie said.

O'Malley scratched at the stubble on his chin and thought for a minute. "Schwartzhofer is going to light out for Germany as quick as he can," he said. "Problem is, we got no clue where he's holed up in the meanwhile. And he's got at least a few hours head start on us."

Natalya emerged into the room, dressed in what appeared to be a traditional Muslim-style burqa, but without the head or face cover common to women of the area. She took a seat at the table and crossed her legs.

"I could not help but overhear," Natalya said. "If I may, the German will wish to take unregistered transport. He will not wish attention to be drawn, as he will not like to have us find him, or any other adversaries he may have acquired."

Mackie nodded. "My family has friends in this area," she said. "It looks like I'm up to bat."

* * *

"Altan!" Mackie said, her arms wide to draw her old friend into a tight embrace. "It's wonderful to see you."

Altan Gulden returned the embrace, then drew back to hold Mackie at arm's length as two regarded each other. Altan was a handsome man, with dark, piercing eyes, a smooth-shaven face, sharp features and a hawk-like nose. He wore a white suit with a mandarin collar, and his raven-black hair was parted in the center, close-cropped in the back, but hung down past his eyebrows in the front.

Finally, he gave Mackie's arms a familiar squeeze, then leaned in and kissed her on each cheek. "Mackenzie," he said. "It has been too long. We were children when last we met! If I may say so, you look lovely."

She nodded. "Thank you, Altan. You look quite handsome yourself." She gestured to O'Malley. "This is my associate, Tennessee O'Malley."

Altan quirked an eyebrow. "The noted archaeologist?"

O'Malley tipped his hat and gave a nod. "The same. I'm honored to meet you."

"Please," Altan said. "The honor is mine. But the sun is high and it is quite warm. Let us step inside where we can talk in a bit more comfort."

Altan beckoned a valet to park Mackie and O'Malley's Jeep, then turned without further comment and led the two into his rather expansive villa. Inside, the classical Grecian structure was designed to allow for the maximum air flow, bringing the temperature down to a near-comfortable level. The trio walked through a lavish outdoor courtyard with an impressive garden, fountains and statuary that O'Malley was certain was of original vintage, and not copied. The adventurer also noted men with guns posted at several points along their journey.

"Excuse me, Mr. Gulden?" he said.

"Doctor," came the reply.

"I'm sorry?"

"Doctor. I have a doctorate from Yale University. But you may call me Altan."

"My apologies. I studied at Northwestern, myself. Not so posh as Yale."

Altan shrugged. "A doctorate is a doctorate. But you had a question?"

"Yeah. What's with the armed guards?"

"These are dangerous times, Dr. O'Malley. The Germans overrun this entire area of the world. I prefer to keep my home safe, even if it is a false sense of security. I've no illusions, you see, that my security could overcome the German army, but they keep lesser threats out; insurgents and the like."

"Gotcha. And you call me O'Malley." He shot a pointed look at Mackie. "All my friends do."

"Indeed."

Altan led Mackie and O'Malley to a shaded table across the courtyard, which had already been spread with a selection of fresh fruits and a pitcher of tea, three glasses of which had already been filled and set out. He bade his guests sit, then took a seat himself. After helping himself to a slice of apple, the Turkish man sat back and regarded his guests. Even in the shade, his white suit seemed to gleam brightly, and there was something in his sharp eyes, O'Malley thought, that somehow belied the friendly smile on his lips.

"Now," he said, "to business. What brings you after all these years to Ahmetli? Certainly, I assume, not the climate, and this is a long way to travel for a social visit, even for old friends such as us."

Mackie nodded. "You're right, I'm afraid. We are, in fact, tracking a German who has something very important of ours in his possession. We need to get it back."

Altan nodded. "I see. And you believe, somehow, that I would have information on his whereabouts?"

Mackie held up her hand. "I don't mean to offend you, Altan. It's just that you were a man of some influence in these parts–I presume this is still the case."

Altan spread his hands in a gesture of acquiescence.

"We figure," O'Malley cut in, "That the German would've had to come through here on his way to Izmir, where he'd have the best chance to catch a quick flight back to the fatherland. We thought you might've heard something."

Altan cracked a half-smile and looked at O'Malley. "You speak of your rival archaeologist, Dr. Hans Schwartzhofer."

O'Malley nodded. "No point in denial. So he's been through here?"

Altan took a drink and observed his glass. "Have you had our tea? I am of the opinion that Turkish tea is the best in the world." He gestured to Mackie and O'Malley's glasses. "Please. I'm sure the heat has made you thirsty and hungry. Help yourselves."

O'Malley opened his mouth to retort, but Mackie kicked him under the table, then lifted her glass. "Of course," she said. "How rude of us not to partake of your hospitality." She took a long drink, then nodded her appreciation.

Grudgingly, O'Malley followed suit. He had to admit, the tea was good, but he had little patience for the niceties of polite society. Still, he could play the game when he had to.

Mackie was the next one to speak up. "Altan, I do apologize, but our situation is rather urgent. Could you please give us any information you have? I would consider it a great personal favor to my family."

Altan took another drink, placed the glass in front of him, and folded his hands. "Very well, then. Dr. Schwartzhofer did pass through here, earlier today, on his way to Izmir. It is said that he was in quite a hurry. He did not linger, and he

had an entourage of hired help, as well as two Nazi officials, both of whom dressed in black, and had on their arms bands with that crooked cross of theirs. They wore, I am told, pins on their lapels that resembled dual lightning bolts."

O'Malley and Mackie, looked at each other and said, simultaneously, "He's working with the SS."

For some reason this struck them both as inexplicably funny and they giggled like school children. Altan watched them, his face a mask of calm. After a few minutes, the laughter died down and Mackie wiped the sweat from her forehead. "Wow," she said. "I'm feeling a little lightheaded."

Altan smiled. "It must be the heat."

"Must be," Mackie said, but the words came thick and she found them hard to pronounce.

"No," O'Malley said. "Somethin's wrong. I feel..." he tried to stand, then fell to his knees. As he tried to stand, he found himself gazing into the glass of tea. He looked at Altan as realization dawned. "You son of a bitch," he said. "What did you..."

O'Malley and Mackie both collapsed.

* * *

Waking up was like swimming through tar. Even when she came to, Mackie wasn't certain she was awake. Her head felt thick and heavy, her mouth felt dry and fat, and the room in which she sat was dark. As her eyes adjusted and the fog lifted, she came to realize that she couldn't move her arms or legs. She was seated, and somehow bound to the chair.

She cast her gaze around and saw, dimly, the shape of another seated person not very far away. Though she couldn't make out his features, she deduced from the familiar shape and stature that it was likely O'Malley.

"Ten!" she stage-whispered. "Ten, are you awake?"

An incoherent mumbling was her only response.

"Ten, come on! Wake up!"

She heard his lips smack a few times in the dark, then: "Where the hell are we? I'm gonna kill that son of a bitch."

"I'm not sure," she said. "A basement, maybe? You also tied down?"

A few grunts followed. "Yeah. Yeah, I'm hog-tied, too."

"Now what?"

"Now we wait."

Time passed slowly in the dark. Neither O'Malley nor Mackie had much to say, so both sat and stewed in silence. A few minutes passed before Mackie spoke up.

"Ten?"

"Yeah."

"I lied, earlier. I do know what we're after."

"Ya don't say. I never would've guessed. Also, I already figured it out. It's the eye of the *Graeae*."

"The who, now?"

"The Graeae. Roughly translated, 'Grey Witches.'"

He could sense her nod in the darkness. "The blind women that Perseus encountered on his quest to kill Medusa."

"It belongs with the Greek government. It's from their mythology, it should be on display in their national museum, not in someone's private collection."

"Marie says it's dangerous."

"To Hell with what Marie Laveau says! That witch probably wants it for herself!"

She could hear his chair shifting on the floor. "What are you doing?"

"Working on something. Anyway, I know about the eye. It's supposed to be the first of the treasures of Perseus, and it's said that when you get them together, aside from the powers each one can give you, that they can lead you to the head of Medusa."

"Imagine what would happen if Hitler got hold of those things, Ten. That's why we can't let it get back to Germany, or let it sit in some museum waiting for someone to steal it."

He huffed in the darkness. It was a sound of resignation that went against most of his instincts. "I know. Just hold on a second. If I can...there! My hand is free."

He worked for a minute more and announced, "I'm loose. Give me a minute and I'll..."

The door opened, and the light shining in blinded both of them. O'Malley put his hands behind his back and sat up straight, praying whoever it was hadn't seen him free. A figure entered and stood regarding them for a second, a black silhouette against the sunlight. When the figure spoke, it was with Altan's voice.

"My dear Mackie," he said, "I do apologize for this, but you must understand I had little choice."

She squinted in an effort to see him beyond what was silhouetted in the light. "You drugged me!" she said.

Altan entered the room, his hands folded behind his back. "I did," he said. "They wanted me to kill you outright, but I couldn't bring myself to commit such an act to a childhood friend."

"I'm flattered," she deadpanned.

He walked to a corner of the room to grab an empty chair for himself. This he pulled in front of the two and sat. He leaned forward, hands folded in his lap. "I wish I had a better excuse," he said. "What I told you about them was true, mostly. They did come here earlier today, and they were as I described. What I failed to mention was that they were still here, hiding. I have staff, family, and friends to think of, Mackie. I had to make a choice."

"And what about me, Altan? I'm a friend, too."

He nodded. "Which is why I didn't kill you. I told them I did. Told them you were poisoned, and the drug did slow your vitals so that at a cursory examination, you appeared dead. Thank Allah they had no doctors with them."

"How long?" O'Malley said.

Altan turned to regard the rugged adventurer. O'Malley pushed. "Come on, Altan, how long were we out? And what are you going to do with us?"

"A few hours," Altan said. "They have long since departed. And I cannot let you go to follow them, that much is certain. They would send others back, and visit an unholy vengeance upon my house."

"So what, then?" Mackie said. "You can't just keep us here."

"No," he said. "No, I cannot. This leaves me in a quandary. I thought of putting you on a plane back to America, but this would only result in you continuing your crusade against Schwartzhofer, which would put me back in the same position. I need to think on what to do."

"You're a damned fool, Altan," O'Malley said. "Do you have any idea what they're carrying? How dangerous it is?"

"No," Altan said simply. "Do you?"

O'Malley blinked twice and stammered, then said, "As a matter of fact, I do. And it's bad!"

Altan smiled. He stood and brushed off his pants. "I will have food sent. At this time, your hands will be untied, but the door will be barred from the outside." He nodded and turned back to Mackie. "I am sorry, Mackenzie. I truly am."

"Yeah," Mackie said. "So am I."

He turned to leave the room. At that moment, O'Malley sprang from the chair and charged. He barreled Altan to the ground, and there was a *CRACK!* as Altan's head hit the floor.

Two armed guards swung into the room. O'Malley came to his feet, the palm of his open hand hitting the chin of the nearest guard, whose head snapped back. O'Malley grabbed the guard's rifle and twisted clockwise, forcing the weapon free while swinging the first guard around so that he was between O'Malley and the second.

The second guard, unable to bring his weapon effectively to bear, cried for help and maneuvered into the room. Out of the corner of his eye, O'Malley could see several other guards running towards the building from other areas of the compound. He also saw something else–a faint blur of movement that something in his mind refused to believe was there, and he knew if he looked directly at it, he'd see nothing.

Natalya. She was here.

O'Malley cracked the first guard alongside the head with the butt of the rifle, and the guard went senseless. O'Malley took a bead on the second guard, just as the guard brought his rifle to bear on Mackie.

"I'll kill her!" the guard cried in broken English. "Drop rifle, or I kill her!"

"No, you won't," O'Malley said, and pulled the trigger. The rifle cracked, and the guard fell to the floor.

The sounds of a scuffle erupted outside. Guns fired, and men gurgled their death rattle.

O'Malley turned to look, and there was Natalya, engaged in a battle with two guards. The other two down, cut from navel to throat, but when she'd made the kill, she'd revealed herself. He took aim and fired again, felling one of her two foes as she drove her dagger through the forearm of the second, who dropped his rifle and staggered back before pulling a sword with his good arm.

O'Malley nodded, confident that the Fox could handle him. "I like those odds much better," he said, then turned back to Mackie.

"Well," O'Malley said, "That's some friend you got there, darlin'."

"Quiet, you," she said. "I've known him since I was a little girl. How could I have seen that coming?"

"Didn't say you could. It's still a bitch."

Natalya appeared at his side. "Thank goodness," she said.

"You're late," O'Malley replied. "You were supposed to be following us."

"And I do apologize. This compound is huge and by the time I arrived, you were already drugged. I had to wait for him to come to you, to find you."

Mackie looked dumbfounded. O'Malley shrugged. "The guy was your friend, not mine. I figured some backup from the Fox, here, couldn't hurt."

She moved to Mackie and worked to free her. O'Malley looked over his shoulder to make sure there were no more guards coming. "Better hurry up with those bonds, darlin'. I reckon we've only got a few minutes at most before those gunshots bring the rest of the compound down on us."

"Indeed," she muttered. "And thank you. For the aid out there."

He shrugged. "You pulled my bacon out of the fire earlier. We're even."

The ropes came free and Mackie stood, stretching the stiffness from her limbs.

"Come," Natalya urged. "We must go, quickly. Izmir is but two hours from here. They may already be there, but Nazis or no, it will likely take them some time to charter an aircraft when they arrive. If we hurry we may still have time to catch them."

"Somehow I doubt it," Mackie said. "If Schwartzhofer is working with the SS, I can almost guarantee they radioed ahead for a plane to be fueled and ready for takeoff. If they filed a flight plan, I can probably follow them, but dollars to doughnuts they're headed for Berlin. Anyone got any ideas how an American girl is supposed to land a plane in Berlin?"

"We'll think of something," O'Malley said. "Let's get gone."

He bent to search the guards, coming up with several stripper clips' worth of spare ammunition, and two Lugers with a couple of spare magazines each. He also stripped the guards of their belts and holsters, tucking the Lugers safely in.

"Burns my behind, having to use these Nazi guns," he said, "But Lord knows what Mackie's buddy did with my Webleys. I'll be putting in a requisition to have those replaced."

"Duly noted," Mackie said, moving into the compound and helping herself to a Luger and a couple spare magazines as well. "Now let's get out of here." She cast one last glance at Altan, laying senseless on the stone floor, and couldn't help but pray that he'd be okay.

* * *

The trip to Izmir was without incident–the group's jeep was still where they'd left it, and two hours later, they found themselves in the midst of a bustling port city on the shores of the Aegean Sea. Mackie directed them to head straight for the airfields, where she'd hangared her personal Curtiss T-32 Condor, the plane which had gotten them to Turkey in the first place. She wanted, she said, to check on the plane and get it fueled and ready to go at a moment's notice. Once that was complete, the plan was for her to contact via telegraph some friends she had working behind the lines in Germany for Special Operations Executive, a British underground spy and resistance agency. She believed if Schwartzhofer did make it to Germany, her friends would be able to let them know, and possibly slow him down (or even stop him) so that they could recover the gem. It was a long shot, she said, but the best shot they had.

O'Malley and Natalya hung back while Mackie talked with the grounds crew, giving instructions for her aircraft to be taxied out of the hangar, fueled, and prepped for takeoff. O'Malley noticed money change hands. Within minutes, the aircraft was rolling out of the hangar and onto the tarmac. As Mackie moved forward to examine the plane, Natalya tugged on O'Malley's sleeve, and she pointed off into the crowd. O'Malley turned his gaze where she indicated and saw nothing.

"What's the problem?" he asked.

"There is a man there, dressed in a gray suit, who has been observing us since we arrived."

O'Malley scanned the crowd again and spotted the man Natalya indicated. The man was reading a newspaper...far too obviously.

"Something's not right," he said.

Natalya nodded. "I have had a creeping feeling since we arrived. There is danger here, something..." her eyes went wide and she dashed across the tarmac. "Mackie!" she cried. "Mackie, get away!"

Mackie turned to see Natalya and didn't hesitate–after enough adventures together she'd learned to trust the Fox's uncanny senses. She ran towards Natalya, and met the girl halfway...

...just as one of the grounds crew drew a Luger and fired. Natalya leapt and bore Mackie to the ground, the bullet barely missing both women, who were thrown flat, Mackie on her back and Natalya on top of her. Then the hail gunfire started, apparently from everywhere. A bullet whizzed past O'Malley's ear, close enough for him to feel the sting as it flew by. He drew his guns and dove for cover, scanning for the shooter.

Halfway between him and the wrecked aircraft, Mackie and Natalya were crawling for cover as fast as they could. He breathed just a little easier as they made it behind a wall of crates about thirty feet from where he crouched. He picked out a relatively safe route to the women and made a dash for it. Another bullet tore through his leather jacket, grazing his arm, but he managed to maintain his hold on both Lugers and continued, making it to where Mackie and Natalya huddled.

"Everyone okay?" he cried over the cacophony. Mackie and Natalya both nodded.

"This day just gets better and better!" he continued. "Anyone catch how many there are, and where?"

"We can't even get to my plane!" Mackie said. "There'd better not be any damage; I've already lost one this year and this is getting expensive!"

"Yeah, well, maybe we oughtta avoid the Middle East till this whole war thing clears itself up," O'Malley said. "Not that it matters none right this minute!"

He took a deep breath. "I'm going to poke my head up and have a look. Get ready to cover me." Guns drawn, he popped up and fired at the first glint of metal he saw. A couple seconds later, he sank back down, panting. "Sweet Jesus," he said. "They're everywhere! Um...I don't know what to do."

He popped up, squeezed off a few shots, then ducked back down again. "I think I got a couple," he said. "We're less outnumbered, now."

Natalya's face was grim. She put on her mask and said, "Cover me," then was just gone.

"Wonderful," O'Malley said. "How the Hell do I cover a woman I can't even see?"

Mackie ducked around the side of the crates and squeezed off a couple shots of her own. "It's the way she works," she said. "Just watch out of the corner of your eye."

O'Malley slid a couple of crates apart, just a crack, so that he could get a line of fire, and watched. Seconds later, two of their assailants gurgled and went down, and the Fox was plainly visible standing behind them. Several others swung their guns towards her, and she saluted them. O'Malley squeezed off four shots, and two went down. Natalya vanished again before the others could pull their triggers.

"Damn," O'Malley said. "She's good, I'll give her that. If she can keep this up, we may get out of this alive."

When Mackie didn't answer, he said, "What, no comment? Mackie?" and turned to see her being held by a muscular Turk who had his hand over her mouth, and a C98 at her temple.

"Guns down!" the Turk barked. O'Malley did as instructed, dropping the guns to the ground.

"Hands up! Stand!"

He folded his hands behind his head and stood up. "Don't you hurt her," he warned.

Then, a familiar voice reached his ears from the Tarmac beyond. "That is up to you, Doctor O'Malley," it said with a heavy German accent. O'Malley turned, a scowl on his face, towards the source of the voice, where a middle-aged man with white hair, a bulbous nose, and a slight paunch stood, his hands wide, a Luger clutched in one fist.

"Schwartzhofer," O'Malley spat. "I reckoned you to be long for Germany by now."

Schwartzhofer clicked his tongue and shook his head, "And that, *herr* O'Malley, is your chiefest weakness. You always assume the obvious path. No, I knew you would come here after me. I knew you would chase me. I am not foolish enough to think that either Altan would keep his word to me, or that you would not overcome him. He will pay in time, but in the meanwhile, I set this trap for you. Do you like it? A great show, is it not?"

He spun and leveled his gun on an apparently empty area. "And you," he said, "can cease your tricks. You are not the only one who has training in the mental disciplines."

In an instant, the Fox was visible to all present. Schwartzhofer clapped his hands in glee as his men—at least thirty robed Turkish and Arabic mercenaries—kept their guns trained on the heroes, and took a few cautious steps towards the Russian. "So it is the infamous Fox, is it not? I wonder what the people of your nation would do if a German captured you and was the one to expose your secret? Shall we find out who you are? I admit, I have always been curious."

To her credit, Natalya kept silent, though it was clear to O'Malley she was on a hair trigger. Her eyes darted around at the various gun-toting goons, as though seeking either escape or victim. She could blow at any minute.

"Fox!" he cried. "Stand down. You can't help Mackie this way!"

She hesitated, trembling, then threw her swords down, and dropped her gun belt to the ground as well. One of the mercenaries crept forward, swept up the weapons, and moved to present them to Schwartzhofer, who took the swords and admired them.

"Incredible craftsmanship," he said. "Unless I am mistaken, you liberated these from the New York Metropolitan museum, did you not? The swords of the Czar Nicholas I. And to think I am so lucky as to hold them in my hand. Edged in silver, you know."

"What do you want, Schwartzhofer?" O'Malley said. "Spit it out, already."

"To *beat you,* Doctor O'Malley!" Schwartzhofer said. "And I have! Oh, you can forget about the gem. I don't even have it with me—I am far from a fool."

"Sent it back to the Fatherland already, with those SS goons?"

Schwartzhofer strode across the tarmac and backhanded O'Malley across the face. "Never speak ill of the great work the *Schutzstaffel* do for the glory of Germany! You Americans once claimed Manifest Destiny to conquer a continent. We shall conquer a world–it is already said the hand of God protects the *Führer*–now he will have the treasures of Perseus as well, and no army on Earth will stand against him!"

O'Malley spat a bright red gob on the ground, and grinned. "You know, Schwartzhofer, I always knew you were a little nuts, but I never figured you for buying into that Nancy-boy mystic mumbo-jumbo. And let's be real–you're no supporter of the *Reich*. You'd sell your own grandmother for enough green. Hitler's no different to you than any other employer."

Schwartzhofer raised his hand to strike again, then caught himself, and pointed at O'Malley, then began to laugh.

"You have me," he said. "You do know me too well. The SS are on their way back to Germany, and they do believe they bear the gem with them." He turned away and walked back to the tarmac. "For my part, I have a gigantic pile of money, with which I shall abscond before they even have a chance to evaluate the fake for what it is. I have no desire for the power and glory of Germany. My own power and glory, on the other hand..." he turned back to O'Malley. "Think of it, O'Malley! We could hunt down the Treasures of Perseus! We could recover the head of Medusa, and then it would be *we* who are unstoppable! What do you say, my old friend?"

"I ain't even going to justify that with a response," O'Malley said.

Schwartzhofer shrugged again. "As you wish," he said. "But since I cannot have you simply chasing me down, either..."

He pointed his gun and fired. Mackie let out a yelp, and both she and the Turk holding her fell to the ground. "Sich zurückziehen!" he cried, and his men scattered as Schwartzhofer disappeared behind a building.

"Mackie!" O'Malley cried, and ran to the woman, who was breathing, but shallow and with difficulty.

She coughed, and blood spattered on her lips. She tried to crack a smile, and whispered, "Ow. That's going to leave a scar, isn't it?"

The Turk who was holding her tried to drag himself away. O'Malley turned Mackie's face away, shielded her ears, and shot him in the head. Then he turned back to his friend.

"Oh, God, Ten," she said. "It hurts. It hurts really bad."

"It's okay, Mackie," he said. "It's gonna be okay. We're going to get you a doctor." He lifted his head and cried, "Help me! Somebody help me!"

She gripped his shirt. "Natalya," she said. "Where's Natalya?"

"I am here," the Russian woman said, kneeling beside the two. She looked at O'Malley. "Is it bad?"

"I don't know!" he said. "I don't know, I'm not a doctor! Somebody get some help!"

Natalya gripped his shoulder and said, "Do you speak Turkish? Try calling out in Turkish."

He swallowed and said, "Right. Turkish, I'm not thinking."

He stood and called out again, in Turkish, and caught the attention of a police officer who had just arrived on the scene. Minutes later, Mackie was in the back of an ambulance and en route to the local hospital. He looked at Natalya. "Let's get to the Jeep. I want to make sure she gets there safely. Then I'm going to find Schwartzhofer and put him down like a rabid dog."

* * *

It didn't take much questioning–even without Mackie's contacts–to track the German down; he had become so overconfident that he wasn't exactly being subtle. Still, it took time, and night lay like a blanket over Izmir as Natalya and O'Malley approached the villa outside the city where Schwartzhofer had holed up. The building was large, fenced-in, and was of vaguely rectangular shape, with rounded corners, a sort of turret at the front left, and a flat roof. There were porches on the ground and second floors, supported by pillars, and the place was crawling with armed guards.

"Damn," O'Malley whispered. "He ain't makin' this easy."

It was said it was the home of a German diplomat, which was both a benefit and a drawback to the heroes. It meant that it'd be hard to get into the place, but it also meant that Schwartzhofer wouldn't be advertising that he still had the gem.

The Fox scanned the grounds for a moment and said, "This should not be a great problem. I have broken into more secured places than this."

"Yeah," O'Malley grunted. "The Met comes to mind."

Natalya didn't respond, but he could almost sense her smiling behind her mask. She nodded for O'Malley to follow her and moved off into the shadows. Knowing this was her area of expertise, O'Malley lit out behind her.

For three hours they circled the complex, studying the movements of the guards and their numbers, until Natalya was satisfied, and then, at her signal, the two dashed towards the fence and Natalya leapt over while O'Malley clambered up and over as fast as he could. From there, they made for a portion of the villa's outer wall where there was a gap in the security. No alarm rose.

"So far, so good," whispered O'Malley.

Swiftly, the Fox drew from her knapsack a rope and grappling hook, which she hurled up the wall with razor precision. The hook caught, and she urged O'Malley up. The process was quick, and before long, both were on the roof of the building, the hook and rope coiled back within Natalya's pack. She surveyed the area again to be sure they hadn't been seen, and once satisfied, gestured once more for O'Malley to follow her. The two settled in to crouch at the center of the roof, and Natalya nodded.

"They will not see us here," she said, "and as there seems to be no easy roof access, we should not encounter any guards."

"Fair enough," O'Malley said. "What are you thinking?"

"If Schwartzhofer is a guest here, his room will be somewhere on the second floor. This building is not as large as some villas I have seen. It should not take long to locate the room, but we will need to take care not to be seen."

"Tell me something I don't know," O'Malley said.

"Remain here," Natalya instructed. "I will find the location of his room."

O'Malley barely had time to acknowledge the order before she pulled her trick and vanished into the night. After a few moments she reappeared in front of him with news that she'd found the room.

"He appears to be sleeping within," she said, "But something does not feel right."

O'Malley nodded. "Well, darlin', the way I see it, we don't have much choice but to take the chance. Otherwise we sit up here all night or leave without the prize, and that don't do nobody any good but Schwartzhofer."

"I do not disagree," she said, "but it seems strange, does it not, that our adversary would be so open about where he is?"

O'Malley shrugged. "He's always been overconfident. But you're right. It does smack of a trap. What do you suggest?"

"As you say," Natalya replied, "We have few options. I merely suggest caution."

She moved off towards the far right corner of the house, O'Malley close behind. After scanning the ground for guards, she pulled herself down and swung onto the balcony, allowing O'Malley to see how she accomplished the task. Though no acrobat, the rugged archaeologist managed the feat with some difficulty, and landed unseen next to her.

"Not bad," she remarked, and moved to the door. She tested the handle to find it locked, and produced a set of lock picks from her pack, with which she went to work. A minute later, a barely audible click sounded, and the door swung open on softly creaking hinges. The two crept into the room where Schwartzhofer snored, in deep sleep.

This is too easy, O'Malley mouthed, and Natalya nodded in response. O'Malley leveled his pistol at the sleeping form, but Natalya caught his wrist and shook her head. She was right, he knew; as badly as he wanted revenge, this wasn't the time, place or way. Not only would it draw attention, he couldn't just kill a man in cold blood while he slept, no matter who it might be. That wasn't the way the Society did business. His hand shook for a moment, his mouth drawn into a tight line, and then he lowered the gun back into its holster.

The two searched the room top to bottom with little success—Natalya found her swords, which she belted on, but the gem was nowhere to be seen. Then, at last, Natalya sighed and looked pointedly at the bed upon which Schwartzhofer still slumbered. O'Malley's face fell and his expression alone said, "You've got to be joking."

The Fox glided forward, took a knee, and wormed her arm between the mattress and box springs, watching Schwartzhofer intently the entire time. After what seemed like an eternity, and with no small amount of difficulty, she pulled her arm forth, clutching in her hands a small box, a bit larger than a man's fist, plain in decoration with a padlock fastening it shut. This she placed on the floor and examined top to bottom. When she was satisfied, she again inserted her lock picks into the mechanism. The lock clicked, and there was a sound not unlike a quiet whistle. Natalya looked surprised, and lifted her hand to note a needle stuck in her wrist.

She swooned; O'Malley ran to catch her before she slumped to the floor. He cast a glance over his shoulder—the box was open and sitting at its center was what appeared to be an enormous, rough cut but perfectly clear sapphire. He pocketed the gem, then placed Natalya's arm around his shoulders.

"Can't make anything easy, can you, darlin'?" he whispered, and made back for the porch.

That was when the light clicked on and he turned, his gun leaping into his hand, to discover Schwartzhofer, his own gun trained on O'Malley and Natalya.

"Please," Schwartzhofer said. "The gem, if you don't mind."

"Or what?" O'Malley said. "You'll shoot us? It'd draw the house security here in seconds, and I'm guessing you don't want your diplomat buddy knowing you still got the Eye."

"True," Schwartzhofer said, "Though killing two intruders intent on assassinating me is something else entirely. The Gem is still in your pocket. Removing it from your corpse will be an easy task. If you shoot, on the other hand, well, you see where that leaves you. You have a choice, Doctor O'Malley. Give me the Eye and surrender. I will turn you over to the

authorities and you'll spend the gods only know how long in prison. Perhaps you will be executed. If you do not, you will certainly die here."

O'Malley started to lower his gun, then frowned and said, "Nah, to Hell with it," raised and fired.

But Schwartzhofer was nowhere to be seen.

"Dammit!" O'Malley cursed, scanning the room. He looked to Natalya, who was barely hanging on to consciousness. "Don't you die on me, girl," he said. "Come on; we have to get moving!"

Lifting her onto the roof was no longer an option–this was going to have to go down the hard way. He guided her out into the hall, where he fired off four shots in quick succession, dropping two guards. He leaned over the balcony, where three more ran in from outside. These he dropped with three more well-placed shots. His Luger spent, he ducked back along the wall and re-holstered it, then drew his other pistol.

"Leave...me," Natalya said.

"Not in a million years," he replied. He looked around frantically. In minutes this building would be crawling with guards. His gaze turned to the nearest turret, which housed the spiral staircase that led up from the first floor. No good trying that. He turned back to Schwartzhofer's room. It was a long shot, he knew, but there didn't seem to be much other choice.

"You still with me, darlin'?" he said.

She groaned and tried to nod, but her head lolled on her neck. Her grip around his shoulder tightened, though, a good sign. She was still fighting. He half-dragged her back into Schwartzhofer's room and onto the balcony. He looked over and judged the fall to be about fifteen feet. The drop would hurt, but if he could control it, he might survive it.

Then something hit him, solid and metal, across the back of his head. He blacked out for a minute, then saw stars. Suddenly, the floor was gone beneath him; he was in mid-air. His hands flailed out, brushed against something solid–searing pain shot through his left hand and a wave of nausea rose within him as he broke his finger. His right hand shot forth and grabbed it; he was dangling from the fence over the ground, and Schwartzhofer was there on the balcony, a Luger pointed at O'Malley's head, his arm around Natalya's throat.

"The Eye!" Schwartzhofer shouted. "Give it to me or die right now!"

Natalya's head lolled forward, just enough for O'Malley to see her eyes, glazed, clouded...

...and then clear. She stomped her foot down on Schwartzhofer's, her boot heel crushing into the German's bare foot. Schwartzhofer let out a scream. Natalya grabbed his gun hand, tugged forward, swung her right leg back and around, and threw her body weight forward and around. Schwartzhofer suddenly found himself stumbling forward, no longer holding his hostage. He looked around in time for Natalya to catch him with a slash across his face with her dagger. He threw his hands up in a vain effort to ward off the attacks, but a swift kick from the Fox sent him backwards, over the balcony.

O'Malley let go, dropped to the ground, and rolled. The impact hurt, but he was fairly certain nothing was broken. Natalya followed after, far more clumsily than O'Malley would've expected. She hit the ground and pitched forward, to her hands and knees. O'Malley ran to help her up.

"How in tarnation did you manage that?" he said.

"Adrenaline," she mumbled, then lost her footing again. "We need to go. Now."

"But Schwartzhofer..." He turned to look where the German had fallen, but there was no sign of the man.

"Go!" Natalya grunted. "Your vengeance can wait!"

He hoisted the girl up and made for the fence. The going was surprisingly smooth, as most of the guards had entered the house. He looked left and right, uncertain which way would be less likely to yield guards. He knew that the security was professional; *someone* had to be left out here to keep an eye on things.

His gaze fell to his jacket pocket. *It can't be,* he thought. Then he shook his head and muttered, "What the hell."

He lowered Natalya to the ground and dug out the gem. Natalya looked up at him and croaked, "We have no time to admire treasure. We must go!"

"Hush up a minute," he said. "I'm tryin' something."

He brought the gem to his eye and gazed in. Suddenly, he had a clear view of every single angle of the compound. He knew where every guard was, and exactly where the safest path out lay, but more than that, it was as though just for the next few minutes, the entirety of time and space was open to him. Every action he and Natalya might take was there, along with the potential consequences. It was a blur, a cacophony of sight and sound that sent him reeling as his mind tried to comprehend the myriad progressions of cause to effect. His mind was full of possibilities, of knowledge, of places, dates, locations, the fates of people he'd never before seen.

"I'll be damned," he said. "It works!"

He concentrated as hard as he could, but drawing an individual thread from the weave was worse than a needle-in-a-haystack scenario. He wished like Hell that Natalya was healthy; her mind was better trained than his. But he was all

they had–Natalya was losing consciousness, fast. He gritted his teeth and forced his mind through what was turning out to be a pounding headache, to focus on one thread after another. At last, he found what appeared to be a safe path through the back gate–if he timed it just perfectly.

He hoisted Natalya once again, and together they edged their way in the shadows towards the rear gate, and managed to slip out into the darkness.

* * *

"Can I see it?" Mackie asked, and O'Malley brought the gem forth and placed it in her hands. She was still in a lot of pain, but managed to sit up in her bed and grip the gem in one hand, her other closed over the wound in her rib cage. "It's beautiful," she breathed.

O'Malley nodded. "It sure is. Damn thing works, too. Showed us the way out of that compound. But damn if I ever want to look into that confusing thing again!"

Natalya nodded. O'Malley noted that the Russian still seemed a bit pale, but that the anti-toxin the hospital had administered seemed to have taken the worst of the poison out of her, and given the necessary secrecy of Schwartzhofer's operation, it was unlikely that her secret identity would be revealed to the world. They'd told the hospital that she had fallen in the street and pricked her finger on the needle, which was discarded alongside of the road. The origin of the poison would remain a mystery, and a generous donation to the hospital on behalf of the Brotherhood of William St. John ensured that there would never be a headline about the Hollywood starlet's treatment.

She exchanged a glance with O'Malley and nodded at him. He returned the nod.

"I know," he said. "That's twice you saved me. I owe you one."

She shook her head, "And twice you have saved me. We are, as you say, square."

"You know," Mackie said, "It's not always a game of score keeping."

"Yeah," O'Malley said, "Yeah, it is. It's part of what keeps us going." He patted Mackie on the leg. "Now you get better, soon. We got more work to do."

"Oh?" Mackie said.

O'Malley nodded. "Schwartzhofer's still out there somewhere, and that gem? The way out of the complex ain't the only thing it showed me. I know where the next of Perseus' treasures is, and if Schwartzhofer looked through it, too, he may already be on his way there."

Natalya rolled her eyes and cursed in Russian. "It never ends, does it?"

O'Malley shot her a look and grinned. "Not if we're lucky."

INTRODUCTION: THE CUT SCENE

We're going to forego the usual detail of the "what is role playing?" section here to address the genre of this specific product. However, here's a quick rundown of just what role playing is, for those who do happen to be new to the game, followed by a section on just what we mean by "Pulp".

A ROLE PLAYING GAME

We will assume that you have at least some idea of what a role playing game is if you've picked this up; if not, suffice it to say that role playing is like playing cowboys and Indians, or cops and robbers when you were a kid, but with rules in play to avoid things like, "I shot you!" "No, you didn't! I'm bullet proof!", and with the exception that you generally talk out your stories instead of acting them out. All of this will become clear as you read further into the book. In essence, role playing is an exercise in collaborative storytelling, where you get together with your friends, each taking on the role of a single character in a larger story guided by one of your friends who acts as the Game Master, a sort of master of ceremonies who controls everything in the world that is not one of the other players' characters. The Game Master sets the stage and the elements of the story, from the weather down to the shadowy guy in the long coat standing at the mouth of that alley in the seedy section of town, and generally gives the players an obstacle to overcome or a goal to achieve through their characters. Often you work together, as a group, rather than in competition, to reach this goal just like the protagonists in a novel or movie.

To play, you'll need paper, pencils, and dice: one four-sided, three or four six-sided, one eight-sided, two ten-sided (of different colors, or one having "Tens" listed on it, i.e. 10, 20, 30, etc.), one twelve-sided, and one twenty-sided. How these dice come into play will become clear as you read through the rules, but note that when you see a designation like "2d6," that means "roll two, six-sided dice." When you see a reference to % dice or "percentile dice", roll the 2d10 (that's two, ten-sided dice) and read them as a percentage score from 1 (01) to 100 (00) rather than adding them together. If you don't have a "tens" die, designate one of your tens as the "tens" die before rolling, and read that one first.

That's the basics. The details will clear themselves up as we go on.

A PULP GAME

It's all well and good to say that this is a pulp role playing game. But what exactly is "pulp?" Ask seven people, and you may well get seven different answers. It's difficult to define "pulp." To take it back to its roots, the term refers to the fiction magazines of the 1920's through 50's, and is named for the cheap wood pulp paper upon which the magazines were printed. But clearly we're not playing a game about people reading magazines.

The pulps, though underappreciated in so-called "legitimate" literary circles, form a vitally important milestone and landmark in Western literary history. In the pages of the pulps, authors like Robert E. Howard practically invented the sword-and-sorcery subgenre of heroic fantasy. Men like H.P. Lovecraft and Robert Bloch brought supernatural horror into its own; science fiction found its first audience in the pulps. Guys like Raymond Chandler brought hard-boiled crime fiction into the public eye (no pun intended!). Without the pulps, authors like Kelley Armstrong, Laurell K. Hamilton, Stephen King, Clive Barker, and Neil Gaiman might not be around—or at least nearly as well-known—as they are today. It was in these cheap magazines, often thought distasteful and tawdry by the general public, that science fiction, horror, and fantasy literature came of age and took on a life of its own.

This game makes no pretentions of bringing role playing into a new level. It's just about fun. What we're trying to do here is look at a few specific subgenres of fiction often found in the pulps, and at the common parlance usage of the word today. No longer does "pulp" refer solely and specifically to old magazines. Rather, when people hear the term "pulp" today they think of high action, often set in the era during which the magazines were published, that is, the 20's, 30's, and 40's, and often with some small element of the supernatural. Pulp today speaks of hard-boiled detectives, fedora-wearing action heroes, and steampunk gadgeteers rocketing to battle with their jet packs against bloodthirsty Thule cultists of the Third Reich.

Before you can begin a pulp game, you have to decide what tropes you're going to use. There are two specific subtypes of pulp that we will be looking at here: literary pulp, and serial pulp, for lack of better terms.

LITERARY PULP

The important thing to remember in literary pulp is that it tends to be very dark. Literary pulp abounds in shades of gray. Hardboiled detectives working a series of grisly, inhuman murder cases must often struggle with their own personal demons as they track down the killer, who may or may not be entirely human. This is the type of story in which the femme fatale plays a major role; never trust a woman with plump, red lips, spectacular gams, and a skirt slit to her thigh. Protagonists in literary pulp are more properly called "antiheroes" than heroes. Wealthy businessmen by day are vigilante crimefighters at night, be it through the use of gadgets or psychic powers that enable them to see the darkest corners of their prey's heart.

Literary pulp is visceral, violent, and often gory. It deals with personal turmoil as well as action and suspense. In film terms, it's more akin to a noir, or a psychological thriller than to lighthearted fun and adventure. Frank Miller's Sin City, and Dark City from director Alex Proyas are excellent examples of films that use the tropes of literary pulp. There's always a twist, and rarely is the twist good. Literary pulp tends to take the world we know and turn it on its ear in a very crooked and skewed way. This is because most literary pulp had a message to convey about the darkest nature of humanity. Robert E. Howard's fiction, both sword-and-sorcery and supernatural horror, dealt with the constant struggle of barbarism with civilization.

Thus, if it's dark and gritty you're after, this is the kind of game you'll want to run. Very likely in a literary pulp game you won't have arcanist player characters; magic is dark and alien and almost everyone who uses it ends up evil or changed into something less than human. It's something to be fought against, not used for the benefit of mankind. If an arcanist does exist in this kind of game, he's going to be mysterious, dark, and mistrusted.

Characters in literary fiction will be gumshoes, hooligans, and socialites, potentially with a mentalist thrown in here and there for that touch of the otherworldly. Gadgeteers may exist, but they'll be of the "Dark Knight" variety, shadowy vigilante figures who tend to kill criminals because the courts won't do their job and keep scum off the streets. Pugilists will likely be the most moral characters in a game like this, simple fighters who see something wrong and seek to set it right in their simple-minded ways.

SERIAL PULP

While literary pulp is generally more true to the roots of the genre, serial pulp is what people tend to think of when they hear the term. Serial pulp is action, excitement and over-the-top heroics. It's the story that harkens back to the Saturday morning matinees of the 50's, which would always end with a cliffhanger to bring kids back for more next week, just to see how their favorite hero escapes. In serial pulp you get the fedora-wearing hero battling his nemesis with fisticuffs on top of a moving train. Guns are often more for show and suppressive fire than actual implements of destruction. In the serials, things tend to be very black-and-white, extremely ethnocentric, and uniquely western in outlook. If you've ever heard the term "Good Guys wear White Hats and Bad Guys wear Black Hats," that describes serial pulp perfectly (though the phrase was used to describe spaghetti westerns, the idea stands firm). In a serial pulp, there may (and generally should) be twists and betrayals by friends, but the major adversaries should be definitely and despicably evil. Villains twirl moustaches and set elaborate traps for the heroes, who are paragons of liberty and justice–maybe a bit rough around the edges, but still representative of all that is best in the western mindset.

All bets are off in this type of game, so long as the action stays light hearted and furious. Gadgeteers will have wild and over-the-top toys like ray guns, rocket packs, and flash bombs. Arcanists will weave complex invocations that speak of other dimensions. Mentalists will see the evil that hides within mens' hearts. Gumshoes will spout memorable clichés such as, "We'll always have Paris." Raiders will grumble about making things up as they go along and getting too old for this stuff as they go toe-to-toe with more Nazis than you can shake a stick at. For modern inspirations for a serial fantasy style game, see Sky Captain and the World of Tomorrow, Disney's The Rocketeer, or the archetype of modern serial pulp, the Indiana Jones movies.

Likely, your game will be somewhere between literary and serial pulp, and that's great! This brief introduction is just to give you something to think about and is, of course, far from complete. A simple web search should turn up hundreds of sites on the various aspects of pulp fiction and its sub-genres.

TOOLKIT APPROACH

One final note: players familiar with ***Castles & Crusades*** will notice that at its core, ***Amazing Adventures*** is extremely similar to that game. Indeed, you should be able to pick up ***Amazing Adventures*** with very little adjustment. The play is nearly identical to that in C&C. However, you may also notice a great deal of options spread throughout the game in sidebars. The SIEGE engine is eminently adjustable and adaptable to many styles of play, and these sidebars are designed to give you options to tweak your game to fit your preferred style. For example, don't like the 3-18 attribute range? There's an option to replace the range with just the -3 to +3 bonus. Don't like passive Challenges created by the hit dice of opponents? An option is present for opposed check rolls. Indeed, the whole of Book Two consists of optional rules for customizing characters and injecting elements of action and/or horror into your game. The intent is that you will pick and choose the options you like, and create your own flavor of pulp from the adaptability of the SIEGE engine.

So what are you waiting for? Go! Play!

BOOK ONE: MARVELOUS MEN OF MYSTERY

The first thing you'll have to do, to play this game, is create your character. Your character is a sort of archetype through whose eyes you will see, whose ears you will hear, and whose mouth you will speak in the fictional world of the game. There are several basic steps to creating a character, with advanced options presented in chapter two. The steps are as follows. Don't worry if it seems complicated; it'll break down pretty simply once you dive in.

Assign Attribute Scores

Choose Primes

Choose Languages

Choose a Character Class

Choose an Alignment (Optional)

Equip Your Character

Choose spells,gadgets,or powers (if an arcanist, gadgeteer,or mentalist)

Record Fate Points

Generally speaking, a basic character can be created for this game in ten to fifteen minutes' time, once you get the hang of it. If using the advanced options in Book Two, it might take a bit longer, but not much.

ATTRIBUTES

Attributes (also called "Ability Scores") represent a character's physical and mental traits. All characters have six attributes:

Strength (Str)
Dexterity (Dex)
Constitution (Con)
Intelligence (Int)
Wisdom (Wis)
Charisma (Cha)

Each attribute has a numeric score ranging from 3 to 18. Each attribute score also has a corresponding modifier, which is a bonus or penalty added to or subtracted from certain die rolls during the game as detailed throughout the rules.

There are two types of attributes: primary and secondary. Of the six attributes each character has, the player selects three to be primary attributes. The remaining attributes are secondary. The distinction is important when determining the outcome of many actions in ***Amazing Adventures***. When a character uses a class ability, such as a hooligan attempting to pick a fat gangster's pocket or a raider tracking a rival archaeologist through a dark forest, an attribute check is rolled to determine if the action is successful. Each class ability has an attribute check associated with it. If the class ability's associated attribute is one of the character's primary attributes, the character has a greater chance of successfully performing the task. The same principle holds true for the other aspects of the game in which an attribute check is required.

Attribute checks are explained in greater detail later. For now, just remember that the selection of primary and secondary attributes significantly affects the possibility of success for many actions in the game. Attribute checks associated with a primary attribute are significantly more likely to succeed than those actions performed with a secondary attribute.

THE SIX ATTRIBUTES

STRENGTH: This attribute reflects physical strength, including the ability to lift or move heavy objects and make powerful attacks. The modifier affects melee combat and damage, and all checks for which strength is the primary influence. Characters can easily carry twice their strength, and can, for brief periods, military press 10x their strength and dead lift 15x their strength score in pounds.

DEXTERITY: This attribute represents a character's reflexes, manual dexterity and hand-eye coordination, including the ability to dodge and defend against attacks. The modifier affects armor class, ranged combat and all checks involving dexterity.

CONSTITUTION: This attribute reflects overall health, and also represents a character's ability to withstand pain, suffer physical damage, avoid fatigue and fight off sickness or poison. The modifier affects hit points, and it applies to all checks involving constitution as the prime attribute.

INTELLIGENCE: This attribute reflects mental aptitude. It represents a character's ability to learn quickly, apply that learning effectively and use deductive reasoning. The modifier affects the number of arcane spells a character can cast each day, the number of languages a character can learn and all checks involving intelligence as the prime attribute.

WISDOM: This attribute reflects depth of personal experience, the ability to make well-considered decisions or judgments, and represents a spiritual connection to a deity. The modifier affects certain types of spell casting, some psionic powers, attempts to turn the undead and all checks involving wisdom as the prime attribute.

CHARISMA: This attribute represents strength of personality, willpower, leadership and attractiveness. It is the degree to which a character is able to influence others. The modifier affects other creatures' loyalty and reactions to the character, and all checks involving charisma as the primary influence.

GENERATING ATTRIBUTE SCORES

Characters are generated via a point-buy attribute system. At character generation, each attribute starts at 6, and the player begins with 45 points to spread amongst his or her ability scores. No single attribute can begin above 18.

Normally, attribute scores only increase or decrease during the course of a game as a result of magic, poison, curses or other extraordinary events. Should an attribute score change during game play, the modifier changes to correspond to the new score, if applicable. It is possible for an attribute score to fall below 3 or exceed 18 during game play. However, attribute scores for characters that fall outside of this range are rare, and are usually associated with monsters, high-level villains, powerful magical items or other entities controlled by the Game Master.

OPTIONAL: RANDOM GENERATION METHOD

Some GMs and players like to randomly generate attributes. In this case, simply roll 4d6, keeping the highest three scores. Do this six times, and arrange the scores as you see fit.

OPTIONAL: GETTING RID OF THE SPREAD

In practice, the 3-18 spread for attributes only matters insofar as it generates a bonus or penalty to SIEGE checks. If players and GMs wish to get rid of the spread, it's possible to simply play with bonuses. In this case, all abilities should begin at -2, and players have 25 points with which to raise them. No ability can be raised above +3. If a player needs more points, she can lower one or more attributes to -3, gaining one point for each attribute lowered from -2 to -3.

ATTRIBUTE MODIFIERS

Each attribute score has a corresponding modifier that can alter die rolls in the game. The modifier is a number added to (or subtracted from) a d20 roll when a character uses an attribute to take an action, make a saving throw or use a class ability. For example, a character attempting to bend the bars of a prison cell would have his or her strength modifier applied to the roll. The amount of damage delivered to a foe is likewise affected by the attribute modifier. A positive modifier is called a bonus and a negative modifier, a penalty. Higher attribute scores have higher bonuses, and lower attribute scores have larger penalties. So, whether fighting a nasty fishman or hungry cave bear, or avoiding the charms of a femme fatale, attribute modifiers play a decidedly important role in the game.

ATTRIBUTE MODIFIERS

1	2-3	4-5	6-8	9-12	13-15	16-17	18
-4	-3	-2	-1	0	+1	+2	+3

PRIMARY AND SECONDARY ATTRIBUTES

There are two types of attributes in ***Amazing Adventures***: primary and secondary. Primary attributes are those physical or mental abilities in which a character is particularly well trained or very experienced in using. Secondary attributes are those the character uses with only average skill. A player selects the character's primary attributes after choosing a class.

Player characters have three primary attributes. Each class has one primary attribute associated with it that cannot be changed. The player selects the others. For example, the primary attribute for the gumshoe class is dexterity. If the player chooses to play a gumshoe, this forms one primary attribute. The player may then select any two more primary attributes. The remaining attributes are considered to be secondary.

SIEGE CHECKS

As mentioned before, the distinction between primary and secondary attributes is important. Almost all non-combat actions (for which the Game Master deems a roll is necessary to determine success or failure) are resolved by an attribute check, or SIEGE check. To make a SIEGE check, a character rolls a d20, adds any relevant bonuses, and attempts to equal or better a Challenge Class, or CC.

The CC is determined by adding the Challenge Base (CB) to a Challenge Level (CL) determined by the GM. Generally speaking, the CL will combine the hit dice or level of the opponent with any situational bonuses or penalties the GM feels appropriate.

Checks made against Primary Attributes have a CB of 12, while checks against Secondary Attributes have a CB of 18. This makes it significantly easier to succeed at a check if you have a Prime in the ability in question.

For example, if Natalya the Fox is trying to slip past the sentries at a Nazi-fortified camp, she makes a Dexterity check for her Move Silently class ability. Since Dexterity is a Prime attribute for Hooligans, her Challenge Base for the check is 12. If the Nazis have an average of 4 Hit Dice, this sets the CL for the check at 4. Adding 12+4 gives us 16 for the final Challenge Class; Natalya needs a 16 or better on her Dexterity check to slip unnoticed past the guards.

If, on the other hand, the GM decides that the sentries are exceptionally alert and actively looking out for spies, he may decide that they get to add their Wisdom bonus as well. In this case, the GM decides that they have a Wisdom score of 13, giving them a +1. This +1 could then add to the CL and make it a 5, for a total CC of 17.

A more thorough discussion of the rules and use of checks, called the SIEGE engine™, is located in the Game Master's section of the rules. For now, it is just important to understand that checks involving the use of a primary attribute are far more likely to be successful than checks involving secondary attributes.

LANGUAGES

Every character begins play with the ability to speak his or her native language. That is, the language that is common to the region from which he hails. American characters speak English; German characters speak German, etc. Beyond this, characters receive bonus languages equal to twice their intelligence bonus, which they can speak, read, and write fluently at the beginning of play.

Learning new languages is not something that can normally be done overnight. Characters should be encouraged to learn new languages during the course of play if they desire, but unless they retire for a year or so to study, they should not be allowed to read, write and speak the language immediately. For example, Quinton, who speaks only the Queen's English, travels with Erik, a Romany mentalist who speaks the Romany tongue fluently. The player tells the Game Master that Quinton is going to study the language while they travel; the Game Master may allow him to get by with the new language within a few months, but to not become fluent for several years of travel. Languages can be an important part of the game and can offer very challenging roleplaying obstacles if the Game Master is not overly generous in handing them out and the player is intrigued enough to unravel ancient societies' customs with halting words and hand gestures.

ADDITIONAL LANGUAGES

Astute readers will note that ***Amazing Adventures*** gives characters double the number of starting languages that they get in ***Castles & Crusades***. The rationale for this is simple: genre emulation. In pulp tales, the heroes are often educated and erudite, and generally speak more languages than your average Joe. As you'll see later, members of the Raider class (p. 42) get even more languages, making them useful companions indeed, on international travels!

CHARACTER CLASSES

The next step in creating a character is to choose a class, or broad archetype of the kind of character you wish to play. In ***Amazing Adventures*** the character classes are the Arcanist, Gadgeteer, Gumshoe, Hooligan, Mentalist, Pugilist, Raider, and Socialite. Each of these classes represents a very broad and general picture of a classic Pulp archetype. The Raider, for example, is the academic explorer who plumbs ancient tombs and temples for lost treasures. The Gumshoe is the hard-boiled detective or rough-and-tumble FBI agent battling organized crime.

If these archetypes seem too broad and general, fear not! After you choose your initial class, you will be given a chance to customize that class to your liking through Generic Class Abilities, Backgrounds, Knowledge Skills, and Traits. For now, just choose the archetype that most closely suits your character concept; we'll build on that later.

Finally, given the wide variety of styles and sub-genres within Pulp, players should check with their GM to ensure that the class they wish to play is appropriate. Not every pulp story includes mystical or supernatural abilities, after all. In such games the Arcanist and Mentalist are inappropriate, as may be the Gadgeteer, depending on the amount of super science or steampunk the GM wishes to include.

THE ARCANIST

The warm, swamp air of the Louisiana Bayou filled the shadowy, ramshackle structure, filled with fetishes, skulls, gris-gris bags, and shrunken heads. An attractive woman, half black, half Creole, huddled over a bowl filled with incense that emitted a sickly-sweet odor as she chanted in pidgin French. Her eyes rolled back into her head, she cast her face towards the sky, her hands held out as she felt the Loa, Baron Samedi, mount her back and enter her mind.

Marie, it spoke to her. Marie Laveau. You can feel them, 'can't ya, girl? You can feel them comin' on down!

"Oh, yes," she whispered with a soft drawl. "I feel it. They's a-comin indeed!"

Hidden in plain sight are those who strive to understand the oft-forbidden and widely feared arcane magics of the multiverse. These few must have no fear in their quest for knowledge, as delving into the arcane involves powers and energies poorly understood by those bound to mortal planes. If not harnessed with care, unleashing these magics can cause catastrophes of great proportion and slay those who dabble in this art. The reward, however, for the diligence and willingness to plumb the depths of these magical energies is potentially great indeed. Arcanists bind themselves to this task, seeking to master eldritch sorceries and unravel the riddles and meanings of the world. They use their powers to reshape the world around them and, in some cases, to bring great world leaders to their knees.

Arcanists are the archetypical magic-users, and they are vastly superior to all others at understanding and harnessing the magic that ebbs and flows through the multiverse. They come from all social strata and can be found in all positions in

society. They may be employed by business tycoons, religious organizations, world leaders or other powerful individuals to whom they act as guides and advisors, but almost always in secret. Many seek to dominate national (and even world) politics, and often succeed. More often though, arcanists work in solitude, far away from the prying eyes and keen ears of enemies, spies and other arcanists who often consider them to be untrustworthy and dangerous competitors in the quest for arcane lore. In wind-swept towers or black Egyptian tombs, far from the din of civilization, such arcanists find the solitude, quiet and safety necessary to pursue their research and carry out their oft-times dangerous experiments.

Though they come from many walks of life, all arcanists have a few characteristics in common. They tend to be intelligent, observant, diligent and have an exacting eye for detail. Their unyielding search and thirst for knowledge of the eldritch powers often generates a self-serving egomania in the most powerful of arcanists. And, as they become ever more competent in harnessing eldritch sorceries and bending the world about them to their will, they suffer little distraction and afford interlopers little forgiveness when their work is interrupted.

Woe to the foes of these powerful magic-users. Incurring their wrath can mean the unleashing of horrid and terrible magics few can comprehend, and fewer still are capable of combating. An arcanist's enemies are laid waste by balls of blue flame and bolts of lightning called from elemental planes or even by servants of the rulers of the nether worlds, conjured forth to act on the arcanist's behalf. They can make objects disappear and transport themselves many miles away, see into the darkness and build walls of force no man can pass. The greatest of arcanists are powerful beyond measure.

An arcanist's pursuits and studies, along with their intense focus upon the arcane, mean a life of laboring over ancient tomes of knowledge. This leaves arcanists little time to learn and become proficient in any but the most common of weapons, and not at all capable of wearing bulky clothing that hinders the intricate somantic movements needed to cast some of their most powerful spells. Yet this matters little to them, as arcanists realize their wits and arcane powers are far more powerful than any gun or sword, and that conjured servants offer far more protection than any arcanist could possibly need.

ABILITIES

SPELLS: An arcanist casts arcane spells. arcanists can only cast a limited number of spells, from each spell level, per day. The number of spells an arcanist can cast is limited in two ways. The first, and perhaps most important, is by the amount of mystical energy the arcanist has to expend. This is determined by his pool of Mana Energy Points (MEP). Mana Energy Points represent the amount of arcane energy the arcanist can channel through his or her person before becoming utterly exhausted. The act of casting a spell is extremely draining, and failing at spell casting can even be damaging to the body of the arcanist. For this reason, Constitution is a vital attribute for all arcanists.

BEGINNING MEP: Arcanists start play with d4 + Con bonus + Primary Spell casting Attribute bonus in MEP. At each additional arcanist class level, a character in a spell casting class gains 1d10 additional MEP.

The second limitation is the preparation the arcanist undergoes each morning. The arcanist Spells Per Day Table (p. 30) lists the number of spells per day an arcanist may prepare of each spell level. For example, a 5th level arcanist can prepare six 0 level spells, four 1st level spells, and two 2nd level spells per day.

PRIMARY SPELL CASTING ATTRIBUTE: Spells are based upon a Primary Spell casting Attribute chosen by the Arcanist at character creation, and representing his or her philosophy towards and method of understanding magic:

Those Arcanists with a scientific outlook towards magic use Intelligence. These are often men and women who spend long hours studying arcane tomes, dusty manuscripts, and ancient scrolls to unlock the secret formulae hidden therein.

Those who believe magic comes from an innate gnosis, or intuitive understanding of the mystical forces at work in the world, cast spells based upon Wisdom. These men and women tend to be those who believe they are blessed by their chosen deity or have an innate connection with the natural world. The fire-and-brimstone preacher that calls down the wrath of God, a nature-worshipping druid, or a Sufi mystic, are good examples of this type of caster.

Finally, those who believe magic comes from sheer force of personality and will cast spells based upon Charisma. These are the hypnotists and enchanters who exercise their force of personality to affect and control other people. An arcanist's primary spell casting attribute need not be a Prime, though for obvious reasons it often is. An arcanist may only cast spells from the spell list for his primary spell casting attribute. This attribute cannot be changed, once selected.

BONUS SPELLS: With a high primary spell casting attribute score, an arcanist gains bonus spells and an appropriate amount of MEP with which to cast those spells. If the character has an attribute of between 13-15, they receive an extra 1st level spell and 2 extra MEP. If the attribute score is 16 or 17, the arcanist receives an extra 1st and 2nd level spell and 5 extra MEP (2 for his first level spell, and 3 for his second), and if 18 or 19, the arcanist receives an extra 1st, 2nd, and 3rd level spell and 9 extra MEP (2, then 3, then 4 MEP, as he gains the respective spells).

Bonus spells and corresponding MEP are only acquired when the arcanist is at a high enough level to cast them. Thus, if a character has an ability of 16, he gets a first level spell immediately, plus 2 MEP. When he is able to cast second

level spells, he gets his bonus second level spell and the additional 3 MEP, for a total of 5.

For example, a 4th level arcanist with an 18 intelligence receives four 0 level spells, four 1st level spells, and three 2nd level spells, plus an additional 5 MEP. No bonus 3rd level spell is acquired until the arcanist reaches 5th level, at which point he gains his bonus 3rd level spell and 4 bonus MEP with which to cast his bonus spell. See the Magic section for more information.

ABILITY	BONUS SPELLS	BONUS MEP
13-15	Level 1	2
16-17	Levels 1 and 2	2 and 3
18	Levels 1, 2, and 3	2, 3, and 4

SPELL BOOK: An arcanist must prepare spells before casting them by studying from a spell book. While studying, the arcanist decides which spells to prepare. Spell casting and spell descriptions are covered in detail in the Magic section (p. 81).

The number of spells that an arcanist has in their spell book at the beginning of play is equal to the number of spells they can cast at first level. For example, a 1st level arcanist with 14 Intelligence can cast four 0 level spells and three 1st level spells (2 + 1 bonus). So, the character would begin play with a spellbook containing four 0 level and three 1st level spells. The spells in the spell book can either be chosen by the Game Master, the player, agreement between the two or randomly (use the Spell List Charts to determine).

At each subsequent level, the arcanist may add one new spell to her spell book, of any level up to the maximum level she can cast. Thus, upon reaching sixth level, an arcanist may add any one spell from levels one to three to her spellbook.

Spells can also be discovered by scouring ancient tombs and books of arcane knowledge in the course of play. When finding a new spell, the arcanist may make a spellcraft check with a CL equal to the level of the spell being learned. Success means the spell can be entered into her books; failure means she cannot yet understand the formulae before her and may try again upon reaching a new level of experience.

SPELLCRAFT: The arcanist can identify spells and magic effects. The CL for Spellcraft checks relating to various tasks are generally based upon either the level of the spell or effect being identified (in the case of lingering or persistent effects), or the level of the arcanist who is casting or maintaining the spell or effect (in the case of consciously maintained effects or those in the process of being cast). A spellcraft check is always made using the arcanist's primary spell casting attribute, and attempts to identify spells or effects cast by arcanists with the same spell casting attribute are always made at a +2. A charisma-based caster, for example, attempting to identify an effect cast by another charisma-based caster, would gain +2 to his check. However, if the charisma-based caster was attempting to identify a spell cast by an intelligence-based caster there is no special bonus to do so.

PRIME ATTRIBUTE: Constitution

ALIGNMENT: Any

HIT DICE: d6

WEAPONS: Small Melee Weapons, archaic ranged weapons, handguns

ABILITIES: Spell casting

Level	HD	BtH	EPP
1	6 HP	0	0
2	d6	+1	2,601
3	d6	+1	5,201
4	d6	+1	10,401
5	d6	+1	20,801
6	d6	+2	42,501
7	d6	+2	85,001
8	d6	+2	170,001
9	d6	+2	340,001
10	d6	+3	500,001
11	+3 HP	+3	750,001
12	+3 HP	+3	1,000,001
13+	+3 HP	*	+250,000

* +1 per four levels.

SPELLS PER DAY

Level	0	1st	2nd	3rd	4th	5th	6th	7th	8th	9th
1st	4	2	–	–	–	–	–	–	–	–
2nd	5	2	–	–	–	–	–	–	–	–
3rd	5	3	–	–	–	–	–	–	–	–
4th	6	3	1	–	–	–	–	–	–	–
5th	6	4	2	–	–	–	–	–	–	–
6th	7	4	2	1	–	–	–	–	–	–
7th	7	5	3	2	–	–	–	–	–	–
8th	8	5	3	2	1	–	–	–	–	–
9th	8	5	4	3	2	–	–	–	–	–
10th	9	5	4	3	2	1	–	–	–	–
11th	9	5	5	4	3	2	–	–	–	–
12th	9	5	5	4	3	2	1	–	–	–
13th	9	5	5	4	4	3	2	–	–	–
14th	9	5	5	4	4	3	2	1	–	–
15th	9	5	5	4	4	4	3	2	–	–
16th	9	5	5	4	4	4	3	2	1	–
17th	9	5	5	4	4	4	3	3	2	–
18th	9	5	5	4	4	4	3	3	2	1
19th	9	5	5	4	4	4	3	3	3	2
20th	9	5	5	4	4	4	3	3	3	3

THE GADGETEER

"I swear, Bucky, the nubile woman purred. I would never lie to you. You know that. You and I, we've been through so much together...can't you trust me?"

"I'd love to, Baby," Bucky said. "But I just can't. Fortunately, I've got my Newson's Magnificent Lie Detector Goggles with me. Let's just see how truthful you are."

Bucky withdrew the awkward-looking goggles from his coat and slipped them over his eyes, giving him the odd appearance of a man with the eyes of an insect. He reached for the dial on the side, turned it all the way up. There was a popping sound, a shower of sparks, and a whiff of ozone, and Bucky pulled the smoking contraption off his head and dropped it to the floor.

"Damn things never worked right," he said, and drew his radium blaster on the woman. "Let's try a different tactic, yeah?"

The gadgeteer is a super hero long before the golden age of superheroes, who uses toys such as X-Ray goggles, ray guns, rocket packs, and wrist radios. Whether he soars in the blue skies with his rocket pack, takes down villains with his bronze gamma ray gun, or sees through walls with his incredible X-Ray specs, this is the character whose very name screams SCIENCE!

Gadgeteers come in two varieties: those who spend long hours in a lab inventing new equipment with which they will battle the forces of evil, or those who have a special "Gadget man" that invents their equipment for them. In game terms, the difference is mostly flavor-based and will be dependent upon which attributes the character designates Prime, though there are advantages to both types of character. In either case, many gadgeteers often adventure for the sheer thrill of it. Others do what they do out of an overdeveloped sense of justice, or a need for vengeance against those who have wronged them or their loved ones.

Since gadgeteers are often on the front lines of the battle against crime, Dexterity is of paramount importance to these characters, but a quick wit and dashing persona are also invaluable to their pursuits, especially if they have a gadget man, so Wisdom and Charisma are also important. Those gadgeteers who invent their own toys will also want a high intelligence score.

ABILITIES

GADGETS: The gadgeteer has one primary ability – Science! This manifests in a number of specialized pieces of equipment, or gadgets, that become a permanent part of his arsenal. A gadgeteer may create these gadgets himself, or have a special scientist friend or sidekick (NPC) who equips him for his mission. If the gadgeteer creates his own gadgets, they cost more, but the gadgeteer is less likely to lose his source of equipment, and will have the ability to create gadgets "on the fly." These "instant" gadgets represent small pieces of equipment he happens to have on his person that he just thought he might need some day. These types of gadgeteer must choose Intelligence as one of their Primes and have either the Science or Mechanics background (if using Character Backgrounds).

On the other hand, the gadgeteer receives a substantial reduction in cost for having a scientist who creates gadgets for him; in this case, however, he stands a chance of losing his contact through kidnapping, death, or even a disagreement, and cannot create "on the fly" gadgets. The gadgeteer with a weapons man must choose Charisma as one of his primes. The gadgeteer must choose at character creation which form of gadgeteer he is, and may not change this decision.

Gadgeteers gain their toys through the expenditure of "Gadget Points." To obtain a gadget, the gadgeteer must choose a spell (any spell) from the Arcanist spell lists. He then "buys" that spell at whatever level of effect he desires (and can afford); it then becomes a permanent gadget on his equipment list, and he can use it whenever he likes. For example, buying the Arcane Bolt effect at first level will have different effects than purchasing it at fourth level.

GADGET POINTS: The gadgeteer begins play with 1d6+1 gadget points, plus his Intelligence Bonus (if he creates gadgets himself) or his Charisma Bonus (if he has a gadget man). Every additional level thereafter, he gains gadget points equal to 1 plus half his gadgeteer class level, rounded up.

A gadgeteer may save gadget points for use in purchasing larger gadgets down the line, or in the case of a self-creator (see below) to use on emergency gadgets, but must spend a minimum of three points on gadgets at character creation. If the character does not have three points at character creation, he then must spend all of his starting points on gadgets with which to begin play. The cost to purchase a gadget is as follows:

SELF-CREATED GADGETS: Cost is equal to the minimum Arcanist caster level to cast a spell, plus one. Thus, purchasing a third-level effect (buying fireball to create a gun that shoots an explosive charge, for example), costs seven gadget points (An arcanist would have to be sixth level to cast this spell). Purchasing a zero- or first-level effect such as Arcane Bolt or Light costs two points (a first-level arcanist could cast either of these spells). Here is a quick breakdown of gadget costs:

Gadget Level	0	1	2	3	4	5	6
Point Cost	2	2	5	6	9	11	13

NPC-PROVIDED GADGETS: Cost is equal to the spell level, plus one. Thus, the same gun made for the character by his personal inventor costs four points (Fireball is a third-level spell).

ON THE FLY GADGETS (INT): Gadgeteers who create their own gadgets can come up with emergency pieces of equipment on the fly. These gadgets may never duplicate any effect higher than that of a zero-level spell, cost three gadget points to create, and require the Gadgeteer to pass a CL 4 Intelligence Check. Once a gadget is created, it becomes a permanent part of the Gadgeteer's arsenal, just as if he had purchased it at character creation or upon achieving a new level. However, if the Gadgeteer chooses, he can decide at the end of the game session to have the on-the-fly gadget "break down," at which point he loses the gadget and regains the spent point. Only on-the-fly gadgets can break down to get points back, and once the points are spent, they are spent for the entire play session.

IMPROVING GADGETS: When a gadgeteer decides to create a new effect, there is no rule that states the effect must be installed in a brand new gadget. For example, a gadgeteer at level one creates what he calls "Tesla Gloves," or gauntlets that allow him to use the Shocking Grasp spell. By sixth level, he wishes to create a "Tesla Gun," picking up the Lightning Bolt spell. He can, if he chooses, install the Tesla Gun effect right into his existing gloves, giving him the option to use the effects in both. In general, only complimentary or similar effects should be installed together in a single gadget, but the GM has final say in whether a gadget can be improved in this manner.

JURY RIG (INT): The gadgeteer is a master of machinery. He has the ability to effect miraculous (if sometimes temporary) repairs on equipment that others might write off for junk. To perform this ability, the gadgeteer makes an Intelligence check at a CL determined by the GM, based on how wrecked the item in question is. In general, jury rigging an item takes either 15 minutes or 1 hour per level of CL added to the check, dependent upon whether the gadgeteer wishes a temporary or permanent fix. Thus, for a CL 5 repair, the jury rigging would take either 1 hour, 15 minutes for a temporary "quick fix," or 5 hours for a permanent repair. A quick-fix item requires constant maintenance, and the gadgeteer must make a Wisdom (not Int)-based saving throw every hour he wishes to keep the thing running, with a CL equal to that required to fix the machine in the first place. This represents his ability to keep a machine going through sheer determination, elbow grease, spit, and good intentions. If a Wisdom save is failed, the machine breaks down and cannot be repaired again.

In addition to taking longer, permanent fixes also suffer an additional +2 to the CL, representing the fact that it's more difficult to make it work for good than it is to get it running "for now."

Building and Running the Gadgeteer

Game Masters are advised to carefully adjudicate and monitor any gadgets purchased by this character, as some spells, when handed unrestricted to a player character, can result in serious game imbalance. A character, for example, who has the ability to create a Prismatic Sphere whenever she feels like it is nigh unstoppable. For this reason, the following guidelines are offered:

1. No spell effects above sixth level be possible through this class, and a gadgeteer should not be able to purchase a gadget that reproduces effects of a higher level than one level below the level he currently is, with a minimum of 1 (i.e. a first- or second-level gadgeteer may purchase first-level effects, but no higher).
2. At the GM's option, the level limit for gadgets can be suspended at character generation, but it is recommended that no more than one gadget ever be owned that is higher than the gadgeteer's normal limit.
3. Any spell that causes direct damage requires a normal ranged attack roll by the character, regardless of the spell effect in question. Thus, creating a ray gun through the Arcane Bolt spell effect still requires the gadgeteer to make a ranged attack roll with his gun (though the GM may allow a bonus to hit, say, +5, for energy bursts that home in on the target). Even area effect spells such as Fireball even require such an attack roll; failure could mean the gadgeteer himself is in the burst area, having to make a Dexterity save for half damage!
4. If a desired spell effect appears on more than one spell list, the Gadgeteer should consider the Charisma-based list first, for purposes of level/cost determination. If a spell is not on the Charisma list, the Wisdom list is second in priority, and the Intelligence list last.
5. While gadget effects are based upon spells, they should be properly restricted to avoid unbalancing the game, and the player should clearly describe what each gadget in his arsenal is. Never should a gadgeteer's player say, "I'm using my Arcane Bolt effect." Rather, he should say something like, "I pull out my homing-blast delta pistol."

6. If the gadgeteer fails to describe his gadget properly and falls back on the spell name for his effect, appropriate penalties should be put into play. Perhaps the gadget malfunctions temporarily to comical effect. Perhaps a penalty to any rolls associated with the gadget is imposed, until the proper terminology is used. Don't unduly harm the character with these, but hammer home the idea that flavor and mood are important to the game.
7. Finally, remember that spells purchased are the beginning of creating a gadget, not the end. If a player wishes to do something that is not strictly defined in a spell effect, the GM should work to modify an existing spell and/or cost and restrict the effect based on the closest available spell.

   For example, if the player wishes to have, say, a robot snake monster, the GM may score this as "Summon Monster," except the purchase gives a permanent robot snake instead of summoning various living creatures, and base the HD and HP of the robot on the guidelines listed in that spell, assigning an appropriate AC as she sees fit. The trick here is to place fair restrictions on gadgets such that the class doesn't unbalance the game, while not restricting the gadgeteer's creativity.

   Likewise, in the case of on-the-fly gadgets, if an appropriate zero-level spell is not available but the player wishes to do something that is roughly the same power level and would make the game fun and interesting, roll with it!

PRIME ATTRIBUTE: Charisma or Intelligence (Dependent on the source of the gadgets)

ALIGNMENT: Any

HIT DIE: d6

WEAPONS ALLOWED: Small melee weapons, medium melee weapons, handguns, and gadgets.

ABILITIES: Gadgets

Level	HD	BtH	EPP
1	6 HP	0	0
2	d6	+1	2,601
3	d6	+1	5,201
4	d6	+1	10,401
5	d6	+1	20,801
6	d6	+2	42,501
7	d6	+2	85,001
8	d6	+2	170,001
9	d6	+2	340,001
10	d6	+3	500,001
11	+3 HP	+3	750,001
12	+3 HP	+3	1,000,001
13+	+3 HP	*	+250,000

*+1 per four levels

THE GUMSHOE

It was a black night, and thick with fog and rain. The kind of night that feels like someone's thrown a wool blanket over your head and choked off your air passages with a rubber hose. All I wanted was to sit in my office and down a quart of bathtub gin.

Unfortunately, that's when she walked in, with eyes like midnight and gams that could crack a walnut. I knew nothing good could come of this meeting.

Of course, I asked her how I could help.

The hardboiled detective, be it private investigation or homicide, who with his trusty snub nose revolver always finds himself in way over his head, The gumshoe is a specialist in tracking down and capturing fugitives from the law. Hardboiled P.I.s, homicide detectives, and FBI agents all fall into this category. The gumshoe is as attuned to the alleys and shadows of the streets and able to move amongst the seedier elements with relative ease. Most gumshoes tend to be lawful in alignment, seeking to bring fugitives and anarchists to justice. There are a few, however, who are neutral or even chaotic, serving whoever pays the most and just as easily being bought off by those they seek to bring in as those who hire them to hunt criminals. For this reason, and the fact that they often succeed where the local law enforcement does not, these freebooters are often looked upon with disdain and sometimes outright contempt by legitimate legal authorities.

Even still, the services of gumshoes are in great demand, for the lawless aren't few, and are rarely bound by the restrictions that hamper legitimate authority. Thus, someone who is able to work for the law, but outside it, is often the only solution. In the end, if you want someone found, nobody has the skills to help like a gumshoe. Just make sure you're okay with the prey being delivered dead or alive.

ABILITIES

CLIMB (DEXTERITY): This ability allows a gumshoe to climb up, down, or across a slope, wall, steep incline (even a ceiling with handholds) or unusually angled natural or man-made slope or incline that others might find it difficult or impossible to climb. When doing so, the gumshoe moves at one half the character's normal speed. A failed check means the gumshoe makes no progress this round. A check that fails by 5 or more means that the character falls and takes full falling damage. Nothing can be carried in the hands while climbing. Unlike a hooligan, the gumshoe must make climb checks even when climbing typical natural slopes and man-made inclines.

CAT AND MOUSE (WISDOM): The gumshoe can track down the location of missing persons or wanted individuals within a given community, or trail a mark through a city. A successful cat and mouse check allows the gumshoe to pick up a trail and follow it for one hour through a combination of physical evidence and asking the right questions of the right people. The CL of this check generally depends upon the size of the community in which the gumshoe is searching, and its disposition towards the missing or wanted individual.

The size of the community in which the Gumshoe seeks the prey also determines the number of checks required to track down his quarry.

- A small, one stoplight town requires 1-2 checks.
- An average-sized town requires 1d4+1 checks before the gumshoe reaches the end of his search.
- A city increases the number of checks required to 2d4
- A metropolis requires 2d6 checks.

Even then, "coming to the end of his search," does not necessarily mean that the gumshoe has captured his prey. It could possibly mean that the prey has fled to another community, though following a lead to its logical conclusion will always yield the most likely community to which the prey has fled, thus initiating a new round of checks when the gumshoe reaches the new area. The table below provides some suggested modifiers, but is not a comprehensive list of all possible adjustments.

CONDITION	CL MODIFIER
One stoplight town	+0
Average town	+2
Small city	+4
Metropolis	+6
Per three members in group sought	-1
Per 24 hours prey has been missing	+1
Prey laying low	+4
Community friendly towards prey or prey's class or affiliation	+3
Community afraid of prey or prey's class or affiliation	+2
Community lawful or good, prey chaotic or evil	-2
Community hostile towards prey or prey's class or affiliation	-3

At sixth level, the gumshoe becomes adept enough at his tracking abilities that each check requires only a half hour, and at twelfth level, each check requires only fifteen minutes. Note that these checks should always lead to role playing opportunities, clues found, or NPC's with whom the character can speak to acquire information; never should an adventure boil down to a die roll and information handed out; it defeats the entire purpose!

HIDE (DEXTERITY): Gumshoes can conceal themselves extremely well in urban environments. With a successful dexterity check, gumshoes can conceal themselves so well as to be unnoticeable by most passers-by. They cannot move and hide at the same time.

Gumshoes cannot hide themselves if being observed, even casually, before the attempt is made. If the observer is momentarily distracted, the Gumshoe can attempt to use this ability. While the observer looks away, the gumshoe can attempt to get to a hiding place of some kind. The attribute check, however, is at a -10 penalty because the gumshoe has mere seconds to find a suitable hiding spot.

MOVE SILENTLY (DEXTERITY): The gumshoe is able to move silently in urban areas with a successful dexterity check. The gumshoe can move up to one-half the character's normal speed at no penalty. At more than one-half and up to the character's full speed, the character suffers a -5 penalty. It's practically impossible (-20 penalty) to move silently while running or charging. Gumshoes may attempt to use this ability in wilderness environs, but at an additional -5 penalty.

While the descriptions seem similar, hiding and moving silently are two different things. One is the ability to remain visually concealed, the other to move without sound. Gumshoes cannot hide and move silently at the same time until they reach 3rd level. At this level and beyond, a Gumshoe can attempt both but must make a successful hide and move silent check at-5. In this case, movement is reduced to one quarter the normal movement rate.

TAKE 'EM DOWN: Gumshoes possess an extraordinary ability to combat their most common foes, criminals, due to intense training and study of the enemy's fighting techniques. When fighting hooligans, thugs, or other gumshoes, a gumshoe inflicts extra damage. This damage bonus is +1 at first level, with an additional +1 gained at every level beyond first. For example, a fifth level gumshoe would inflict an additional 5hp of damage for each successful hit against thugs, hooligans, or other gumshoes.

PRECISION SHOT: A P.I.'s best friend is his snub nose, and one never knows when a shot that takes out a chandelier can save the day. At second level, gumshoes gain a +1 to hit with a handgun at ranges of less than thirty feet. At fourth level, the gumshoe reduces all range penalties for hitting with a handgun by half. At seventh level, when using a handgun, the gumshoe ignores any cover bonuses the target gains to AC. At tenth level, the gumshoe gains an extra shot per round with a handgun. At twelfth level and every three levels thereafter, the gumshoe may fire one extra (cumulative) bullet at a single target with one attack roll, which may not be combined with the extra shot granted at tenth level.

FACE IN THE CROWD (CHARISMA): Beginning at third level, through quick changes of clothing and posture, the gumshoe can disguise or impersonate to blend into a crowd. This disguise is not complete; it is used to throw off a tail, stalk prey without being noticed, or other similar effects. Impersonating specific individuals is not possible with this ability, though affecting a change in gender, race, or even social class is possible. This effort requires 1d4 rounds to complete and can include an apparent change of height or weight no more than one-tenth the original (generally through standing straighter or on tip-toes, or slouching). The Game Master makes the character's check secretly so that the character is not sure if it is successful. The following modifiers are applied to a disguise check when appropriate.

Sex difference	-2
Race difference	-2
Age difference	-2 per 10 years
Social class difference (higher)	-2 to -10 (GM's discretion)
Social class difference (lower)	+2 (it's easier to be a pauper than a prince)

Success indicates a disguise good enough to fool normal observers, though those actively looking for such a disguise may increase the Challenge Level of the check, perhaps significantly. As such, this ability is generally used to remain discreet and inconspicuous, rather than for any sort of actual impersonation.

ADVERSARY: At sixth level, the gumshoe has become famous (or infamous) enough to have drawn the ire of a specific organization whose members or affiliates he has plagued once too often. However, this can work to the gumshoe's advantage, as he becomes intimately familiar with the signs, tactics, and operations of this organization. When combating or dealing with members of this organization, the gumshoe gains a +2 bonus to hit and to AC in combat. Further, all attribute checks related to dealings with this organization are made at a +2 bonus. This includes all gumshoe class abilities. The organization should be specific, but need not be world-spanning or infamous. For example, a gumshoe could have "The Reds, a local gang in the East End of Philadelphia," just as easily as he could, "The American branches of the Yakuza." Game Masters should monitor this choice to ensure that the Adversary is appropriate to both the character and the campaign.

PRIME ATTRIBUTE: Dexterity

ALIGNMENT: Any

HIT DICE: d10

WEAPONS: Small melee weapons, medium melee weapons, handguns, sub-machineguns, rifles and shotguns

ABILITIES: Climb, cat and mouse, hide, move silently, take 'em down, deadeye shot, face in the crowd, adversary.

Level	HD	BtH	EPP
1	10 HP	+1	0
2	d10	+2	2,001
3	d10	+3	4,501
4	d10	+4	9,001
5	d10	+5	18,501
6	d10	+6	36,001
7	d10	+7	72,001
8	d10	+8	145,001
9	d10	+9	290,001
10	d10	+10	580,001
11	+5 HP	+11	870,001
12	+5 HP	+12	1,120,001
13+	+5 HP	*	+250,000

*+1 per level

THE HOOLIGAN

The sentries were half-asleep. It had been far too quiet over the past few months on the Eastern front, and the long shifts on the parapets of the ancient castle were enough to send the most acutely-attentive man to slumber. She was counting on that.

Natalya Abramova slipped through the shadows of the Bavarian forests and scaled the walls of the castle as though there were ready-made steps for her to take. The up-and-coming Hollywood starlet moonlighted as the cat burglar known as the Fox for her blood-red costume and stylized mask, and plied her skills in a more heroic fashion as a member of the adventuring Brotherhood of William St. John. For her, life was about the thrill of risk, the joy of a good con, the satisfaction of getting over on a target who never even knew she was there.

The Fox glided along the walkways, coming up behind the first sentry. Her knife flashed and with barely a gurgle the first guard slipped to the ground. Three more to go, and her companions could approach home-free…

The archetypal ne'er-do-wells, these characters can be cat burglars, thieves in the night, or bootleggers. They may be mob enforcers (or even bosses, at higher levels), suave con-men, or common street thugs. They are rebels against the mainstream, be it with or without a cause.

Some make their living by burglary, robbing wealthy marks and pilfering the goods on the black market. Others are street urchins and pickpockets. Still others find their skills best suited to plundering ancient catacombs and tombs, unraveling riddles in dark caves, and seeking ancient treasure from the forgotten places of the world, avoiding the laws and the lawmen of the more civilized areas of the world. Whatever their preference, the hooligan lives for the thrill of the chase, of pulling something off right under the noses of the feds, and getting away with it. To perform these acrobatic feats of daring, they must be exceedingly dexterous, nimble of hand and foot, but also must be quick-witted with sharp senses.

A slick combination of mental acumen and hand-eye coordination, the hooligan is a foe to be feared and an acquaintance never to be trusted. Hooligans tend to be chaotic or neutral in alignment, though there do exist thieves with honor that have their own code, though the distribution of abilities of this class makes practitioners of the shadow arts that are of a lawful and good persuasion rare beyond rare.

ABILITIES

BACK ATTACK: In general, a hooligan avoids face-to-face combat if possible and prefers to use stealth to attack an opponent from behind, striking the back, lungs, kidneys, or another vital area. A hooligan who is thus able to attack an unaware opponent from the rear, gains a bonus to hit and to damage. To catch an opponent unaware, a hooligan must make a successful move silently check to sneak up behind

the foe, or make a successful hide check while behind the opponent. A hooligan that succeeds in one or the other of these can make a back attack at a +4 bonus to hit. A successful hit inflicts double the normal damage.

When making a back attack, a hooligan must use a close-quarters melee weapon. This weapon must be shorter than the character's arm. A hooligan can only back attack living creatures that have a discernible anatomy. The hooligan must be able to see the target well enough to pick out a vital spot, and then must be able to reach it.

As the hooligan gains experience, the damage inflicted increases and can be applied with a ranged weapon, such as a handgun. At 5th level, a back attack deals triple damage, and at 9th level a back attack inflicts quadruple damage or double damage with a ranged weapon within thirty feet. A back attack cannot be combined with the sneak attack ability.

CASE TARGET (WISDOM): Using this ability, the hooligan can determine information and weaknesses about a potential opponent or target through detailed observation and deductive reasoning. A hooligan must spend 1d3x10 minutes observing an opponent before a check is allowed. A successful check results in knowledge of the approximate level or Hit Dice of the opponent within 10%, alignment, hidden weapons or unusual items, distinguishing habits and mannerisms, and any other details that might not be apparent to normal observation. The Game Master must decide what the hooligan can learn about the target and deems appropriate to convey. If used on a location, the check can reveal security measures and weaknesses, location and disposition of guards, entry and escape points, etc.

CLIMB (DEXTERITY): This extraordinary ability allows a hooligan to climb up, down, or across a slope, wall, steep incline (even a ceiling with handholds), or unusually angled natural or man made slope or incline that others would find

impossible to climb. When doing so, the hooligan moves at one-half the character's normal speed. A failed climb check means that the character makes no progress. A check that fails by 5 or more means that the character falls from the currently attained height, and must suffer falling damage. Hooligans cannot carry anything in their hands while climbing. When climbing typical natural slopes and manmade inclines, such as a cliff faces or steep steps, a hooligan does not need to make an attribute check to climb the surface. It is only when climbing very sheer and difficult grades where there are few to no hand- or footholds that a check needs be made.

HIDE (DEXTERITY): Hooligans use this ability to conceal themselves from others. A successful check means that the Hooligan is hidden so well as to be almost invisible. The hooligan can move up to one-half normal speed and remain hidden. Hide checks suffer no penalty in this circumstance. At more than one-half and up to full speed, the character suffers a -5 penalty to the check to remain hidden. It's practically impossible (-20 penalty) to hide while running or charging.

If the character is being observed, even casually, he cannot hide. If observers are momentarily distracted, though, the character can attempt to hide. While the observer averts its attention from the character, the character can attempt to get to a hiding place. This check, however, is at a –10 penalty because the character has to move quickly to the hiding place. A hooligan cannot hide if there is nothing to hide behind or conceal oneself with. Deep shadows can count as concealment at the Game Master's discretion.

LINGO: Hooligans often use a street language known only to those in the trade, called their lingo. Code words, hand signals, demeanor, and other signs comprise the lingo, which is often a pidgin version of a real language. The lingo can be used to convey complex ideas. The language may vary to some degree both geographically and culturally, making the lingo unique to each region, city, or even within a city.

LISTEN (WISDOM): A hooligan can use this ability to listen intently and hear noises that others might not detect, even through an obstacle such as a door. Generally, a successful check at the character's CB indicates that the hooligan has detected some sort of noise. The hooligan can hear soft sounds, like a whisper or cat stalking, while outside or in the open and up to a range of 30 feet. It also indicates success if the hooligan is listening for sounds on the other side of a door, but the hooligan must be adjacent to the door. However, exactly what is heard is up to the Game Master's discretion as each case is unique. If listening through a stone wall, the hooligan suffers a -10 penalty to the check. For other materials, vary the penalty as appropriate. A hooligan can retry this ability once a round.

MOVE SILENTLY (DEXTERITY): This ability allows a hooligan to move so silently that others cannot hear the movement. The hooligan can use this ability both indoors and outdoors. A hooligan can move up to one-half the character's normal speed at no penalty. At more than one-half and up to the character's full speed, the character suffers a -5 penalty. It's practically impossible (-20 penalty) to move silently while running or charging.

While the descriptions seem similar, hiding and moving silently are two different things. One is the ability to remain visually concealed, the other to move without sound. Hooligans cannot hide and move silently at the same time until they reach 3rd level. At this level and beyond, a Hooligan can attempt both but must make a successful hide and move silent check at-5. In this case, movement is reduced to one quarter the normal movement rate.

OPEN LOCK (DEXTERITY): A hooligan can use this ability to open any sort of mechanical lock that would normally require a key to open. A successful check indicates the lock has been opened. This ability requires the use of a set of hooligan's tools, including picks, blank keys, wires or other appropriate tools. A hooligan may only make one attempt per lock. If that attempt fails, the hooligan cannot try to open the same lock again until gaining one more level as it is beyond the current ability of the hooligan to pick it. The CL to pick a lock is at the GM's discretion but generally equal to the level of the locksmith who created the lock to begin with.

PICK POCKET (DEXTERITY): A hooligan can use this ability, on a successful dexterity check, to remove the contents of a pocket or pouch (or otherwise take something from a person) without being noticed. Success may require the hooligan to cut the purse or pouch from the target.

This ability also allows the hooligan to perform "sleight of hand" maneuvers. A successful dexterity check indicates the hooligan has hidden or moved an item in such a manner so that observers are not aware of where the item has been hidden. Such typical maneuvers are hiding a coin, sliding a card up a sleeve, performing the shell game, and the like.

TRAPS (INTELLIGENCE): A hooligan may use this ability in three manners: finding, disabling or setting traps. Each use requires a separate attribute check and each check may be made only once in a given circumstance. The player must also describe how the actions are being performed to use this ability.

To find a trap, a hooligan spends time intently studying and searching an area to deduce possible trap locations. It takes one round to locate a trap in a specific area such as a lock or a doorknob, and one turn to locate a trap in a 10 by 10 foot area. A successful check indicates the hooligan finds one trap, if any are present. The trap discovered is the simplest or most obvious trap in the area. If multiple traps are in an area, multiple successful checks are required to find them all. A hooligan can find magical traps with this ability, although it may be much more difficult than finding mundane traps.

To disable a trap, a hooligan must first know its location. Once a trap is located, a successful check means the hooligan has disarmed the trap. The attempt can only be made once and failure indicates that the hooligan set off the trap. A hooligan can disarm a magic trap, although it may be much more difficult than disarming a mundane trap. In most cases, hooligan's tools are needed to disarm a trap. Generally, it takes 1d4 rounds to disarm a trap, depending on its complexity.

To set a trap, or to reset a previously disabled trap, a hooligan must make a successful traps check. If a hooligan is resetting a trap that was previously disabled, the hooligan gains a +5 bonus to the check. The amount of time required to set or reset a trap depends on the complexity of the trap, typically taking 1d4 rounds.

SNEAK ATTACK: At fourth level, the hooligan can target vital areas any time an opponent is unaware, not just when their back is turned. Even if an opponent or victim is aware of the hooligan, so long as they are unsuspecting of an attack, a hooligan can use the sneak attack ability. For example, a hooligan could be having a conversation with a potential victim while hiding a snub-nose Saturday night special up his sleeve, intending to strike once a piece of vital information is learned. Or, a hooligan could be perched in the shadows of a tree, waiting for the perfect opportunity to use a blowgun, a bow, or (in later pulp settings) a silenced firearm. Alternately, if an ally is currently in combat with a foe, the hooligan can take advantage of the situation, and strike the opponent in a vital area while his attention is split. Unlike the back attack, sneak attack situations do not necessarily require a previously successful hide or move silently check, although the game master could require success in one or both, depending upon the circumstances if necessary.

A hooligan making a sneak attack gains a +2 bonus to hit and a +4 bonus to damage. Ranged weapons can be used for sneak attacks if the target is within 30 feet. A hooligan cannot aim with deadly accuracy from beyond that range. A sneak attack cannot be combined with back attack. At eighth level, this bonus increases to +3 to hit, and +5 to damage, and at twelfth level the bonus increases to +4 to hit and +6 to damage.

PRIME ATTRIBUTE: Dexterity

HIT DIE: d6

ALIGNMENT: Any

WEAPONS: Small melee weapons, handguns, sub-machineguns, rifles and shotguns, explosives

ABILITIES: Back attack, case target, climb, hide, lingo, listen, move silently, open lock, pick pockets, traps, sneak attack

Level	HD	BtH	EPP
1	6 HP	0	0
2	d6	+1	1,801
3	d6	+1	3,501
4	d6	+1	7,001
5	d6	+2	14,001
6	d6	+2	25,001
7	d6	+2	50,001
8	d6	+3	100,001
9	d6	+3	200,001
10	d6	+3	400,001
11	+3 HP	+4	650,001
12	+3 HP	+4	900,001
13+	+3 HP	*	+250,000

*+1 per 3 levels

THE MENTALIST

Natalya hated it when her roguish stealth abilities failed her. The last sentry spun on her when she accidentally stumbled over a loose rock, and spat, "Identifizieren Sie sich!"

She focused her mental energies on the area, feeling every inch of her body become one with the castle and sensing her opponent, the tension in his limbs, the quick beat of his heart, the beads of sweat on his forehead. Somehow, she knew exactly what his next move would be.

She slid her rapier from its scabbard and used it to parry the barrel of his sten gun aside, then neatly stepped inside his personal space before he could bring it to bear, sinking her dagger smoothly into his chest. She lifted her mask and kissed him as his last breath escaped, then whispered. "They call me the Fox, moya lyubov. Sleep well."

As his lifeless form slid to the ground, Natalya shrugged. "They always die of a broken heart," she muttered, then moved to signal her companions. It was good to have other abilities to fall back on when one's training failed, was it not?

Not all mystical power arises from alien forces or from the arcane energies that permeate the lands. Some men and women have the ability to call upon special inner reserves of strength and ability, reserves that manifest as a power commonly known as mentalism, or psionics.

With a colorful assortment of psychic abilities at her disposal, the mentalist leads the way in matters of the occult, but this power comes with an exacting toll. Mainstream society tends to distance itself from her out of fear and mistrust for a type of power they neither have nor can understand. Arcanists, too, shy away from the mentalist, perhaps bitter towards the mentalist's ability to naturally call forth powers that arcanists must work long and hard to achieve.

Many mentalists revel in the dark perception society holds of them, using it to reinforce their own mystique, while others seek to break down these barriers and gain acceptance amongst mainstream society. It is difficult, however; few are likely to trust someone who can read your feelings or thoughts, or even control the same.

Because of the fear and mistrust associated with their abilities, and because of the more focused nature of their power, psychic adventurers must learn certain combat skills to survive in the shadows and seedy underbelly of the world. Thus, they gain a better BtH progression than do arcanists.

ABILITIES

MEDITATION (WIS): Mentalists can, with a successful Wisdom check, enter a trancelike state that cleanses the mind and rests the body. Entering this trance requires 1d12 minutes, and the trance can be maintained by a number of hours equal to the character's level plus her wisdom bonus. One hour of uninterrupted meditation is as good as two hours of sleep. Also, while meditating, the character does not feel the effects of hunger, thirst, or discomfort, though he still suffers any damage resulting from these conditions. While meditating, the character's natural rate of healing doubles (see healing, p. 179).

MENTAL RESISTANCE: At level five, Mentalists gain an extraordinary mental and emotional resilience. All saving throws based on Intelligence, Wisdom, and Charisma gain a +2 bonus. At level eight, this bonus increases to +3, and at level twelve, to +4. Beyond level twelve it increases by +1 per four levels of experience.

PSIONIC POWERS: At levels one, three, five, and seven, the character may choose one new psychic power from the "basic" list. Beginning at level nine, the character may choose new powers from either the "basic," or "advanced" powers lists. Advanced powers have prerequisites that must be met before they can be chosen. After Level 12, Mentalists may continue to select new powers at every odd level. In addition, at first level, the Mentalist gains additional basic powers equal to her Wisdom bonus. Thus, if a Mentalist has Wisdom of 18, she gains four basic powers at first level.

PSYCHIC SENSES (WIS): Psychic senses are also known as "sixth sense" and "ESP." They represent the psychic's ability to perceive the world around him in ways different than others. He can sense a few seconds into the future, thereby detecting potential dangers before they happen, can feel the presence of other psychically or magically active people, can sense taint in a place where atrocities have been committed, etc. In practice, this ability functions much like a magic user's various "Detect" spells, though not as specific. Rather than knowing an item is magic, or that a person has malicious intent, for example, the GM might inform the psychic that she has an odd feeling about this place, person, or thing. Psychic Senses can also lead a character to discover clues or important items with a successful Wisdom Check; this ability grants a +2 bonus on any active search or perception-related task attempted by the psychic. Lastly, a psychic character always gets to make a Wisdom check to avoid surprise.

PRIME ATTRIBUTE: Wisdom

HIT DICE: d6

ALIGNMENT: Any

WEAPONS: Small melee weapons, medium melee weapons, handguns, sub-machineguns, rifles and shotguns.

SPECIAL: Meditation, psionic powers, psychic senses

Level	HD	BtH	EPP
1	6 HP	+0	0
2	d6	+1	1,801
3	d6	+1	4,001
4	d6	+2	8,001
5	d6	+2	16,501
6	d6	+3	33,001
7	d6	+3	65,001
8	d6	+4	130,001
9	d6	+4	260,001
10	d6	+5	520,001
11	+3 HP	+5	780,001
12	+3 HP	+6	1,040,001
13+	+3 HP	*	+260,000

* +1 per 2 levels

THE PUGILIST

"Savage" Steve McPartland set his back to the wall, his faithful Rottweiler Bluto at his side. The dog's back arched, his sharp teeth bared, and snarled at the group of Triad assassins in a semicircle around the two.

"Okay, Gents," Steve said. I'm not really sure what I did to get you all angry with me, but I'm sure we can work this out like men?"

The first Triad came in fast, with a dagger strike aimed right at Steve's head. Steve caught his wrist in one hand, forcing the dagger high, then grabbed for the assassin's armpit with the other, easily lifting the lithe Asian man and slamming him head-first into the wall. He let go and the man sprawled senseless to the splintered wood of the docks.

He turned to the rest of the assassins and grinned. "That's what I'm talking about. Who's next?"

The pugilist is the master of hand to hand combat, a professional boxer, traveling martial artist, or lowly pit fighter whose fists of iron are matched only by the damage he can soak up and still keep on going. These characters tend to be simple, viewing the world in terms of "Good" and "Bad," but are often loyal and good to have in your corner, especially when the fists start flying.

Pugilists are rough-and-tumble men and women who love to mix it up and get down and dirty. Generally, at least in the western world, a pugilist has little time or patience for talk or negotiation; they'd rather just beat something to a pulp. There are those, however, who have the wisdom to see their physical exploits as a path to inner peace; honing the mind, to them, is as important as honing the body, and using their body as the lethal weapon it is, for these wandering philosopher-monks, becomes a last resort.

Regardless of their philosophical outlook, pugilists eventually become so adept at fisticuffs and hand-to-hand fighting that they can take on just about anyone. A pugilist can be a professional boxer or wrestler, a trained martial artist, or just a street kid who had to come up using his fists to make a name for himself. Many pugilists work as bouncers in local bars, as wrestlers or fighters for the entertainment of the locals, or even as enforcers for the local crime syndicate.

ABILITIES

DOWN AND DIRTY: The Pugilist likes to get in close, grab and pin. Thus, at level two he starts to become quite adept at the process. At level 2, the pugilist gains a +1 on all attempts to initiate or break free from a grapple, as well as all opposed strength and dexterity checks. This bonus improves to +2 at level 5, to +3 at level 8, and to +4 at level 11.

Whenever a pugilist successfully grapples an opponent, he may immediately and for each round thereafter that the grapple is maintained, automatically deal damage as though he had made a successful unarmed attack. The pugilist may choose to inflict subdual damage instead of lethal damage in this case. However, the opponent may attempt to break the hold every round; if so, the pugilist must make a new grapple check with a CL equal to the opponent's hit dice and Strength or Dexterity bonus (whichever is higher).

TOUGH AS NAILS (CON): The pugilist's mental mastery over their body imparts a +1 bonus to all constitution-based saving throws. The bonus increases to +2 at 3rd level, +3 at 6th level, +4 at 10th level and +5 at 15th level.

UNARMED ATTACK: A pugilist specializes in unarmed, hand-to-hand combat. Pugilists gain attacks and improve in the amount of unarmed combat damage inflicted as shown on the table. The pugilist also gains the ability to make an off-hand attack at 6th level. The pugilist may choose whether the attacks inflict normal damage or subdual damage.

When pugilists gain the extra off-hand attack, they do not incur the penalties to their 'to hit' die rolls as described in the combat section as long as both attacks are unarmed attacks. A pugilist fighting with a one-handed weapon can make an unarmed attack as an off-hand attack, but the pugilist suffers the standard penalties for two-weapon fighting. Likewise, a pugilist with a weapon in his or her off-hand may make an extra attack with that weapon, but suffers the usual penalties for two-weapon fighting.

UNARMORED DEFENSE: A pugilist knows how to use his or her body for defense, and gains an AC bonus that

increases with experience as indicated on the Pugilist Special Abilities table. This bonus does not stack with that from any other armor; the pugilist gains no AC bonuses from a Pulp Costume (see Pulp Armor).

DEFLECT MISSILES: At 2nd level, pugilists gain the ability to deflect non-magical projectiles, including but not limited to, arrows, axes, bolas, bolts, bullets, clubs, daggers, darts, hammers, harpoons, javelins, nets, rocks, and spears. The pugilist must have at least one hand free to use this ability. When a character would normally be hit with a ranged weapon, the character can make a dexterity check with a CL equal to the BtH bonus and Dexterity bonus of the attacker. If the check succeeds, the pugilist deflects the weapon and suffers no damage. This can be done once per round for levels 2-6, twice per round for levels 7-11, three times per round for levels 12 to 16 and four times per round for levels 17-20. If the pugilist beats the attack roll by more than 5, he has caught the projectile instead of deflecting it.

The pugilist must be aware of the attack to use this ability. An attempt to deflect a ranged weapon counts as a pugilist's primary unarmed attack. If a pugilist is high enough level to have a secondary unarmed attack, the pugilist may still make the secondary attack if the deflect missile ability has only been used once or twice. If three or more missiles are deflected, the secondary attack is considered used.

FAST MOVEMENT: At 3rd level and higher, a pugilist moves faster than normal. A pugilist carrying a medium or heavy load loses this extra speed. See the Pugilist Special Abilities Chart for the increase in speed.

ROLL WITH FALL (DEX): At 4th level, a falling pugilist is able to absorb the impact from a fall by rolling with the damage. He takes damage from a fall as if the fall were 20 feet shorter than it actually is. The pugilist must succeed at a Dexterity Check with a CL of 1 per ten feet fallen to use this ability. At 6th level, the pugilist, on a successful save, takes half damage from a fall instead of reducing the fall by 20 feet.

IRON CONSTITUTION: At 5th level, a pugilist gains +1 to all saving throws versus disease and poison. This saving throw bonus increases by one for every level past 5th. For example, a 10th level pugilist receives a +6 bonus. After 10th level, the +1 bonus is gained once every other level to a maximum bonus of +10 at 18th level.

SUBMISSION HOLD: Starting at level six, the pugilist can place a submission hold on an opponent, rendering them helpless and eventually unconscious. If the character is able to grapple the opponent and maintain the hold for at least one round, the opponent must make a Constitution Save each round after the first (assuming he is unable to break free) at a CL equal to the brawler's strength bonus and hit dice or level. Failure means the opponent is rendered unconscious for 1d4 rounds. This unconsciousness is normal, though deep, and the opponent can be roused by vigorous efforts (if an ally spends an entire round shaking, slapping or otherwise stimulating the unconscious character, allow a base Constitution Save to awaken) or taking damage.

GRANITE JAW (CON): At 6th level, the pugilist can take half damage from any blunt or bashing source (fists, clubs, staves, etc.) by making a Constitution Check with a CL equal to the damage dealt. This ability cannot be used against damage from piercing or bladed weapons, or from bullets.

FAST HEALING: At 7th level, a pugilist's body naturally heals faster than normal. Each day, a pugilist heals 1d4+1 hit points per level as long as rest, sleep and meditation is possible. The pugilist must be in a serene environment, under no physical duress or mental stress, must be able to sleep undisturbed for 12 hours, and meditate undisturbed for 6 hours. Food and water should be plentiful.

DEATH STRIKE: At 12th level, a pugilist gains a fearsome and deadly attack. Some call this the quivering palm. Others the five-point exploding heart. Still others of a less showy persuasion just snap necks, create aneurisms, or blast cartilage into their opponents' brains. The pugilist can use the attack once per week. The attack must be announced before an attack roll is made. The pugilist must be of higher level than the target or have more levels than the target's hit dice. If the pugilist successfully deals damage with an unarmed attack, the death strike succeeds. Thereafter, the pugilist can choose to try to slay the victim at any later time within 1 round per level of the pugilist. The pugilist merely wills the target to die, and the victim makes a constitution check. If the victim fails, it dies.

For example, a 10th level pugilist successfully strikes a 5th level gumshoe. The pugilist can then attempt to will the character to die any time within the following ten rounds. Should the gumshoe fail a constitution saving throw, the gumshoe dies.

PUGILIST SPECIAL ABILITIES

Level	Unarmored AC	Primary Unarmed Attack	Secondary Unarmed Attack	Fast Movement
1	10	1d4		
2	11	1d6		
3	12	1d6		40
4	12	1d6		40
5	13	1d8		40
6	13	1d8	1d4	50
7	13	1d8	1d4	50
8	14	1d8	1d4	50
9	14	1d10	1d6	50
10	14	1d10	1d6	60
11	14	1d10	1d6	60
12	15	1d10	1d6	60

PRIME ATTRIBUTE: Constitution

HIT DIE: d12

ALIGNMENT: Any

WEAPONS: Any melee weapons, archaic ranged weapons

ABILITIES: Down and dirty, tough as nails, unarmed attack, unarmored defense, deflect arrows, fast movement, fists of stone, roll with fall, iron constitution, choke hold, granite jaw, fast healing, death strike

Level	HD	BtH	EPP
1	12 HP	+0	0
2	d12	+1	1,901
3	d12	+2	4,001
4	d12	+3	8,501
5	d12	+4	20,001
6	d12	+5	40,001
7	d12	+6	80,001
8	d12	+7	160,001
9	d12	+8	325,001
10	d12	+9	550,001
11	+6 HP	+10	750,001
12	+6 HP	+11	1,250,001
13	+6 HP	*	+ 250,000

*+1 per level

THE RAIDER

Tennessee O'Malley hung by one hand over a gorge that from his vantage looked bottomless. For the time being, he was stable, but he watched one of his prized tomahawks tumble into the ravine. Cripes, he thought, it must be a thousand feet down! Then, on the heels of that, he muttered, "This really isn't my day. I loved that hatchet."

He gripped the sapling desperately with one hand, his other flailing for another hand rest. At length he found a solid grip on the rock and started to pull himself over the ledge. At least the idol representing the ancient and lost cult of the Red God was still secure in his pouch.

With a gasp, he made it over the ledge back onto solid ground and was relieved to see that his competitors' men were nowhere to be seen. At least one thing had gone right today. Of course, making it on foot to a town in the desert heat was going to be a challenge. He stood, brushed off his khakis, adjusted his hat, and set off. There were cliffs and rock formations nearby that could provide shelter, and if he remembered right, the ancient natives that once populated this area had reliable means of finding water amongst the shrub-like growths in the area.

He checked his Webley revolver, blew some dust from the chambers, and re-holstered it.

That was when the thundering sound of approaching horses reached his ears…

The Raider is an adventuring scholar who plumbs deep tombs in search of the treasures of lost worlds. Most raiders are well-schooled and many hold positions as historical researchers or professors of ancient civilizations or religions. They are historians, archaeologists, anthropologists, and seekers of knowledge as well as of treasure and fortune. But more than that, they just live for the thrill of adventure and the excitement of discovering something new and never-before-seen. They spend their days waiting for the chance to–at least for a little while–hang up their coat and tie in exchange for a leather jacket, work boots, and their trusty .45 to seek some long-lost artifact that could change the face of scholarship forever.

Raiders come from all philosophies and outcomes, and there are honorable, forthright and trustworthy Raiders who seek to preserve ancient treasures for all, just as there are greedy, dishonorable scum who work for the highest bidder, and ruthless collectors seeking only to pad their own personal store of antiquities.

Since their stock in trade is ancient worlds, civilizations, languages, and artifacts, Intelligence is paramount to the Raider, but Constitution and Dexterity are also important for avoiding the many pitfalls and traps left by the builders of ancient tombs, and for surviving the punishment these traps and pitfalls deal out when stumbled upon.

ABILITIES

BONUS LANGUAGES (INTELLIGENCE): Raiders are studied in many languages and customs. As such, the Raider gains two additional languages per point of intelligence bonus at character creation, rather than one. These bonus languages cannot be used to trade for extra Knowledge skills (if this option is used; see p. 64), but even if the Raider chooses to trade languages for knowledge skills, he still gains the bonus languages per this ability.

For Example: A character with an Intelligence Score of 18 normally would gain six languages for his +3 bonus. The GM has chosen to use the optional Knowledge skills system and the Raider chooses to take three Knowledge skills instead of three of his languages. However, due to this class ability he still gains three bonus languages, which may not be traded for Knowledge skills. Thus, he gains six languages and three Knowledge skills. If he chooses not to take any Knowledge skills, the Raider could be fluent in nine languages!

CRYPTOLINGUIST (INTELLIGENCE): Masters of ancient and forgotten languages, raiders often need to decipher and interpret legends and secret writings to acquire more knowledge. This ability allows the raider to decipher writing in an unfamiliar language, a message written in an incomplete or archaic form or a message written in code. If the check succeeds, the character understands the general content of a piece of writing. It takes ten turns to decipher each page of a script. A cryptolinguist check may be made only once per writing.

DISGUISE (CHARISMA): With a successful check in this ability, raiders can use their knowledge of other lands and customs to disguise themselves or impersonate people and cultures. The ability allows the raider to impersonate general types of people, as well as individuals. For example, a European raider might impersonate a Bedouin, or pass for a local in an alien country.

For a general impersonation such as a soldier or a member of a different race, the effort requires a few props, makeup, and 1d3x10 minutes of work to complete. Where specific individuals are being impersonated, at least one month's preparation time is required to avoid detection. A disguise can include an apparent change of height or weight of no more than one-tenth the original height or weight of the raider. The Game Master makes the character's disguise check secretly so that the character is not sure of its success. The following penalties are applied to a disguise check when appropriate: sex difference -2, race difference -2, and a -2 for an age difference of more than ten years.

A successful disguise does not fool an observer in all instances. Success indicates that the raider is disguised well enough to fool normal, non-suspicious observers. If a suspicious individual observes the raider, the Game Master may allow the observer an intelligence check to see through the disguise. If a raider is impersonating a particular individual, all who know that individual are permitted to make a wisdom check to detect the disguise. If the observer would recognize the impersonated individual on sight, the check is made at+4. If the observer is a friend or close associate, the check is made at +8 and if intimate, the check is at +12.

LEGEND LORE (INTELLIGENCE): Raiders are masters of myth and archaic knowledge. With a successful attribute check, a raider gains or remembers some relevant information about local notables, a legendary item, a noteworthy place or any other relevant bit of information. Gaining the information may entail speaking to local inhabitants and/ or doing research. The information might prove useful in diplomacy, entertaining, or otherwise influencing others. The ability also might impart a full or partial understanding of local or secret languages, including the local lingo of the criminal underworld, the secret druidic language or raider signs.

The check will not reveal the powers of a magic item, but may give a hint to its history, general function or activation. The Game Master gauges the challenge level of the check based on whether the knowledge is: Common known by at least a substantial minority of the local population (CL 1); Uncommon but available, known by only a few people in the area (CL 5); Obscure, known by few, and hard to come by (CL 10); Extremely Obscure, known by very few scholars and sages, possibly forgotten by most who once knew it, or possibly known only by those who don't understand the significance of the knowledge (CL 15 or higher, depending on the knowledge in question).

SCALE (DEXTERITY): This extraordinary ability allows a raider to climb up, down, or across a dangerous natural slope or inverted incline that others would find impossible to climb. When doing so, the raider moves at one-half the character's normal speed. A failed scale check means that the character makes no progress. A check that fails by 5 or more means that the character falls from the currently attained height and must suffer falling damage. Nothing can be carried in the raider's hands while climbing. When climbing typical natural slopes and inclines, such as steep but rocky hillsides, a raider need not make an attribute check to scale the surface.

SURVIVAL (INTELLIGENCE): In wilderness environments, raiders can provide shelter for themselves and others, and can provide decent food and water for several people, all without the need for an attribute check unless it is a large number of people. The raider can forage and hunt for food and water. The raider must spend 8 hours hunting and gathering to produce enough food and water to feed 2-8 people for a day. If the raider wishes to feed or shelter a larger group of people than the die indicate, a successful wisdom check is necessary. If successful, the raider must spend an additional 8 hours gathering food to feed and water an additional 2-8 people. This additional effort allows the raider to gather food and water for up to 4-16 creatures. The raider can only hunt and forage for food twice per day.

For example: A raider is attempting to feed 12 people. For 8 hours of effort, the raider feeds 2-8 people automatically. The result is a 6, so the raider has to feed 6 more people. On a successful wisdom check, the raider can forage for another 8 eight hours and feed 2-8 more people.

In addition to the ability to provide food and shelter in the wilds, a raider can automatically determine where true north lies in relation to the character in normal wilderness environments.

TRAPS (WISDOM): A raider is able to detect and build simple traps in a wilderness environment, or in ancient structures (such as lost tombs, ancient mazes, etc). When passing within 25 feet of a wilderness or primitive trap, a raider is entitled to an attribute check to spot it. When actively searching for traps, the raider receives a +2 bonus to the check. It takes one round to locate a trap in a 5 x 5 foot area, or one turn spent searching to locate a trap in a 25 x 25 foot area. A raider cannot find magical traps with this ability.

A raider can set simple traps in a wilderness environment. These include snares, pit traps and similar devices. Raiders cannot set complicated mechanical traps such as those found on treasure chests or on doorways. On a successful traps check, the raider successfully builds and conceals a snare or pit trap. Snares can capture and hold creatures of up to medium height, and pit traps can be dug to deliver 1d4 points of damage (halved if the creature falling in it makes a successful dexterity saving throw). Raiders can also disable simple wilderness traps (of any type they can build) with little or no effort. No traps check need be made to do this.

RESIST ELEMENTS: Raiders spend a great deal of time in inhospitable climes seeking lost treasures. This toughens them against the elements. At 2nd level, raiders gain a +2 bonus to saving throws against fire, water, earth, air, cold and lightning attacks.

FAVORED WEAPON: Raiders often have a specific type of gun, sword, whip, or other weapon that they favor above all others. At third level, the Raider chooses one weapon in his arsenal with which to specialize. When using this weapon or a weapon of the same type (any .38 caliber revolver, for example, or any bullwhip or any .45 Auto Pistol), he gains a +1 bonus to hit and damage. At Fifth level, this bonus increases to +2 to hit and damage. At tenth level, the bonus is +3 to hit and damage. At twelfth level, the Raider may choose a second weapon with which to specialize, gaining +2 to hit and damage with that second weapon.

PRIME ATTRIBUTE: Intelligence

HIT DICE: d10

ALIGNMENT: Any

WEAPONS: All

SPECIAL: Bonus Languages, Cryptolinguist, Disguise, Legend Lore, Scale, Survival, Traps, Resist Elements, Favored Weapon

Level	HD	BtH	EPP
1	10 HP	+1	0
2	d10	+2	2,100
3	d10	+3	4,301
4	d10	+4	8,601
5	d10	+5	17,501
6	d10	+6	35,001
7	d10	+7	70,001
8	d10	+8	140,001
9	d10	+9	280,001
10	d10	+10	560,001
11	+5 HP	+11	840,001
12	+5 HP	+12	1,120,001
13+	+5 HP	*	+280,000

*+1 per level

THE SOCIALITE

The museum was awash with police and reporters. Word of the theft earlier in the evening had quickly spread throughout the city and everyone wanted a piece of it. Tennessee O'Malley and Mackenzie, "Mackie" Gleeson stood at the fringes, watching the circus.

"We're never getting in there," O'Malley grumbled. "Should we call Nat?"

Mackie shook her head. "No good. She's got stealth, but she doesn't know anything about mummies. That's your job. But don't worry about it. I've got this. Follow me and keep it quiet."

She ducked and weaved through the gauntlet of reporters and cops. A few flashes turned her way, but she ignored them. She could feel O'Malley at her back. He

was nervous about all this. The man needed to start having faith in other people once in awhile.

She walked up to the front doors of the museum like she owned the place, which wasn't far from the truth. The officer at the front door held up a hand as she approached; she flashed him a winning smile.

"Hi there, Jim," she said. "Please don't give me any trouble. You know me, and you know well how much money my family has invested in this museum. Now, my colleague here is an expert on Ancient Egypt, and you're going to let us in so he can take a look."

"This isn't a good idea," the officer said, but stepped aside for Mackie and O'Malley to pass.

The connected diplomat or wealthy debutante with money, power, and prestige to match his or her pretty face, this person has the looks, connections, and personal magnetism to open doors when guns are a bad idea. While many socialites come from rich families, not all are wealthy unto themselves. A socialite could be temporarily or permanently cut off from family funds from disgracing her family name or even just because her parents want her to learn to live on her own. Alternately, she could be "new money," an up-and-coming movie starlet or the wife of a country-boy-turned-senator.

Socialites adventure largely out of boredom and desire for excitement, though there are exceptions, young debutantes who want something of their own, not related to the reputation of their family (though most are not above exploiting their family name to get where they need to go). These tend to become adventurers and thrill-seekers, gathering allies to their side based on their charisma and self-confidence. The socialite makes the perfect "face" for a group, being the consummate diplomat and/or seductress.

Charisma is the most important attribute for socialites, as most of their abilities are based upon this attribute. However, Dexterity and Constitution help keep her alive in the perilous situations in which she may find herself, and Wisdom is of importance in knowing where her family and reputation hold influence, and in keeping herself and her allies safe from rash decisions.

ABILITIES

CHARM (CHARISMA): The Socialite can attempt to charm another person to do her bidding. This ability works exactly as the spell Charm Person, save that the Socialite must make a Charisma Attribute check against a CL equal to the level or hit dice of the person she is attempting to charm. Her effective "caster level" for purposes of duration, effect, etc., is equal to her Socialite Level. At Fifth level, the socialite can instead of charming a subject, attempt to through subtle seduction and subliminal suggestion Command the subject as per the second level arcanist spell, if she desires. At twelfth level, if she so desires, she can attempt to Mass Charm instead of charming or commanding a single target. This ability can be used once per day at first level, twice per day at fifth level, three times per day at tenth level, and at fifteenth level, the socialite can perform this ability at will.

CONNECTED (CHARISMA): The socialite (or her family) has friends and acquaintances everywhere. Whenever the PC's need help, information, a friendly face, or resources, the Socialite can attempt to call in a favor from one of these friends. This requires two checks. First, the Socialite must make a Wisdom Check to locate a friendly name or face in the current area where the PC's are adventuring. Failure means the socialite's family has no friends in this area. Second, the socialite must make a Charisma check to call in the favor. The GM determines the CL of this check based on the reputation of the socialite, the number of favors previously (and recently) called in, and other social factors at the GM's discretion. Success means the acquaintance is willing to help, but such help may (again, dependent upon social factors at the GM's discretion) come at a price.

EXALT (CHARISMA): This is the socialite's ability to inspire companions and listeners, allowing them to surpass their normal level of performance. Some socialites invoke this ability through oration, while others use battle cries or sheer acting and demeanor. With a successful attribute check, a socialite can help allies succeed at a task. The ally gets a +2 bonus on any action requiring an attribute check, including class ability checks, saving throws and standard attribute checks. This ability does not affect attack rolls. The allies must be able to see and hear the socialite, and must be within 60 feet. The Game Master may rule that certain uses of this ability are infeasible. The socialite can use this ability once per day per level, and can maintain the effect for a number of rounds equal to the socialite's level. As the socialite rises in levels, the bonus imparted increases as well. It rises to +3 at 6th level, +4 at 12th level and +5 at 18th level.

EMBOLDEN: At 3rd level, the socialite's confidence and fearlessness in the face of danger instills courage in their companions and followers. Any companions or followers within 30 feet of the socialite gain a bonus of +1 to strength, constitution, dexterity, and intelligence saving throws, and a +2 to wisdom and charisma saving throws. This ability can be used once per day and lasts a number of rounds equal to the socialite's level. This ability cannot be used in conjunction with demoralize or exalt.

FASCINATE: At 4th level, a socialite gains the ability to place a single intelligent creature into a trance. The creature to be fascinated must be able to see and hear the socialite, and the socialite must also see the creature. The creature must be able to pay attention to the socialite. The distraction of a nearby combat or other danger will prevent the ability from working. The socialite can use seduction, music, poetry, chanting, speech, whistling, playing an instrument or any combination of the above, as long as some verbal element is included. Socialites can use this ability three times per day, and can maintain the effect for a number of rounds equal to their level.

When a socialite uses this ability, the target makes a charisma saving throw to resist the socialite's charms. The CL of this

check is equal to the socialite's level plus her Charisma bonus. If the saving throw fails, the creature sits quietly and listens to the socialite for up to the full duration of the effect. While using this ability, a socialite must concentrate, as if casting or maintaining a spell. While fascinated, the target is treated as if prone and also suffers a -4 penalty to all saving throws and a -5 to armor class.

If the creature's saving throw succeeds, the socialite cannot attempt to fascinate that creature again for 24 hours. Any threat that is obvious to the fascinated creature, such as the casting of a spell, drawing of a sword, aiming of a weapon or actually taking damage, automatically breaks the effect.

As the socialite rises in levels, the power of the fascination increases as well, allowing the socialite to further influence the listener through suggestion. These specialized uses of the fascinate ability can only be performed on creatures who are under the influence of the socialite's fascinate ability. At 5th level, a socialite may attempt a charm person on a fascinated creature. At 8th level, a socialite may attempt to implant a suggestion into a fascinated creature. At 12th level, a socialite may attempt antipathy/ sympathy on a fascinated creature.

As the socialite gains experience, the number of creatures that can be affected by the fascination, or one of its specialized uses, increases. The number of creatures is equal to two fewer than the level of the socialite. For example, a 4th level socialite can fascinate 2 creatures, a 6th level socialite can fascinate 4 creatures, and a 12th level socialite can fascinate 10 creatures.

At 18th level, a socialite may attempt a mass suggestion on a large crowd of fascinated creatures, as per the mass suggestion spell. In each case, the targets receive a saving throw to attempt to break the fascination.

DEMORALIZE (CHARISMA): At 5th level, the socialite, with a successful Charisma check, may cause fear, dread, or hopelessness in the ranks of foes and enemy forces. This Charisma check has a CL equal to the average hit dice or level of the foes he seeks to affect. Enemies to the socialite's immediate endeavor suffer a penalty of -4 to charisma checks.

In addition, the affected foes must successfully save versus fear at a -4 penalty or suffer a -1 penalty to hit. This ability can be used once per day and lasts a number of rounds equal to the socialite's level. The number of creatures that can be affected increases as the socialite gains levels. At 5th level, the socialite can affect up to 5 creatures. The ability affects up to 10 creatures at 7th level, up to 25 creatures at 9th level, up to 50 creatures at 12th level and 100 creatures at 16th level. This ability cannot be use in conjunction with embolden and exalt.

EXHORT GREATNESS: At 9th level, a socialite can inspire greatness in one other person. For every two levels the socialite attains beyond 9th, the socialite can inspire greatness in an additional ally. To inspire greatness, the socialite must use some sort of oration, inspiring speech or language. The ally to be inspired must be able to hear and understand the socialite, and must be within 30 feet for the effect to take place.

A person inspired with greatness gains temporary hit points and attack bonuses for as long as the socialite is within its hearing and the socialite continues to encourage them. This effect lasts for one turn, or six rounds, at 9th level, and the duration increases by one additional round for every level beyond 9th. The ally can move out of the 30 foot radius once the exhortation has begun, but it must still be able to hear the socialite at all times.

The target gains a +2 bonus on all 'to hit' rolls, and gains temporary hit points as if two hit dice (or levels) higher. Apply the ally's constitution modifier, if any, to each bonus hit point roll. See the combat section for a detailed explanation of temporary hit points.

PRIME ATTRIBUTE: Charisma

HIT DIE: d8

ALIGNMENT: Any

WEAPONS: Handguns, Small melee weapons, medium melee weapons, archaic ranged weapons

ABILITIES: Charm Person, Connected, Exalt, Embolden, Fascinate, Demoralize, Exhort Greatness

Level	HD	BtH	EPP
1	8 HP	+0	0
2	d8	+1	1,901
3	d8	+2	3,801
4	d8	+3	8,001
5	d8	+4	16,401
6	d8	+5	33,801
7	d8	+6	67,601
8	d8	+7	135,201
9	d8	+8	250,000
10	d8	+9	501,001
11	+4 HP	+10	751,001
12	+4 HP	+11	1,001,000
13+	+4 HP	*	+250,000

*+1 per level

MULTICLASSED CHARACTERS

Not all characters will fit into the mold of a single character class. If this happens, you may want to explore multiclassing. Multiclassing enables a player to combine the abilities of two different classes, at the expense of much slower progression. Any class may be combined with any other class, with two restrictions: First, a character may not multiclass as two different types of Arcanist (i.e. no Int-based spell casting and Wis- or Cha-based spell casting in the same character). Second, Arcanists and Mentalists may not multiclass, as their powers are antithetical to one another.

In this manner it's possible to, for example, combine Socialite and Hoodlum to create a character who by day is a wealthy playgirl, hosting parties and hobnobbing with the upper crust, and by night is the feared cat burglar Shadowhawk. In Amazing Adventures, not only is multiclassing allowed, it is actively encouraged, to create just the kind of broad range of heroes seen in the pulp magazines.

In order to multiclass, the character must meet all requirements of the class in question; this mostly pertains to primes. A character, for example, with two classes that have two different primes is severely restricted in what attributes she may designate as prime, while a character with but a single class has some wiggle room to choose two of her primes for herself. As with anything, the final combination of classes is at the discretion of the Game Master.

A multiclassed character maintains but a single experience progression. This progression is equal to the total of both classes rounded down to an even hundred, plus two hundred XP per current level the character has, plus 1. Thus, a first level Hooligan/Arcanist requires 4,601 XP to advance to second level. The Hooligan requires 1,601 and the Arcanist 2,601. Adding these together gets 4402...round the "02" down to "00." Then add 200 XP because the character is currently first level, then add one extra. The total is 4601. To advance to third level, the player would again combine the requisites of both classes, adding 400 XP for the character currently being second level. 9,101 would be required.

Multiclassed characters gain all of the abilities of each class, and can use any weapons or armor allowed to either class (provided such does not interfere with other class abilities), but average the hit dice and BtH progression of the classes.

Multiclassing is just that simple. While it may seem an easy path to lots of extra abilities, players will quickly see that the (much) slower advancement of a multiclassed character more than makes up for the extra abilities granted.

TRADING OFF LEVELS

If players and GMs don't like the idea of advancing two classes at the same time, the option exists to advance one class at a time. Under this option, a character begins play with one class. When she gains enough experience to gain a level in this class, she can instead choose to add a level in another class, so long as she meets the prerequisites for that class, as above. When doing so, the character begins a new XP tally for the added class, and all experience gained goes to the new class. When the new class gains enough XP to advance a level, the character can advance the class, or choose to advance her original class. This way allows slightly faster advancement, but is trickier because the player may only pick up new classes in which she already has the Primes. In this case it is important to keep track of both character level–the combination of all levels in all classes–and class level–the level a character has in a single class. Class-based abilities use class level, not character level, unless the character has the same ability in both classes. For example, a Hooligan/Gumshoe would use Hide and Move Silently at character level, since both classes have these abilities, but would use Face in the Crowd at his Gumshoe class level. Finally, as characters get higher in levels, this method of multiclassing might prove to create far more powerful characters from combining classes, despite the slower advancement. Charging players an extra 200 XP per current character level before advancement is allowed may help to offset this power creep.

CLASS AND A HALF

Normally, multiclassing advances the character equally (and irrevocably) in two classes, at a heavy cost of XP and a thinning of the hit points. This third option allows for the character to designate one class as a primary class, and the other class as a set of secondary abilities that the character has less expertise in using. Basically it allows the player to choose one class for his character, and supplement it with some of the abilities of another. This system allows a more lenient manner of combining these abilities, in the spirit of creating new class concepts that are appealing without being too powerful.

Class and a Half characters have a single, enhanced class. Pick two classes; one will be designated the "principal," or "primary" class, and will be the character's "real" class. The other will be designated "supporting." A character combining Gumshoe and Arcanist classes could choose to be either a Private Dick who knows a few spells (Gumshoe primary), or he could choose to be a sorcerer with some training in investigations and tracking fugitives (Arcanist primary). The character will advance and perform ability checks of the supporting class at half the rate of the principal class. A first level character would have the abilities of the supporting class at level zero, gaining the class's first-level abilities but rolling a straight d20 to use them with no bonuses, attribute or otherwise (though any penalties still apply).

Level	Principal Class Level	Supporting Class Level
1	1	0
2	2	1
3	3	1
4	4	2
5	5	2
6	6	3
7	7	3
8	8	4
9	9	4
10	10	5

Experience points for level advancement are determined by adding the principal class's XP to half the XP of the supporting. Hit dice are averaged, rounding in the direction of the principal class (see the table below).

Principal Class HD	Supporting Class HD				
	d4/1	d6/2	d8/3	d10/4	d12/5
d4/1	d4/1	d4/1	d6/2	d6/2	d8/3
d6/2	d6/2	d6/2	d6/2	d8/3	d8/3
d8/3	d6/2	d8/3	d8/3	d8/3	d10/4
d10/4	d8/3	d8/3	d10/4	d10/4	d10/4
d12/5	d8/3	d10/4	d10/4	d12/5	d12/5
d*/**					

d* = hit die for the class

** = fixed HP gained after 10th level

Quick rules:

1. The GM is the ultimate arbiter of which classes can be combined and how they are combined. The GM can (and should) amend the rules to fit their needs and their restrictions trump any rules presented here.
2. Primary Attribute: The character only needs the prime attribute of his principal class.
3. BtH: The character uses the best to hit bonus, and best weapon proficiency list.
4. Armor: Class and a half characters may wear any costume pieces allowed to either class.
5. **CLASS ABILITIES:** The class and a half's supporting class abilities are gained, or not gained, as follows:
    - Arcanist, Gadgeteer, Hooligan, Mentalist, and Raider supporting gain all abilities
    - Gumshoe supporting does not gain adversary or take 'em down.
    - Pugilist supporting gains Down and Dirty, Unarmed Attack, Unarmored Defense, and Submission Hold, but no other abilities.

- Socialite supporting does not gain fascinate

6. Class Combinations must follow the following restrictions:
   - Hooligan, Pugilist, Raider, and Socialite may align with any other class.
   - Arcanist, Mentalist, and Gadgeteer may not combine with each other.

Other class combinations may require some justification, and some are less than practical. As with all rules, the GM has the final say in which classes may combine.

NOTE: These class combination restrictions apply to full multiclassing as well as class-and-a-half combinations!

ROUNDING OUT THE CHARACTER

PERSONALITY

Now it's time to put the pieces together. You've got your attributes and class abilities in place, and have chosen your Primes. But that gives you a general archetype with which to play. More important than what your character can do is, who is he? You need a good idea of your character's back story and history. At very least, you should lay down a detailed sketch. Who were his parents? Were they wealthy or poor? Why does he do what he does? Is it for the thrill of the chase, the adrenaline rush of crawling through deadly ancient tombs, or is it for a sense of altruism, that his exploits might educate or otherwise aid humankind?

Even mundane things can help with this sketch. What does he look like? What color and style is his hair? His eyes? Does he wear glasses? The more detailed your character concept, the better off, especially in a game with as open a system as the SIEGE engine. If, say, your character's father was a doctor and he grew up sitting in the exam room while his dad performed procedures, he may have picked up some basic first aid, or even some more advanced techniques. This background could, when it comes into play, provide bonuses to certain Attribute checks, at the GM's discretion.

If your players are having difficulty coming up with a concept, we point you to the optional "Advanced Character Customization" section (Chapter 2), where we offer options for character backgrounds, traits, and knowledge skills.

ALIGNMENT

One way to quickly help define your character is to choose an alignment. Alignment systems may seem a strange addition to a pulp game, given the shades of gray that generally exist within the genre. However, there are certain subgenres of Pulp in which it is essential to outline the heroic code of the protagonists, particularly when looking at the representation of pulp action we see in the classic Saturday Morning Serials, and the modern aumages to these films, like the Indiana Jones series, or The Rocketeer.

Alignment represents the basic and most essential aspects of a character's worldview and moral outlook. Alignment is a description for the fundamental moral outlook of every sentient creature. Is the character good or evil, chaotic, lawful or even neutral? Alignment is a very basic description and acts as an ethical and motivational guide for characters, non-player characters and monsters.

Alignment should never be used as a box to limit the character; rather, players should choose an alignment whose moral and ethical compass best suits their character's outlook. It's a description more than a guideline. It's not there to tell you how to play your character; rather it's there as a point of reference for other players and the Game Master. That's all. To that end, alignment categories are fairly general and there is much room for interpretation within each category of alignment. A lawful good character may be a modern knight errant, adventuring with the sole purpose of stamping out evil in the land. On the other hand, a lawful good arcanist may devote himself to acquiring ancient arcane magic in order to create a library for the benefit of all. A chaotic evil hooligan may be a roving, murderous bandit robbing and murdering whomever and wherever he can for his own personal hedonistic desires, or he could be a cultist devoted to the wanton destruction of man's accomplishments and eradication of those with whom he disagrees. There is great variation within each of the nine alignment categories described below. They should be used as a general guideline for motivations, actions, ethos and worldview.

Still, Game Masters who don't want to lock their game down with strict alignments can always feel free not to include them in their game, and alignment should generally be considered an optional addition. This will make certain arcanist spells less useful (or at least require them to be re-defined), but other than that should have little effect on overall game play.

There are nine possible alignments: lawful good, neutral good, chaotic good, lawful neutral, neutral, chaotic neutral, lawful evil, neutral evil, or chaotic evil. Each alignment, except true neutral, is composed of two aspects.

LAW AND CHAOS

The first aspect of alignment – lawful, neutral or chaotic – generally represents a character's ideals and world view. These, however, are broad categorizations that go to the core beliefs of a character. Thus, all lawful characters are not the same, nor are all chaotic characters. Each might exhibit traits typically associated with the opposite. The following are general traits of each aspect. "Law" implies honor, trustworthiness, obedience to authority and reliability, and above all, the idea that there is (or should be) a defined order and structure to things.

On the downside, lawfulness can include closed-mindedness, reactionary adherence to tradition and a lack of adaptability. Lawful characters tell the truth, keep their word, respect authority, honor tradition, and judge harshly those who fall short of their duties. Lawful characters can still follow their conscience and can favor new ideas. Chaotic characters can still be honorable and trustworthy. Just because someone values individual freedom and pragmatism doesn't necessarily mean he can't be trusted to have his friend's back in a crisis.

"Chaos" implies freedom, adaptability and flexibility, and a lack of structure and order. On the downside, chaos can include recklessness, resentment toward legitimate authority, arbitrary actions and irresponsibility. Chaotic characters follow their consciences, resent being told what to do, favor new ideas over tradition and keep their word only if they feel like it.

"Neutral" implies a normal respect for authority, with neither a compulsion to obey nor to rebel. Neutral characters are honest, but can be tempted into lying or deceiving others. Animals and other creatures incapable of moral action are neutral.

GOOD AND EVIL

The second aspect of alignment – good, neutral or evil – generally represents behavior and how characters express or impose their ideals, whether lawful, neutral or chaotic. Again, these are broad categorizations. The following are general traits of each aspect. Good implies altruism, respect for life and a concern for the dignity of sentient beings. Good characters make personal sacrifices to help others. Good characters and creatures protect innocent life.

Evil implies hurting, oppressing, killing others and selfishness. Some evil creatures simply have no compassion for others and kill without qualms if doing so is convenient. Others actively pursue evil, killing for sport or out of duty to some evil deity. Evil characters and creatures debase or destroy innocent life, whether for fun or profit.

Neutral characters fall somewhere in between, but most are committed to others by personal relationships. A neutral person may sacrifice himself to protect his family or even his homeland, but he would not do so for strangers who are not related to him. Some neutral characters are simply selfish. Animals and other creatures incapable of complex relationships are neutral.

The combination of the lawful, neutral or chaotic axis with good, neutral or evil creates nine possible character alignments. Although characters of the same alignment possess the same general world view and behave similarly, each will be unique and vary in terms of psychology and life experiences.

LAWFUL GOOD

Characters of this alignment are dedicated to following the strictures of society, respecting law and order. They act for the benefit of others and society, placing great value on truth, honor and life.

LAWFUL NEUTRAL

Characters of this alignment place primary importance on ultimate order, structure and regulation of behavior. Good and evil are largely irrelevant for characters of this alignment because everything flows from the order of law.

LAWFUL EVIL

Characters of this alignment value structure and order, and they place no limit on attaining it, especially if the goal is to their own benefit. They do not value life or concern for others. Ultimately, they seek to impose their ideals on others through strict regulation.

NEUTRAL GOOD

Characters of this alignment have a healthy respect for both law and freedom, typically choosing a road betwixt the two in order to achieve benefits and mercy for all.

NEUTRAL

Characters of this broad alignment typically believe in a balance between law and chaos, and between good and evil. Some seek to maintain existing social institutions, while others simply wish to keep to themselves. Some engage in a crusade to preserve what they view as the natural order of things. Others simply follow their own code, which changes with the situation, tending to favor those that benefit them the most.

NEUTRAL EVIL

Characters of this alignment mirror those of neutral good, but they typically follow a road that benefits themselves instead of others.

CHAOTIC GOOD

Characters of this alignment view the greatest good as being attainable through freedom. Thus they place primary importance on individuality and liberty of action over that of any law or societal structure.

CHAOTIC NEUTRAL

Characters of this alignment value individual freedom, and have no qualms in achieving it by whatever means necessary, be they good or evil.

CHAOTIC EVIL

Characters of this alignment tend not to value anything, disdaining others and often seeking to destroy for their own selfish reasons. They seek power and the ability to wield it as they see fit.

FATE POINTS

Fate Points are a mechanic that provides characters with the means to affect game play in small, but significant ways. They represent the actions of cinematic heroes, who always seem to make those dramatic comebacks, have sudden flashes of insight just in time, or call upon inner reserves of strength to fell the villain just when things look grim.

USING FATE POINTS

A character always has a limited amount of Fate Points, and while the character replenishes this supply with every new level he or she attains, the rate of attrition can far outstrip the rate of gain. As such, players must use them wisely. A character can spend Fate Points to do any of these things:

FORTUNE'S FAVOR: alter a single d20 roll used to make an attack, attribute check, level check, or a saving throw.

MIGHTY BLOW: make a single, earth-shattering attack which also stands a chance of smashing the character's weapon.

YOU MISSED!: Avoid an attack.

JUST MADE IT!: Automatically succeed at a saving throw.

SECOND WIND: Recover lost hit points.

SOUND THE CHARGE!: Double the character's movement for the round.

DOWN BUT NOT OUT: avoid death when reduced to below -10 Hit Points

PROVIDENCE SMILES: gain a Plot Break

Fortune's Favor

When a character spends 1 Fate Point to improve a d20 roll, add a die to the roll to help meet or exceed the target number. The type of die rolled is dependent upon the character's level and shown on the fate point table (p.52). A character can declare the use of 1 Fate Point to alter a d20 roll after the roll is made—but only before the GM reveals the result of that roll (whether the attack or check or saving throw succeeded or failed). A Fate Point that comes up 6 explodes just like a roll of a natural 20, but does not implode on a roll of 1.

Mighty Blow

When a character spends 1 Fate Point to make a single, earth-shattering attack, the attack automatically hits the opponent; no attack roll is needed. Also, the attack does double the maximum possible damage for the attack. However, the character must then make an unmodified d20 roll; a result of 1-9 on the d20 means that the weapon shatters as a result of the mighty blow (firearms are ruined from blowback). This ability is useful only in melee combat, and extra damage from special attacks such as sneak attacks does not double. A Fate Point can be used to achieve this effect only once per game session.

You Missed!

A character may spend 1 Fate Point to avoid a single attack that targets her. Critical hits may only be avoided if they would reduce the character below 0 hit points, and this costs 2 Fate Points.

Just Made It!

A character may spend 1 Fate Point to automatically succeed at a saving throw. This Fate Point must be spent before the character rolls the saving throw. If the character rolls the saving throw and fails, he may still use "Just Made It!" but this requires the expenditure of 2 Fate Points.

Second Wind

A character who has lost more than half of their current total hit points (and is still conscious) may, once per day, spend two Fate Points to recover half of all the hit points they have lost (round up). For example, a character who has 25 hit points when at his maximum has suffered 15 points of damage, reducing him to a current total of 10 hit points. He may spend two Fate Points to instantly recover 8 hit points, but may not catch a Second Wind again for another 24 hours.

Sound the Charge!

A character can spend a Fate Point to double their allotted movement for a single round. This includes the ability to move full movement and still attack, rather than half, as described on (p 149).

Unlike a normal Charge maneuver, characters spending a Fate Point can move up to their full base movement and attack, but do not gain a bonus to damage or penalty to Armor Class. However, spending a Fate Point to Sound the Charge effectively doubles the distance a character can cover to take a charge maneuver in order to gain this bonus and suffer this penalty (see Charge, p. 171). In effect, this maneuver allows a character to move up to their full base movement and make a normal attack, or to double the distance up to which they may make a charge maneuver.

Down But Not Out

When a character falls to at least -10 Hit Points or below, he is normally considered dead. Not so, if he has Fate Points to spend. Down But Not Out costs three Fate Points, and results in the character being reduced to exactly -9 Hit Points, and stabilized. The character must have three Fate Points to spend to use this ability, and may only call upon it once per character level, and if he doesn't use it, it doesn't carry over. So a character who never has to use Down But Not Out at second level doesn't have two uses of it waiting when he gets to third.

Providence Smiles

By spending a Fate Point, a character can gain a small plot break that helps him in some minor way. He gains an

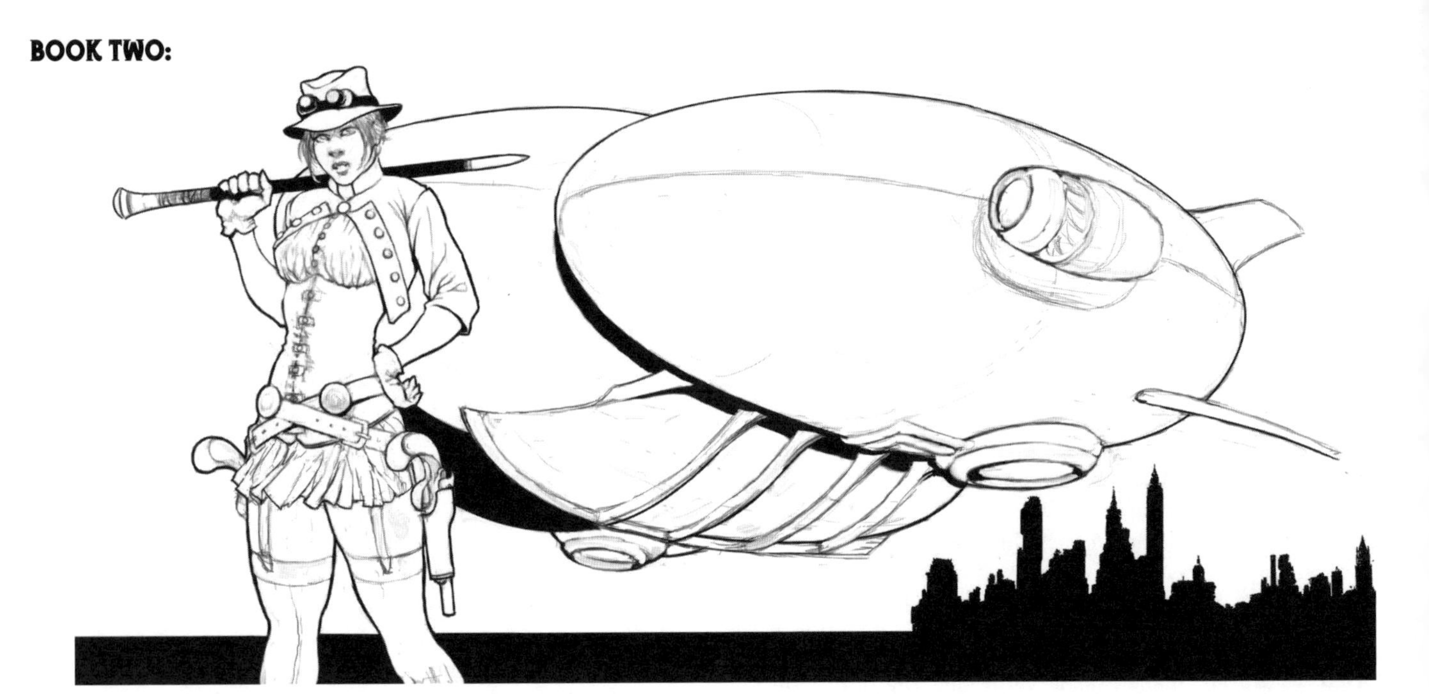

important clue that he overlooked, just happens to be talking to the right person to get the information he needs, or has the cavalry come over the hill while he's in a hopeless situation. The player must describe exactly what the plot break is that his character gains, and the GM always has the right to overrule this use if he deems it improper, or if he has a good reason for the character to be in such a tight spot. If the plot break is overruled, the Fate Point is not spent. Characters can spend a point for Providence Smiles once per game session.

A character can only spend Fate Points once per round. If a character spends a point to strike a mighty blow, he or she can't spend another one in the same round to improve a die roll, and vice versa.

Depending on the hero's character level (see the table below), the die type increases when spending 1 Fate Point to add to a roll. If the character does so, apply the highest result and disregard the other rolls.

CHARACTER LEVEL	FATE DICE ROLLED
1st–4th	1d6
5th–9th	1d8
10th–14th	1d10
15th–20th	1d12

STARTING AND GAINING FATE POINTS

Characters begin the game with 10 Fate Points. Each level thereafter, the character gains additional Fate Points equal to half their new level (rounded down). Any Fate Points not spent do carry over to the new level. Thus, if a first level character makes it to second level with 8 Fate Points remaining, she gains 1 new Fate Point for half her level, which adds to her existing 8, for a total of 9.

In addition, the GM can (and should) award Fate Points as an on-the-spot reward for heroic or dramatic play, the use of clever (in character) banter, noble self-sacrifice, or as "compensation" to the players when the story needs to take a turn that is particularly dark for one or more characters.

Remember, however, that the use of Fate Points creates an extremely heroic game, and awarding too many can result in very over-the-top play, rather than the cinematic bennies that they are intended to represent. It's important to strike a balance between allowing characters to have fate points when needed, and the characters having so many that they never have to worry about failing. In general, and keeping in mind that characters gain additional Fate Points every level, if the GM is awarding half to three-quarters the amount of Fate Points spent in a given game session this is likely a decent balance.

GRITTIER GAMES

Fate points are considered a core part of the ***Amazing Adventures*** rules as they allow the kind of over-the-top heroics and limited "plot immunity" that heroes in pulp tales often display. However, for GMs wanting a grittier game with less emphasis on this kind of heroic play, you can choose to not use fate points, or severely restrict their accumulation.

For a grittier game that still has some use of fate points in play, start characters with five fate points, and still grant them half their level (round down) in additional fate points per level as they increase in experience, but do not hand out additional points for good roleplaying, heroic acts and the like.

PULP EQUIPMENT

Now it's time to equip your character for spy work, adventuring, exploration, and wild heroics! This section lists outfits (Pulp Armor), weapons, and other gear your characters might need during their exploits. We will not concern ourselves with money for starting characters; prices are listed as a period reference only, and for the GM's reference when it comes to "can my character afford this?" questions. In fantasy games, the number of gold, platinum, and silver a character has is part and parcel of the game. In modern or pulp games, where the acquisition of loot isn't as much of a major focus (with the exception of perhaps a single MacGuffin that forms the focus of an adventure), tracking dollars and cents generally just serves to slow the game down.

There's nothing worse for a player than designing a really cool pulp costume for her character and then being unable to afford to buy the outfit! Thus, at character creation, the GM should work with players to determine what type of equipment the character would reasonably have, and simply equip the character as necessary. If a player wants their character to be exceptionally wealthy, it is suggested to the GM to check out the "Wealthy" generic class ability in the next section. From then on, player characters are assumed to be able to purchase within their means. Pugilists, Hooligans and Gumshoes are generally fairly poor—lower to lower-middle-class. Arcanists, Raiders, and Socialites are likely fairly wealthy (though the Arcanist is a toss-up). Mentalists can fall anywhere in the picture, depending on their back story and history. In the end, it's up to the GM and players to come up with a reasonable back story and determine what level of income is appropriate for the game at hand.

PULP ARMOR

Unlike in a traditional fantasy game, one doesn't see characters (with the possible exception of gadgeteers) in the adventure pulps running around covered in chain mesh or steel plates from head to toe. Indeed, in a pulp game it's looks that matter most! The cooler a character's image, the less likely he is to take a bullet to the heart or a knife to the gut.

In a 1920's to 1950's pulp game, no character is assumed to be proficient with armor, and any traditional armor donned will impart penalties. Rather, pulp characters gain AC bonuses to standard exploring or uniquely "pulp hero" clothes. Sure, it's not realistic, but it certainly is in-genre and a heck of a lot of fun! Standard AC bonuses are as follows, as are the pieces that typically should be allowed to stack together to create costumes. No combination of clothing pieces, however, should ever yield more than a +7 AC bonus, regardless of how many costume elements are stacked together.

CLOTHING	AC BONUS	COST	SUGGESTED STACKS WITH:
Fedora	+1	$5	Three-piece suit, trench coat, flight or bomber jacket, evening or formal clothes (men only), mask, scarf or sash, short gloves, cape or cloak
Scarf or Sash	+1	$5	Fedora, trench coat, body suit, mask, evening or formal clothes (women only), flight or bomber jacket, motorcycle jacket, short gloves, cape or cloak, martial arts uniform
Mask	+1	$10	Fedora, trench coat, body suit, scarf or sash, three-piece suit, ceremonial robes, motorcycle jacket, short gloves, cape or cloak, martial arts uniform, studded fetish gear
Body Suit	+1	$10	Trench coat, scarf or sash, mask, short gloves, cape or cloak, martial arts uniform
Ceremonial Robes	+2	$15	Mask, short gloves
Evening or Formal Clothes	+2	$15	Scarf or sash (women), fedora (men), trench coat (men), long gloves (women), short gloves, cape or cloak
Flight or Bomber Jacket	+2	$10	Fedora, scarf or sash, short gloves
Long Gloves	+2	$5	Evening or formal clothes (women) , ceremonial robes (women), cape or cloak, martial arts uniform, studded fetish gear
Short Gloves	+1	$2	All, except Long Gloves
Safari Gear	+4	$20	None, short gloves
Motorcycle Jacket	+3	$15	Mask, scarf or sash, short gloves
Cape or Cloak	+2	$6	Fedora, scarf or sash, mask, body suit, evening clothes, gloves (any), martial arts uniform, studded fetish gear
Martial Arts Uniform	+3	$15	Gloves (any), mask, scarf or sash, cape or cloak
Studded Fetish Gear	+3	$15	Cape or cloak, mask, gloves (any)
Three Piece Suit	+1	$10	Fedora, mask, trench coat, short gloves
Trench Coat	+2	$15	Fedora, three piece suit, evening or formal clothes, body suit, mask, scarf or sash, short gloves

COSTUMES, AC, AND MIN/MAXING

To combine AC bonuses, all pieces in a combination should stack; use the highest AC combination from stackable pieces. This means that a character wearing Safari Gear with a Fedora and trench coat would gain only the highest AC bonus, from the safari gear, and not the bonus from the fedora or trench.

The GM can and is encouraged to override this limitation for specific costume builds, if a player has a really good costume concept. Just be careful not to let AC ratings creep too high; the recommendation of limiting bonuses to +7 should always stand. Some players will undoubtedly attempt to min/max their characters to always score a +7 on their pulp costume. The GM should always feel free to require players to supply a detailed description of their character's pulp adventuring outfit, increasing or decreasing the overall AC bonus based on how subjectively "awesome" the character's costume is.

Alternately, the GM can consider +7 a standard AC bonus and *decrease* this bonus if players *don't* provide a good description of their character's Pulp costume. Consider a certain dour Puritan adventurer created by Robert E. Howard who was *always* described as dressed all in black with simple clothing, boots, a featherless slouch cap, cloak and a green sash. If players fail to give an adequate description of what their character looks like when in the heat of an adventure, their AC bonus can be reduced accordingly.

The table can also serve to help in situations where players are not wearing their costumes, but may be wearing other fancy pulpy clothes. For example, players at a black tie dinner will always be wearing tuxedos and evening dresses, and so would gain an appropriate AC bonus from these.

ARCHAIC WEAPONS

Not every hero goes into a battle two guns a-blazing. Some prefer the finesse or punch of a classic sword, hand axe, or Asian martial arts weaponry. Weapons in ***Amazing Adventures*** are divided into categories: small, medium and large melee weapons, archaic ranged weapons, handguns, sub-machineguns, rifles and shotguns, and explosives. Each class has a list of weapon categories in which they are proficient. Large melee weapons and archaic ranged weapons (with the exception of the pistol crossbow) must always be used two-handed.

For a more extensive listing of archaic and medieval weapons, please refer to our sister publication, ***Castles & Crusades***, which has an extensive list of medieval and fantasy weaponry that can be dropped right into ***Amazing Adventures***. When it comes to pricing such weaponry, the costs here should be sufficient to estimate the cost of any other weapon. For example, any weapon that has a similar cost to a short sword in ***C&C*** would have a cost of $3 or thereabouts in ***Amazing Adventures***.

WEAPON	DAMAGE	RANGE	COST
Small Melee Weapons			
Big Knife/short sword	1d6	5 ft.	$3
Billy club/nightstick	1d6	0 ft./5ft.*	$3
Dagger/small knife	1d4	10 ft.	$2
Hand Axe/tomahawk	1d6	10 ft.	$5
Medium Melee Weapons			
Broad Sword	1d8	n/a	$20
Crowbar/tire iron***	1d10/1d6**	n/a	$5
Fencing Foil	1d4	n/a	$10
Katana / bastard sword	1d10/1d8**	n/a	$30
Rapier / saber / scimitar	1d6	n/a	$15
Large Melee Weapons			
Battle Axe	1d12	0 ft./2ft.*	$20
Spear	1d6	20 ft.	$5
Staff	1d6****	n/a	$2
Archaic Ranged Weapons			
Bow, Long	1d8	100 ft.	$20
Bow, Short	1d6	60 ft.	$15
Crossbow, heavy	1d8	80 ft.	$18
Crossbow, pistol	1d4	30 ft.	$15

*Suffers range penalty to strike whenever thrown, which increases per post-slash increment

**First damage value when using 2-handed; second if only wielding with one hand

***Not intended as a weapon; -4 to all "to hit" rolls

****May be used to make an extra attack as though fighting with a weapon in each hand; standard penalties apply. See "Combat" for details.

FIREARMS

Firearms pose an interesting problem in a game such as this. We want the game to remain fast and furious, without excess rules to bog things down, but certainly it has to be acknowledged that firearms change the playing field quite a bit, and can do things that archaic weapons cannot; amongst these capabilities is the ability to fire more projectiles, faster. For this reason, firearms have special rules concerning recoil and rate of fire. These are detailed under the "Combat" chapter.

In the table below, the following details are present:

- "Caliber" represents the size of the cartridge fired.
- "Range" is the range increment for determining penalties to hit; for each range increment past the first, the weapon suffers a cumulative -2 to hit its target to its maximum range, generally five times its range increment.
- "Dam" is the damage inflicted per shot.
- "Rec" is the recoil penalty suffered (cumulative) for firing multiple shots, if possible.

- "Acc" represents a bonus to hit with this weapon based on its accuracy, which can improve chances to hit, and helps offset recoil penalties.
- "RoF" stands for "rate of fire" and represents the number of shots that can be fired per combat round
  - o A designation of "B" means the weapon is capable of burst fire.
  - o A designation of "A" means it is fully automatic. Details on burst and automatic fire are found in the Combat section.
- "Receiver" is general information about how and where the weapon loads.
- "Cap" is the number of bullets it holds when fully loaded.
- "Cost" is self-explanatory
- "Year" is the year this weapon first became available to the public, which is useful to GM's determining what weapons are available in their game.

For simplicity's sake, assume bullets cost roughly $1.00 per 25 rounds.

WEAPON	CALIBER	RANGE	DAM	REC.	ACC.	ROF	RECIEVER	CAP	COST	YEAR
Pistols										
Walther PPK	.380 ACP	10'	d10	2	1	3	Grip	7	$15	1930
P-08 Luger or Walther P38	9mm Para	30'	d10	3	2	3	Grip	8	$25	1908, 1939
Colt M1911A1	.45 ACP	30'	d12	3	2	3	Grip	7	$13	1911
Browning 1910	.32 ACP	30'	d8	3	2	3	Grip	8	$10	1910
Mauser C96 "Broomhandle"	7.63x25mm, or 9mm Para ("Red 9" variant)	30'	d10	3	2	3	Grip	10	$25	1896
Beretta Model 1931	7.65mm	30'	d10	3	2	3	Grip	8	$14	1931
Colt Model 1917	.45 ACP	30'	d12	4	2	3	Revolver (DA)	6	$8	1917
Sub-machine guns										
Thompson Submachine Gun (Tommy Gun)	.45 ACP	100'	d12+2	4	1	3/A	Box or Drum	30 or 100	$50	1919
Sten	9mm para	30'	d10	3	1	3/A	Box	32	$50	1941
MP-18	7.63x25mm Mauser	30'	d8	3	1	3/A	Drum or Box	20, 30, 50	$100	1918
Shotguns										
20 Gauge Sawed Off Double Barrel	20 Gauge	10'	d8	5	0	2/B	Individual	2	$35	All
Remington Model 11 or Browning Auto 5	12 Gauge	30'	d10	3	0	3	Tubular	5	$37	1949
Remington Model 17	20 Gauge	30'	d10	n/a	0	1	Tubular	5	$42	All
12 Gauge Double Barrel	12 Gauge	30	d10	4	0	2/B	Individual	2	$39	All
Rifles										
M1 Garand	.30	200'	2d8+6	2	2	3	Box	8	$50	1936
KAR-98K	8mm Mauser	200'	2d8+4	n/a	2	1	Clip	5	$60	1935
MAS 36	7.5mm MAS	200'	2d8+4	1	1	3	Box	5	$55	1936
Sharps .50	.50	200'	4d6	n/a	3	1	Cartridge	1	$40	1850
Springfield 1903	.30-.06	200'	2d8+6	n/a	2	1	Box	5	$50	1903
Winchester 1873	.30-30, .44-40	200'	1d12+2	3	2	2	Tubular	7	$40	1873
Machine Guns										
Browning M1918A2	30-06	200'	2d8+6	3	0	A	Box	20	n/a*	1918

*This weapon generally unavailable to non-military personnel.

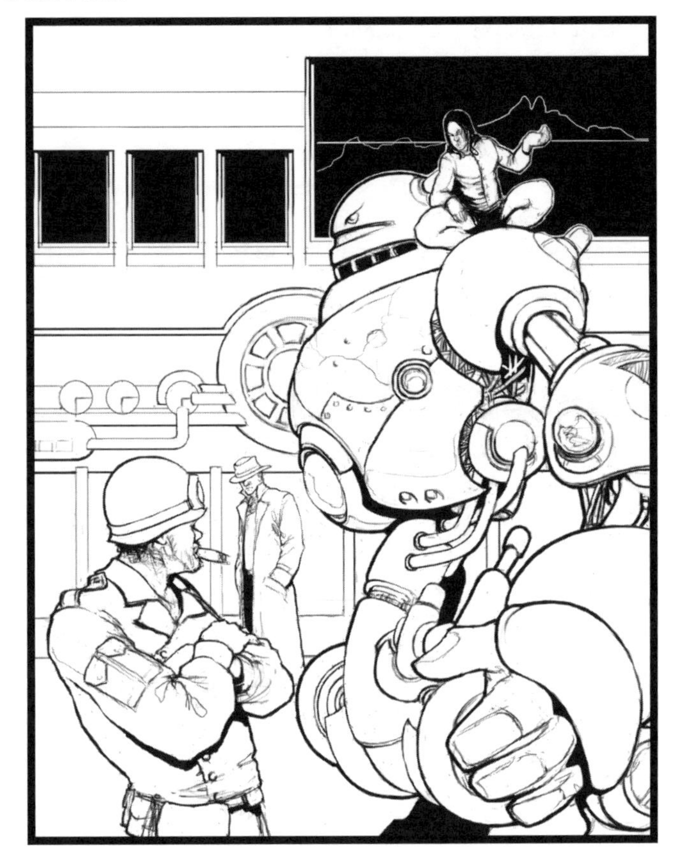

Other Firearms

This table is far from comprehensive. While we hope to expand the table with more firearms in future sourcebooks, those who are enthusiasts on the topic will desire more weapons immediately. Fortunately, a bit of research into just about any firearm you would like to include in your game will show that the table above should allow you to model it accurately enough for in-game use. You will notice that damage is generally based on caliber, as is recoil. Accuracy, Range and Rate of Fire are based on the weapon itself, and are often determined by a combination of caliber and barrel length, among other factors. Reciever, Capacity, Cost, and Year are all simply real-world information.

OTHER GEAR

Finally, we have other useful equipment for adventurers. Clever readers will notice that this is far from an exhaustive list of things someone living in the 20's through 40's might own; since this is a pulp game we are focusing on specialized gear that might come in useful to adventuring and heroic types. GMs should really play "fast and loose" with the type of equipment available. Most pulp heroes have signature equipment, represented by a character's starting gear list, and access to other resources based upon their day job, income, or other factors. Keep your character backgrounds in mind when determining what equipment a character may have on hand in a given situation, but be careful not to undermine other characters, particularly in the case of having a Gadgeteer in the party. On the table below, sizes are listed merely as "Small," "Medium," "Large," or "Huge," as a general reference to the Game Master and players.

GEAR	SIZE	COST
Binoculars	S	$30
Canteen, 1 quart	M	$1.75
Car, standard (Ford Model T)	H	$385
Car, high end luxury (Mercedes Benz)	H	$8,000
Car, luxury (Packard)	H	$2,500
Cigarettes	S	$0.10
Cigarette lighter	S	$5.00
Climbing Gear (includes cable, harness, lanyard, spikes, grappling hook)*	L	$25.00
Cooking/mess kit	S	$6.50
Grappling Hook (without rope)**	M	$10.00
Handcuffs	S	$2.00
Heavy blanket	L	$1.00
Lock Picks***	S	$10.00
Matches, box of 50, "strike anywhere"	S	$0.10
Medical case (Doctor's "black bag," including stethoscope, various medicine samples, a scalpel, sutures, tape, a syringe, thermometer, etc.)	M	$25.00
Motorcycle	L	$95.00
Oil Lamp / lantern	S	$1.50
Pint of oil	S	$0.10
Pipe and tobacco	S	$1.00
Pup tent, two-man (7' x 7')	L	$11.50
Rope or cable, 50 ft.	L	$8.50
Smoking tobacco, 1 oz.	S	$0.10
Watch, Gold pocket	S	$30.00
Watch, wrist	S	$5.00

*Adds +2 to climb or scale checks and prevents falling damage

**Adds +1 to climb or scale checks if used with rope.

***Required for picking locks. Improvised tools, such as a hairpin, can be used, but at a -4 penalty.

The prices above assume 1930's and 1940's era gaming. Game Masters are encouraged to research the prices of the day for keeping with the spirit of the Pulp era, keeping the exact decade (20's, 30's, or 40's) of their game in mind. Knowing, for example, that a trip to the movies cost $0.75, or an uptown bus ride ran the rider $0.05, adds a lot of background flavor to a game. Still, the exact prices of mundane entertainment and daily costs of living is not essential to the kind of high-action gaming that the Pulp genre entails.

BOOK TWO: ADVANCED ACTION HEROES

Now we get into the part where you can alter your character from the basic template provided by your class through Generic Class Abilities, Backgrounds, Knowledge Skills, and Traits. As with most rules in the SIEGE engine, the rules in this section should be considered optional. Game Masters should feel free to disallow or modify the elements below to fit their own games. These sections should be considered "Advanced Rules," which affect character creation, allowing a high degree of customization and individuality even amongst characters of the same class, which reach far beyond the selecting of different primes, but which still maintain the single system task resolution of the SIEGE engine and don't add much complication to the game.

GENERIC CLASS ABILITIES

Generic Class Abilities are abilities that any class can take, simply by sacrificing an existing class ability and adding one of these in its stead. Choosing a generic class ability does not affect the experience progression of a class, and some may have prerequisites that must be met before the ability can be chosen. These allow the customization of character classes to a degree, allowing players to create characters filling a more specific pulp archetype. Generally speaking, players should sacrifice a class ability tied to the same attribute as the Generic ability they are gaining, but this is at the Game Master's discretion.

Please note that if a character sacrifices a class ability that he gains at a later level, for a Generic Ability, he gets the Generic Ability when he would normally gain the sacrificed class ability. For example, the Socialite gains Embolden at third level. If the Socialite chooses to sacrifice Embolden to get Animal Handling, he gains Animal Handling at third level.

Finally, for purposes of sacrificing class abilities, Arcanists, Gadgeteers, and Mentalists can at the GM's discretion, sacrifice a level of spell, power, or gadget point advancement to pick up a generic class ability, essentially reducing their effective caster/power/gadget level by one.

> **SACRIFICING ADVANCEMENT FOR NEW ABILITIES**
>
> Some class abilities advance as the character does, becoming more effective in specific ways as the character goes up in levels. For example, the Gumshoe gains new applications of Deadeye Shot at fourth, seventh, tenth, and twelfth levels. At the GM's option, a character can permanently "freeze" a class ability at a certain level, instead picking up an appropriate new Generic Class ability. However, if this is allowed, the frozen ability can *never again advance*; this is the price of becoming a jack of all trades. GMs should always be careful when allowing the selection of Generic abilities. Take care that the player isn't trading a weak ability for a more powerful one.

TRUE CHARACTER CUSTOMIZATION

If the players and GM determine it appropriate, true character customization can be achieved by "mixing and matching" the class abilities of various classes rather than choosing one of the multiclassing options here. This method is extremely challenging and tricky and runs a high risk of unbalancing the game, so it is not recommended. However, if the GM permits, this method essentially treats all class abilities for all classes as Generic Class Abilities.

Using this method, if a player so chooses (and the GM permits) she can choose a character class as standard and swap out class abilities with abilities from other classes that the GM deems to be of similar or equivalent power. That is to say, players should only swap out abilities with other abilities of the same general level of advantage, and obtain the abilities at the same levels. So, if a character swaps out a non-combat ability (say, the Socialite's 3rd level Embolden Ability), she should not gain something like the Hooligan's Sneak Attack power. Rather, something along the lines of the Raider's Legend Lore ability, or even a single basic Psionic power (which is non-combat related) might be appropriate.

As always, the GM must carefully weigh the options available with such choices and be certain that the abilities the character gains combined with the speed of advancement, do not ruin the overall balancc of the game.

ACE (DEX)

This character is either a classic wheelman or hot dog pilot. He can pull bootleg turns, storm barns, and work a vehicle like Van Gogh worked with color. Instead of adding either a vehicle's Dex bonus or his own when piloting, this character adds *both the vehicle's bonus and his own*. If a vehicle has a penalty to an attribute, the character can treat that penalty as zero (See Vehicle Combat rules, p.181). At fifth level, if the vehicle has a penalty to an attribute, the Ace instead applies a +1 bonus. At fifth level, the character can treat any negatives to a vehicle's attributes as zero. At tenth level, the character adds an additional +1 to all rolls when piloting a vehicle.

ANIMAL HANDLING (CHA)

Pulp adventures are full of stories of heroes with loyal animal companions. Where would the Lone Raider be without Silver, for example? Any Player Character can choose to swap out any class ability and gain Animal Handling in its stead. Any character who chooses this class ability should automatically begin play with an animal of the player's choice (subject to GM approval) that is either trained in the maximum number of tricks possible, or trained for a general purpose.

Animal Handling allows the character to get an animal to perform various tasks with a Charisma Attribute Check. The CL for this check depends on what you are trying to do.

TASK	CL
Handle an animal	1
"Push" an animal	5
Teach an animal a trick	2 to 5[1]
Train an animal for a general purpose	3 to 10[1]
Rear a wild animal	5 + animal's HD

[1]See the specific trick or purpose below.

HANDLE AN ANIMAL: This task involves commanding an animal to perform a task or trick that it knows. If the animal has taken any damage or ability score damage, the CL increases by 2. If your check succeeds, the animal performs the task or trick on its next action.

"PUSH" AN ANIMAL: To push an animal means to get it to perform a task or trick that it doesn't know but is physically capable of performing. This category also covers making an animal perform a forced march or forcing it to perform strenuous activity beyond that which would normally fatigue or exhaust the creature. If the animal is wounded or has taken any nonlethal damage or ability score damage, the CL increases by 2. If your check succeeds, the animal performs the task or trick on its next action.

TEACH AN ANIMAL A TRICK: You can teach an animal a specific trick with one week of work and a successful Handle Animal check against the indicated CL. An animal with an Intelligence score of 1 can learn a maximum of three tricks, while an animal with an Intelligence score of 2 can learn a maximum of six tricks. Possible tricks (and their associated CLs) include, but are not necessarily limited to, the following.

ATTACK (CL 5): The animal attacks apparent enemies. You may point to a particular creature that you wish the animal to attack, and it will comply if able. Normally, an animal will attack only natural, living humanoids or other animals. Teaching an animal to attack all creatures (including such unnatural creatures as undead and demons from beyond the pale) counts as two tricks.

COME (CL 2): The animal comes to you, even if it normally would not do so.

DEFEND (CL 5): The animal defends you (or is ready to defend you if no threat is present), even without any command being given. Alternatively, you can command the animal to defend a specific other character.

DOWN (CL 2): The animal breaks off from combat or otherwise backs down. An animal that doesn't know this trick continues to fight until it must flee (due to injury, a fear effect, or the like) or its opponent is defeated.

FETCH (CL 2): The animal goes and gets something. If you do not point out a specific item, the animal fetches some random object.

GUARD (CL 5): The animal stays in place and prevents others from approaching.

HEEL (CL 2): The animal follows you closely, even to places where it normally wouldn't go.

PERFORM (CL 2): The animal performs a variety of simple tricks, such as sitting up, rolling over, roaring or barking, and so on.

SEEK (CL 2): The animal moves into an area and looks around for anything that is obviously alive or animate.

STAY (CL 2): The animal stays in place, waiting for you to return. It does not challenge other creatures that come by, though it still defends itself if it needs to.

TRACK (CL 5): The animal tracks the scent presented to it. (This requires the animal to have the scent ability)

WORK (CL 2): The animal pulls or pushes a medium or heavy load.

TRAIN AN ANIMAL FOR A PURPOSE: Rather than teaching an animal individual tricks, you can simply train it for a general purpose. Essentially, an animal's purpose represents a preselected set of known tricks that fit into a common scheme, such as guarding or heavy labor. The animal must meet all the normal prerequisites for all tricks included in the training package. If the package includes more than three tricks, the animal must have an Intelligence score of 2.

An animal can be trained for only one general purpose, though if the creature is capable of learning additional tricks (above and beyond those included in its general purpose), it may do so. Training an animal for a purpose requires fewer checks than teaching individual tricks does, but no less time.

COMBAT RIDING (CL 10): An animal trained to bear a rider into combat knows the tricks attack, come, defend, down, guard, and heel. Training an animal for combat riding takes six weeks. You may also "upgrade" an animal trained for riding to one trained for combat riding by spending three weeks and making a successful CL 5 Handle Animal check. The new general purpose and tricks completely replace the animal's previous purpose and any tricks it once knew.

FIGHTING (CL 5): An animal trained to engage in combat knows the tricks attack, down, and stay. Training an animal for fighting takes three weeks.

GUARDING (CL 10): An animal trained to guard knows the tricks attack, defend, down, and guard. Training an animal for guarding takes four weeks.

HEAVY LABOR (CL 3): An animal trained for heavy labor knows the tricks come and work. Training an animal for heavy labor takes two weeks.

HUNTING (CL 10): An animal trained for hunting knows the tricks attack, down, fetch, heel, seek, and track. Training an animal for hunting takes six weeks.

PERFORMANCE (CL 5): An animal trained for performance knows the tricks come, fetch, heel, perform, and stay. Training an animal for performance takes five weeks.

RIDING (CL 5): An animal trained to bear a rider knows the tricks come, heel, and stay. Training an animal for riding takes three weeks.

REAR A WILD ANIMAL: To rear an animal means to raise a wild creature from infancy so that it becomes domesticated. A handler can rear as many as three creatures of the same kind at once.

A successfully domesticated animal can be taught tricks at the same time it's being raised, or it can be taught as a domesticated animal later.

TAMING AN ANIMAL: A character can attempt, with a Charisma check, to calm or tame a wild animal so that it can be handled, or so that it does not feel threatened (i.e. stop it from attacking). The CL for this check is dependent upon the beast's attitude when encountered. The CL listed is for a check to improve the animal's attitude by one step; multiple Checks are allowed, but a failure downgrades the animal's attitude by two steps. An animal downgraded beyond Hostile immediately attacks and no further checks are allowed.

INITIAL ATTITUDE	CL
Friendly	CL 1
Indifferent	CL 2
Suspicious	CL 5
Antagonistic	CL 7
Hostile, Cornered, or Afraid	CL 10

ANIMAL LEVELS: Whenever a character achieves a new level of experience, so does his or her animal companion, gaining a Hit Die and +1 to Attribute Checks and attack rolls.

COMBAT DOMINANCE

The character gains an extra attack with any weapon when fighting opponents with half his hit dice or fewer. In order to use this ability the character must direct all attacks in a combat round against creatures that meet this criteria. The character can split the available attacks amongst qualified creatures as desired. The ability improves as the character increases in levels, granting an additional attack every four levels. The

character can sacrifice one of these additional attacks to allow the ability to apply to ranged combat, but it cannot increase the rate of fire of a firearm; rather, it will allow an additional attack within the weapon's rate of fire before recoil penalties accrue. To acquire this ability, the character must sacrifice a combat-related ability that is gained at fourth level or higher, or must sacrifice two combat-related abilities of lower level.

GREAT FORTITUDE (CON)

The character gains +2 to all Constitution-based saving throws. This does not combine with other class abilities that grant bonuses to all Constitution-based saves, though it will combine with those that grant bonuses to specific saves that also happen to be based upon this ability. At level 5, the character gains an additional hit point at every level gained thereafter. At level 10, the character gains Constitution as an additional Prime Attribute; if he already has Constitution as a Prime, or already has four Prime Attributes, he instead gains an additional +3 to all Constitution-based ability checks.

GENERIC ABILITIES AND ADDITIONAL PRIMES

Some of the abilities here, at tenth level, grant the character an additional Prime. It's easy to see how selecting three of these could result in a character having all six abilities as Prime Attributes. This can result in extremely powerful characters, and while there is precedent for this in the Pulps in such characters like Doc Savage, for a game this may be over-the-top. It is recommended that no matter how many of these Generic Class Abilities take, a character should never have more than four Prime Attributes total. Any remaining attributes boosted by a Generic Class Ability would simply receive the additional +2 to checks gained for characters who already have that ability as a Prime.

For example, if a character has Iron Will and Keen Intellect, but already has Primes in Constitution, Dexterity, and Charisma, when he reaches level 10 he would have to choose whether to take Wisdom (from Iron Will) or Intelligence (from Keen Intellect) as his fourth Prime; the other ability would then gain +2 to all checks instead, stacking with the +1 he got at level 5, for a total of +3.

Remember, all Generic Class Abilities are optional; GMs who feel that these abilities overpower characters too much can choose not to allow them in game.

INDOMITABLE

This character gains an extra hit point per level of experience. At level 5, the character gains two extra hit points per additional level. At level 10, the character gains an extra three hit points per additional level.

IRON WILL (WIS)

The character gains +2 to all Wisdom-based saving throws. This does not combine with other class abilities that grant bonuses to all Wisdom-based saves, though it will combine with those that grant bonuses to specific saves that also happen to be based upon this ability. At level 5, the character gains +1 to all Wisdom-based ability checks related to perception or willpower. At level 10, the character gains Wisdom as an additional Prime Attribute; if he already has Wisdom as a Prime, or already has four Prime Attributes, he instead gains an additional +2 to all Wisdom-based ability checks (adding to the +1 at level 5 for a total of +3)

KEEN INTELLECT (INT)

The character gains +2 to all Intelligence-based saving throws. This does not combine with other class abilities that grant bonuses to all Intelligence-based saves, though it will combine with those that grant bonuses to specific saves that also happen to be based upon this ability. At level 5, the character gains +1 to all Intelligence-based ability checks related to solving

puzzles, academics, or reasoning. At level 10, the character gains Intelligence as an additional Prime; if he already has Intelligence as a Prime, or already has four Prime Attributes, he instead gains an additional +2 to all Intelligence-based ability checks (adding to the +1 at level 5 for a total of +3)

MEDICINE (WIS)

Adventurers often have to deal with allies who are poisoned or infected with some horrible disease, or face enemies that do not wish to be captured, sometimes to the point of committing suicide rather than being brought in for questioning. For this reason, it can be useful to have a working and thorough knowledge of toxins and pathogens, and how to slow or stop their effects. A player character can, at the cost of another class ability of his choice, gain Medicine in its stead. A Character with this ability undergoes years of study and training to learn the signs, symptoms, and makeup of poisons used the world over, and of disease vectors, communicability rates, and cures, so may actually have knowledge of a poison or infection he has never seen before.

Using this ability requires two Wisdom checks. The first check lets the Character divine what kind of affliction the character suffers. The CL of this check can increase depending on how rare or foreign the substance or infection in question is, at the discretion of the GM. The second check is to actually delay or neutralize the toxin or disease. The Character can, on a successful medicine roll, temporarily halt the effect of poisons or illness. This ability allows the Character to stop the poison, bacteria, virus, or other foreign vector from working for one hour per level of the Character. It does not cure any damage the poison or disease has already caused. The process takes one round, and the Character must have an appropriate first-aid kit and the proper herbs and medicines to succeed at the attempt, which can be made only once per individual.

If the roll exceeds the total needed for success by 6 or more, the medic has successfully neutralized the poison or infection. The afflicted creature suffers no additional damage or effect from the poison, and any temporary effects end, but damage or effects that have already occurred are not reversed. Players should keep in mind that some diseases have no cure and some poisons, no antitoxin.

Another use of this ability is to perform general first aid on a suffering or wounded character. If a character has negative hit points and is losing hit points (at the rate of 1 per round, 1 per hour, or 1 per day), a character with this Class Ability can make him or her stable. The CL of the check to do so is equal to the number of hit points the dying character is below zero. A stable character regains no hit points but stops losing them.

Providing long-term care, treating a wounded person for a day or more, allows the patient to recover hit points or ability score points (lost to ability damage) at twice the normal rate: 2 hit points per level for a full 8 hours of rest in a day, or 4 hit points per level for each full day of complete rest; 2 ability score points for a full 8 hours of rest in a day, or 4 ability score points for each full day of complete rest. The CL for this check is the same as for a dying character if the patient is below zero; otherwise providing long-term care has a CL equal to the number of patients being treated simultaneously. The medic needs a few items and supplies (bandages, salves, and so on) that are easy to come by in civilized lands.

NIMBLE (DEX)

The character gains +2 to all Dexterity-based saving throws. This does not combine with other class abilities that grant bonuses to all Dexterity-based saves, though it will combine with those that grant bonuses to specific saves that also happen to be based upon this ability. At level 5, the character gains a +1 to all Dexterity-based checks related to agility, tumbling, acrobatics, and the like. At level 10, the character gains Dexterity as an additional Prime; if he already has Dexterity as a Prime, or already has four Prime Attributes, he instead gains +2 to all Dexterity checks (adding to the +1 from Level 5, for a total of +3)

OVERWHELMING PERSONALITY (CHA)

The character gains +2 to all Charisma-based saving throws. This does not combine with other class abilities that grant bonuses to all Charisma-based saves, though it will combine with those that grant bonuses to specific saves that also happen to be based upon this ability. At level 5, the character gains the ability to Charm a single person, as per the spell "Charm Person," (p. 105). This ability requires no expenditure of M.E.P., but requires a Charisma Check with a CL equal to the level or hit dice of the victim. At level 10, the character gains Charisma as an additional Prime; if the character already has Charisma as a Prime, or already has four Prime Attributes, he instead gains +3 to all Charisma-based checks.

POWERHOUSE (STR)

The character gains +2 to all Strength-based saving throws. This does not combine with other class abilities that grant bonuses to all Strength-based saves, though it will combine with those that grant bonuses to specific saves that also happen to be based upon Strength. At level 5, the character gains +2 to damage with all melee attacks, and can deal 1d4 normal damage with an unarmed attack. At level 10, the character gains Strength as an additional Prime; if the character already has Strength as a Prime, or already has four Prime Attributes, he instead gains +3 to all Strength-based checks.

RELENTLESS WARRIOR (CON)

When the character is reduced to zero hit points, he may continue fighting by making a Constitution Check. The CL of this check is +1 for every five points below zero the character's hit points fall. If the character fails a Constitution Check, or at the end of the battle, he immediately collapses and takes the full

penalty for his current negative hit points (meaning that if he is below -10 hit points, death occurs).

STILL BODY (CON)

This character has mastery over vital bodily functions, and with a successful Constitution-based check can slow them until he or she appears to be dead. To any examination, the character will appear to have no heartbeat, no breathing, no vital functions whatsoever. The character may maintain this state of feigned death for a number of turns equal to the character's level. Anyone examining the character can detect the subterfuge by making a Wisdom check with a CC equal to the character's Constitution check to activate this ability, plus 2. Thus, if the Constitution check to activate this ability was 17, anyone examining the character for signs of life would detect such signs on a Wisdom check of 19 or better.

TRACKING (WIS)

The character with this ability can successfully track any creature in a wilderness setting that leaves a discernable trace. They can also determine characteristics about the creature being tracked. With a successful wisdom check, a character can find and follow a creature's tracks or trail for 5 hours. The character can also hide tracks at the same level of ability. A character can, by sacrificing another class ability, gain the acumen of an expert tracker.

When tracking or hiding tracks from enemies, a character receives a +2 bonus to the attribute check. The Game Master may apply bonuses or penalties for varying conditions, such as the length of time elapsed since the tracks were made, weather conditions, the number of creatures tracked and whether the tracked creature moved through water or a secret door.

A successful track check may also impart information about the creature(s) being tracked. Once a trail is found, a track check can determine the general number and type of creatures being tracked. The number of creatures tracked should be disclosed to the player by using one of the following categories: individuals (1-6), band (6-30), troop (20-100), or army (100+). A character can identify specific animal tracks with no effort. After having tracked a particular type of creature several times, the character can later identify its tracks. At 5th level, a character can identify the specific type of prey being tracked, if belonging to a society with which the character has had some interaction: a jungle tracker, for example, may be able to spot telltale signs of different local primitive tribes.

At 3rd level, a character can ascertain distinguishing characteristics about the creatures tracked, such as whether they are wounded, exhausted, carrying heavy objects or wearing certain armor. The character might even be able to determine if a shaman or arcanist is in the group being tracked. The marks or characteristics determined are limited only by the Game Master's imagination and desire to provide or enhance story elements during game play.

TWO-FISTED

Characters with this ability can fight with a weapon in each hand, so long as the weapon can be wielded in one hand, including handguns as well as melee weapons, allowing the character to make an extra attack each round with the "off-hand" weapon. Normally, when attempting to fight with weapons in two hands, the character suffers a -3 penalty with his strong hand, and a -6 penalty with his "off" hand. Characters with this ability suffer a -3 penalty with each hand at first level. At fifth level, this penalty decreases to -2. At tenth level, the penalty decreases to -1, and at fifteenth level, the character may attack with a weapon in each hand at no penalty. Characters seeking to take this ability should sacrifice an appropriate combat-related Class ability (at the GM's discretion), or two class abilities tied to mental Attributes or social situations (again, at the GM's discretion).

USE/BREW POISONS (INT)

Identifying a poison or antitoxin requires a successful check. To make a poison or antitoxin, the character needs access to a chemistry lab and raw materials costing at least $500. Training in the use of poison means that he never risks accidental poisoning when applying poison to a blade. Moreover, characters with this ability train with poisons of all types, and they slowly grow more resistant to their effects. This is reflected by a +1 bonus to saving throws versus poisons gained. This saving throw is gained at 3rd level.

WEALTHY (CHA)

This class ability is generally only available in games that use the optional Wealth system on page 79. Characters with this class ability have money and friends. These characters automatically succeed in any wealth check (see p. 79) to purchase any mundane item, from a cigarette lighter to an automobile, and whenever an item is encountered that needs to be purchased and is beyond the funds of the party, the Wealthy character adds +5 to her check to make the purchase. In addition, characters with a negative class-based Wealth Rating instead have a Wealth Rating of 0.

WEAPON FINESSE

As with Two-Fisted, an appropriate combat-related class ability should be sacrificed to pick this up. Weapon Finesse allows a character, when using a light melee weapon or rapier, to use her Dexterity bonus in place of her Strength bonus when rolling to hit in combat. At fifth level, she can also when appropriately armed substitute her Dexterity bonus for strength when rolling damage. At ninth level, her flashing blades also provide a measure of defense–she improves her AC against melee attacks (and only melee attacks) by +2 when using appropriate light weapons or a rapier. At twelfth level she gains an additional +1 to AC against melee attacks.

BACKGROUNDS, SKILLS AND TRAITS

Playing a pulp hero requires flare and flavor. To this end, several new aspects besides Generic Class Abilities are added to character creation that allow a high degree of uniqueness and customization to each character, making every ***Amazing Adventures*** character distinct from all others without sacrificing speed, simplicity, or ease of play.

CHARACTER BACKGROUNDS

DETERMINING BACKGROUNDS

There are two methods for determining backgrounds for a character. The first, and preferred method, is that each player can script out his character's back story as he likes, and then work with the GM to choose an appropriate background(s) based on that story. The second method is for players who prefer the "gonzo" nature of random character generation.

In addition, every class should be assumed to have a Knowledge skill in their appropriate class. Thus, Socialites have Knowledge (Socialite) and Gadgeteers Knowledge (Gadgeteer); class-specific Knowledge skills likely will encompass one or more of those listed below, but are considered bonus knowledge based off of the character's chosen path in life.

Method One: Player's Choice

GM's should be careful to adjudicate this freeform method closely, to maintain balance in the game, and in no case should a player ever begin play with more than three backgrounds (not counting their class-specific one). Backgrounds need not be selected from the table below, which is offered only for use with method two and potentially as a list of suggestions for appropriate backgrounds. This list is not all-inclusive; if a player has an idea for a character background not on the table, the GM should work with the player to allow such a new background, so long as it is not already covered by one in the table. A character, for example, who wishes to play a Professor of Ancient History does not need to create "Professor" as a background; rather, he can simply chose "Historian," and say that his character teaches at the local university.

Method Two: Random Generation

To determine background randomly, players should roll a d20 at character creation. The result determines profession to which the character was exposed before beginning his life as an adventurer (and often, the "day job" he currently holds). Backgrounds separated by a slash indicate a choice. A player who rolls a 1, for example, does not have a background in science and medicine–he should choose one of the two.

TABLE: CHARACTER BACKGROUNDS

D20 roll	Background
1	Scientist (type) / Doctor*
2	Mechanic
3	Businessman
4	Reporter
5	The Mean Streets
6	Factory or blue collar work
7	Mathematician
8	Photographer
9	Artist
10	Historian
11	Archaeologist / Anthropologist
12	Writer / Novelist
13	Chef / Restaurateur
14	Theologian / Religious Scholar
15	Lawyer / Law Enforcement
16	Professional Athlete
17	Actor / Actress
18	Politician
19	Roll Twice
20	Roll Three Times

*This does not provide practical, applicable skill in advanced medicine, only "book knowledge" and exposure to the medical field. At best, a player with this skill could make a good guess at a diagnosis for an ailment, perform basic first-aid, and determine if hospitalization and professional treatment is required. If a player wishes his character to actually have the skills of a doctor or surgeon, see the Medicine Generic Class Ability.

USING BACKGROUNDS

These professions represent a character's previous occupations or careers the character tried or held before taking up a life of adventuring (and possibly still holds). In these areas, the character has had special training or experience that provides bonuses in certain situations. Any time a character is able to call upon his life's training or experience, he gains +2 to the check. Situations in which these life paths are appropriate to use are at the discretion of the GM, though players are encouraged to be creative in suggesting the use of such abilities.

FOR EXAMPLE: A group comes to a market place in Egypt, needing to unload some pilfered treasures on the black market. Several backgrounds could be appropriate for use in haggling with collectors. Archaeologist/Anthropologist certainly would be useful in knowing just what the PC's have, as would Religious Scholar if the artifacts are of religious import. Any time a player can justify to the GM's satisfaction that his background could play an important role in an Attribute Check, he gains +2 to his check.

Under no circumstances should these backgrounds replace any class ability; the rules for mimicking cross-class abilities still apply. Thus, a Mentalist with the Politician or Actor/Actress background may attempt to use social skills and contacts and gain a +2 to the check, but still does not add his level as a bonus to the roll, since having contacts and high social standing are generally tied to the Socialite's "Connected" class ability. Characters whose backgrounds complement their Class abilities, on the other hand, do see the benefits of doing so. Thus, a Raider with the Archaeologist background adds his class level and an additional +2 to all Legend Lore checks related to Archaeology.

Likewise, the character's background can serve as an (albeit minor) restriction on his abilities. A character, for example, cannot build an atomic bomb without some sort of appropriate science background, no matter how high his Intelligence score is. If an attempt is antithetical to a character's background, the attempt probably shouldn't be allowed, though as always this is at the discretion of the GM.

IMPROVING BACKGROUNDS

At levels 5, 10, 15, and 20, a character can improve a single background, which then sees its bonus increase by +1. Likewise, characters who randomly roll backgrounds and get redundant results on their initial background selection can opt rather than re-rolling to increase the bonus to the redundant result in this manner. For example, Joe gets 2 rolls on the background table; both come up "Historian." He can choose to re-roll the second result in hopes of getting a different background, or may improve his Historian background, granting +1 to history-related Checks in addition to the normal +2, for a total of +3.

KNOWLEDGE SKILLS

Knowledge skills function similarly to Backgrounds in game, but represent more specialized areas of knowledge and skill. Characters can swap out up to half of their intelligence-based bonus languages (p. 27) for Knowledge skills. Knowledge actually encompasses a number of unrelated skills. Knowledge represents a study of some body of lore, possibly an academic or even scientific discipline. Whereas Backgrounds are more widely applicable, Knowledges grant slightly more information. Ability Checks using a Knowledge add +3 instead of +2.

Bonuses from Knowledges and Backgrounds generally do not combine. Normally, a background and knowledge will provide different, though possibly complimentary, information rather than granting a higher bonus to a single check. Thus, a player who is an archaeologist by background with knowledge in myths and legends does not usually gain +5 to suss out the meaning of an ancient scroll; in this case the archaeology knowledge would allow him to assess the probable age and authenticity, adding +2 to the check to do so, where the myth and legend knowledge would allow him to interpret the meaning of the story on the scrolls, adding +3 to that check. In some circumstances, however, the GM may decide that the situation does merit combining the two, granting a full +5 bonus to the check. This is left to the discretion of the GM.

At levels 4, 8, 16 and 20, all knowledge skills improve, their bonuses increasing by an additional +1. Alternately, at these levels, a character can instead choose to gain a new Knowledge skill. A new Knowledge skill always begins at first level experience. Any

Ability Checks with the new skill add +3 for the knowledge bonus, and +1 for being at first level (if they don't overlap another class's ability). Players should keep track of new skills, and their effective level, on their character sheets.

Some knowledges may overlap with Class Abilities. Such abilities impart an additional +3 to the use of said class ability. A character possessing a skill that mimics the abilities of another class (one of which the character is not a member) still gains +3 to relevant ability checks, but does not add their character level to the check. Skills are not a means to supplant class abilities; rather they are designed to supplement character creation and help to provide a means of character customization. Where overlap with a class or class ability is a gray area, the GM is encouraged to err on the side of the class rather than the skill, i.e. if you're not sure, don't allow the addition of character levels.

TYPICAL KNOWLEDGE SKILLS

Below are listed typical fields of study. There are countless more, and GM's should encourage players to come up with their own, unique ideas. Again, skills that overlap class abilities or step on the toes of another class, should not allow the character's level to be added to the roll. Thus, a non-Socialite with Knowledge (High Society) gains +3 to the check, but does not add character level. Likewise, knowledges do not add to backgrounds—characters gain the benefits of one or the other on any given roll, not both.

Arcane Symbols
Brewing
Confidence Games
Ecclesiastic Tradition
Electrical Engineering
Etiquette
Heraldry
History (Type; Military, European, U.S., etc.)
Magical Traditions
Magic Theory
Mythology (Type; Greek, Roman, Norse, etc.)
Engineering (Type; Mechanical, Civil, etc.)
Politics
Popular Culture
Science (Type: Chemistry, Biology, etc.)
Secret Societies (Type: Specific Secret Society**)**
Strategy and Tactics
Theology (Type; Christian, Muslim, Judaism, Gnosticism, etc.)

In many cases, you can use one of these skills to identify monsters and their special powers or vulnerabilities. In general, the CL modifier of such a check equals the monster's HD. A successful check allows you to remember a bit of useful information about that monster.

For every 5 points by which your check result exceeds the CC, you recall another piece of useful information.

CHARACTER TRAITS

Traits are aspects of a character's personality, background, or physique that make him better at some activities and worse at others. A character can have only a limited number of traits, and each trait provides some benefit. However, traits also carry a corresponding drawback. In addition to their game effects, traits suggest characteristics about the character's personality that might lead to interesting role playing opportunities. Together with a character's class and feat selection, traits offer a way for game mechanics to encourage deeper character backgrounds and consistent role playing.

Traits serve as an interesting starting point for role playing, reminding players of their characters' most prominent strengths and weaknesses. However, role playing a certain aspect of a character's personality does not require possessing the trait. For example, a character can be honest and forthright without the Honest trait. The player should role play the character consistently even though the character's honesty has no effect on his skill checks.

A character can begin play with up to two traits, chosen by the player at the time of character creation. Alternatively, the GM can require players to roll on Table: Character Traits to determine the traits possessed by their characters. Keep in mind, however, that some roll results might be wildly inappropriate for a given character—there's no reason for anyone but an Arcanist, for example, to gain Spellgifted. In such cases, the GM should always permit a reroll.

ADDING TRAITS

If the GM allows it, players may add traits to their characters after 1st level. The GM might allow a player to assign a trait to her character after she has role played the character in a manner consistent with the trait in question, or after a traumatic or life changing experience (after dying, a character might develop the Cautious trait or the Aggressive trait). If the GM includes this option, a character should gain a new trait no more frequently than once every five levels. Since traits add both bonuses and penalties, there is no cost for the acquisition of a new trait, other than the permission of the GM.

BUYING OFF TRAITS

As characters advance in level and ability, they might want to get rid of the traits that they chose at the beginning of play. This is not easy; changing one's personality requires a lot of work and discipline. This costs a character experience points. Buying off a Trait with XP costs 2,000 XP per level of the character

(the older you are, the harder it becomes to effect change in your life). For example, an abrasive character can work on becoming more personable by spending XP to buy off the Abrasive Trait; at first level, the cost to do this is 2,000 XP. At fourth level, the cost to buy off this Trait would be 8,000 XP. This represents the character shifting focus from advancing in her chosen career to making a change in the core of who she is.

DESIGNING TRAITS

Although this section provides a large number of character traits, a player who wants to create a character with a distinctive personality may ask the GM to design a new trait. If that happens, the GM should keep in mind that the traits variant is only effective if the benefits and the drawbacks of the traits are related. If the drawback and benefit of a trait apply to disparate or unrelated aspects of the game, it becomes too easy for a player to choose a trait for her character that provides a bonus on a commonly attempted ability check or skill check while the corresponding penalty applies to a rarely used or never used aspect of play. For example, a trait that gave a bonus to Armor Class and a penalty on attack rolls would be poor design because spell casters make very few attack rolls (making the penalty far less severe) yet continuously gain the benefit-of the increased Armor Class.

As long as the GM and player talk about a new trait ahead of time and view it in light of what skills and abilities the character uses most often, this potential pitfall is easy to avoid.

TABLE: CHARACTER TRAITS

d%	Trait	d%	Trait
01-03	Abrasive	50-51	Nightsighted[1]
04-06	Absent-minded	52-54	Passionate
07-09	Aggressive	55-57	Plucky
10-11	Brawler[1]	58-60	Polite
12-13	Cautious[1]	61-62	Quick[1]
14-16	Detached	63-65	Reckless
17-19	Dishonest	66-68	Relentless
20-21	Distinctive[1]	69-70	Saddleborn
22-24	Easygoing	71-73	Skinny
25-27	Farsighted	74-76	Slippery
28-30	Focused	77-78	Slow[1]
31-33	Hard of Hearing	79-81	Specialized
34-36	Hardy	82-84	Spellgifted
37-39	Honest	85-87	Stout
40-41	Illiterate)	88-90	Suspicious
42-43	Inattentive[1]	91-93	Torpid
44-46	Musclebound	94-96	Uncivilized
47-49	Nearsighted	97-100	Roll again twice[2]

1. Trait has special restrictions (see the text). If you don't qualify, roll again.

2. No starting character may have more than two traits. If a player rolls this result two or more times, the player may choose which two traits to keep.

ROLEPLAYING OF TRAITS

If a player creates a character with one or more of the traits described here, she has three basic choices for how that trait affects the character's personality.

First, the character might view the trait as a weakness. A character with this view might try to hide the trait or make excuses for his behavior. On the other hand, he might seek out others with the trait to feel better about his own idiosyncrasy.

Second, the character might view the trait as a strength. A character might call attention to the trait, encourage others to act in ways that mimic the trait, or simply assume that those without the trait are less worthy than those who possess it.

Finally, the character might not acknowledge the trait at all. A character might adopt this attitude toward a trait for several reasons, each suggesting something different about the character's background and personality.

The character might not be aware of the trait; for example, a nearsighted character might not realize that others see better at a distance because his impairment is mild and the onset was so gradual that he never noticed the change.

The character might be aware of the trait but not want to admit that he possesses it. For example, an abrasive character might realize that his mannerisms affect others, yet find more solace in putting the blame on those whom he offends rather than on himself.

The character might know but simply not care.

CREATING YOUR OWN TRAITS

The list of Traits here is not extensive; if you wish to create your own trait, use the following guidelines.

First, the player and GM should decide what the Trait will generally accomplish, and what it will be called. For example, perhaps the character is crass and irritable, which results in a mildly cruel attitude towards others, but lets them see through flaws due to their suspicious nature? The GM and player may decide to name the Trait Ornery.

Next, it's time to consider the game mechanics. Traits grant a +1 bonus to a circumstantial bonus related to one ability, with an equivalent penalty to a circumstantial bonus related to one ability, which need not be the same ability. For example, see Abrasive, which adds +1 to Charisma Checks to intimidate others in exchange for a -1 to be diplomatic or bluff. Aggressive, on the other hand, gives a +2 bonus to initiative in exchange for a -1 penalty to AC. In this case, the -1 penalty to AC is considered roughly equivalent to the +2 Initiative bonus.

Going back to our new Ornery Trait, the game mechanics seem pretty clear. The character gains a +1 to Wisdom checks to see falsehoods or ulterior motives in others, but a -1

to Charisma checks when trying to be diplomatic or engage in social niceties.

Add a few statements about the way this Trait can be role played, and there you have it!

TRAIT DESCRIPTIONS

Each trait in this section includes a benefit, a drawback, any special limitations regarding its selection by a character, and roleplaying ideas for how to incorporate it into your character's personality.

Abrasive

You are difficult and demanding in conversation, which tends to oppress those around you.

Benefit

You gain a +1 bonus on Charisma checks to intimidate others.

Drawback

You take a -1 penalty on Charisma checks to be diplomatic or bluff another.

Roleplaying Ideas

Characters with this trait might be loud and abrupt or quiet and sinister, but either way, most find them disconcerting or irritating.

Absent Minded

You are fascinated by knowledge and learning and are capable of pursuing complex trains of thought quite quickly. However, your preoccupation with such thoughts makes you a little less aware of your surroundings.

Benefit

You gain a +1 bonus on Intelligence checks to recall information about a subject, area, person, culture, etc. This bonus stacks with the Raider class's Legend Lore ability.

Drawback

You take a -1 penalty on Wisdom checks to spot or listen. This penalty applies even to the Listen class ability, and to the Case Target ability.

Roleplaying Ideas

Characters with this trait might flit from idea to idea, trailing off in mid-sentence or mumbling their way through complex ideas. Conversely, characters with this trait might be extremely articulate but still allow their thoughts to move faster than the pace of a conversation.

Aggressive

You are quick to initiate combat, and you tend to press the attack once battle is joined. Your enthusiasm makes you a dangerous foe, but you sometimes leave yourself open to blows that a more cautious warrior would avoid.

Benefit

You gain a +2 bonus on initiative checks.

Drawback

You take a -1 penalty to Armor Class.

Roleplaying Ideas

Characters with this trait are often hotheaded and quick to anger, or simply think that the best defense is a quick offense.

Brawler

You naturally move close to your opponents when fighting, instinctively grabbing and punching rather than striking with weapons.

Benefit

You gain a +1 bonus on unarmed attack rolls and grapple checks, and may inflict normal damage (1d4) with unarmed attacks.

Drawback

You take a -2 penalty on all other attack rolls.

Special

The bonus from this trait doesn't apply to natural weapons and does not stack with Pugilist class abilities. Pugilists are already natural brawlers. If a character with this Trait gains a level in the Pugilist character class, he loses this trait. This is an exception to the rule regarding the use of experience points to buy off Traits.

Roleplaying Ideas

Characters with this trait often disdain the use of weapons entirely, and some eventually learn more refined martial arts based on their instinctive fighting techniques. Many brawlers might not even be consciously aware that they fight differently from other characters; they simply know that the best way to take someone out of a fight is to grab him or punch him in the face.

Cautious

You are cautious in combat, even a bit cowardly, and you take more care to defend yourself than others. However, this caution renders you susceptible to fear effects.

Benefit

You gain an additional +1 dodge bonus to Armor Class whenever you use the Dodge Combat Maneuver, or when fighting defensively (see p. 175).

Drawback

You take a -1 penalty on saving throws made to resist fear effects.

Special

You cannot select this trait if you have immunity to fear or fear effects. If you later gain immunity to fear, you lose the benefit of this trait. This is an exception to the rule regarding the use of XP to buy off traits.

Roleplaying Ideas

Characters with this trait might consistently urge talking rather than fighting, or they might do little to encourage that their companions avoid combat and simply remain as far away from foes as possible, using ranged weapons or spells.

Detached

You maintain a distance from events that keeps you grounded but limits your reaction speed.

Benefit
You gain a +1 bonus on Wisdom checks.

Drawback
You take a -1 penalty on Dexterity checks.

Roleplaying Ideas
Characters with this trait are likely to be quiet and restrained, but they might be vocal when others falter in their beliefs.

Dishonest
You are naturally deceitful and insincere with others. You have a talent for lying, but have difficulty convincing others when you do speak truthfully.

Benefit
You gain a +1 bonus on Charisma checks to bluff another.

Drawback
You take a -2 penalty on Charisma checks to be diplomatic.

Roleplaying Ideas
Characters with this trait might be portrayed as crafty liars, or lying might simply be second nature to them, making actually telling the truth a difficult chore.

Distinctive
You have some distinctive physical feature such as a scar, a prominent nose, a limp, or some similar characteristic that is hard to disguise or conceal.

Benefit
You gain a +1 bonus on Reputation checks. For information on Reputation, see p.78.

Drawback
You take a -1 penalty on Disguise checks.

Roleplaying Ideas
Characters with this trait might be sensitive about it, or they might play up its presence to gather attention, sympathy, or notoriety.

Easygoing
You are naturally friendly and trusting. Others feel comfortable around you, but this trait also makes it more difficult for you to be pushy or suspicious.

Benefit
You gain a +1 bonus on Charisma checks to be friendly, diplomatic, or gain information.

Drawback
You take a -1 penalty on Charisma checks to Intimidate another, and on Wisdom checks to detect falsehoods, lies, or ulterior motives.

Roleplaying Ideas
Characters with this trait might be more easily manipulated in interactions with NPCs, or they might simply prefer not to argue and instead use their natural talent to learn more about the world around them.

Farsighted
You have difficulty focusing on nearby objects, but your distance vision is more keen than normal.

Benefit
You gain a +1 bonus on Wisdom checks related to spotting things in the distance, or on the fly. This bonus stacks with class or racial abilities to notice secret compartments, unusual stonework, or anything hidden.

Drawback
You have a -2 penalty on Wisdom checks to search areas up close. This penalty also affects to class or racial abilities to search for traps, secret compartments, or anything hidden.

Roleplaying Ideas
Characters with this trait might be sensitive about it, or they might simply be oblivious to its presence, having never known any different way of experiencing the world.

Focused
You can keep your attention on a task despite many distractions; however, events in the background pass you by.

Benefit
You gain a +1 bonus on Attribute checks involving concentration. Situations where this applies are at the GM's discretion.

Drawback
You take a -1 penalty on Wisdom checks to spot something hidden or out of place, or to hear unusual sounds unless you are concentrating on the task of listening or searching a specific area.

Roleplaying Ideas
Characters with this trait often seem single-minded or even obsessive in their focus on a specific task.

Hard of Hearing
You have a slight hearing impairment, and to compensate, you have become more in tune with your other senses.

Benefit
You gain a +1 bonus on Attribute checks involving sight.

Drawback
You take a -2 penalty on Attribute checks involving hearing.

Roleplaying Ideas
Characters with this trait might be sensitive about it, or they might simply be oblivious to its presence, having never known any different way of experiencing the world.

Hardy
You are made of tougher stuff than the average person, but you're not quite as quick to react to dangerous effects.

Benefit
You gain a +1 bonus on Constitution-based saves.

Drawback
You take a -1 penalty on Dexterity-based saves.

Roleplaying Ideas
Characters with this trait might see their physical prowess as normal and look down on less hardy individuals, or they might see it as their duty to play the role of protector and help those less able to endure physical hardship.

Honest

You are naturally straightforward and sincere. This quality helps you persuade people to your viewpoint, but you have difficulty telling lies and seeing deception in others.

Benefit
You gain a +1 bonus on Charisma checks to be diplomatic or make the truth work to your advantage.

Drawback
You take a -1 penalty on Wisdom checks to be dishonest or to sense dishonesty in others.

Roleplaying Ideas
Characters with this trait might be naive and too unsophisticated to lie, or they might be aware of worldly matters and simply choose to take a higher ground.

Illiterate

You cannot read, but you have devoted yourself to learning other skills.

Benefit
Choose any one attribute that is designated Prime for your character. You gain a +1 bonus on checks using that Attribute.

Drawback
You are illiterate.

Special
You can't select this trait if your character is already illiterate.

Roleplaying Ideas
Characters with this trait might be sensitive about not being able to read, or they might not value "book learnin'."

Inattentive

You are alert and skilled at finishing simple tasks quickly, but you have a difficult time dealing with longer, more complex tasks.

Benefit
You gain a +1 bonus on Wisdom checks to spot something hidden or out of place, or to hear unusual sounds unless the listening or searching requires patience and concentration. You also gain a +1 bonus to all Attribute checks involving tasks that can be completed quickly (excluding combat).

Drawback
You take a -1 penalty on Attribute checks involving concentration or focus for more than a few moments, or on ongoing tasks. Situations where this applies are at the GM's discretion.

Roleplaying Ideas
Characters with this trait might flit from subject to subject in conversation, or they might seem typical in most situations but leave most of their long-term projects perpetually unfinished.

Musclebound

You are good at almost everything that requires strength, but less adept than most at tasks that require coordination.

Benefit
You gain a +1 bonus on Strength-based Attribute checks.

Drawback
You take a -2 penalty on Dexterity-based Attribute checks.

Roleplaying Ideas
Characters with this trait are likely to solve problems with physical strength rather than through trickery or finesse.

Nearsighted

You have difficulty focusing on distant objects, but your eye for detail is more keen than normal.

Benefit
You gain a +1 bonus on Wisdom checks to search areas up close. This bonus stacks with class or racial abilities to search for traps, secret compartments, or anything hidden.

Drawback
You have a -2 penalty on Wisdom checks related to spotting things in the distance, or on the fly. This penalty also applies to class or racial abilities to notice secret compartments, unusual stonework, or anything hidden.

Roleplaying Ideas
Characters with this trait might be sensitive about it, or they might simply be oblivious to its presence, having never known any different way of experiencing the world.

Nightsighted

Your eyes are particularly well suited to using some form of night vision, but they are less well adapted to what others consider normal light.

Benefit
Increase your night vision by one level. If you don't normally have it, you gain Duskvision. Duskvision, in turn, becomes Twilightvision. Twilightvision becomes Darkvision, and Darkvision becomes Deepvision.

Drawback
You take a -1 penalty on all Attribute checks and combat rolls when in areas of bright light.

Roleplaying Ideas
This trait might not affect a character's personality at all, but it might make the character prefer going on underground or nighttime adventures.

Passionate

You are made of tougher stuff than the average person, but you are highly suggestible.

Benefit
You gain a +1 bonus on Constitution-based saves.

Drawback
You take a -1 penalty on Wisdom-based saves.

Roleplaying Ideas
Characters with this trait might be gruff and place extreme value on overcoming physical obstacles, or conversely, their weakness against magical enchantments might leave them fascinated and fearful of such things.

Plucky
You have a strength of will not reflected in your limited physical gifts.

Benefit
You gain a +1 bonus on Wisdom-based saves.

Drawback
You take a -1 penalty on Constitution-based saves.

Roleplaying Ideas
Characters with this trait might be annoyingly positive-minded, or they might only show their mental resilience in times of dire need.

Polite
You are courteous and well spoken.

Benefit
You gain a +1 bonus on Charisma checks made to be diplomatic.

Drawback
You take a -2 penalty on Charisma checks when attempting to intimidate another.

Roleplaying Ideas
Characters with this trait might be honestly polite and kind, or they might simply be adept at mimicking social conventions to get what they want.

Quick
You are fast, but less sturdy than others.

Benefit
Your base movement rate increases by 10 feet, and you gain +1 to initiative.

Drawback
Subtract 1 from your hit points gained at each level, including 1st (a result of 0 is possible).

Roleplaying Ideas
Characters with this trait typically try to stay away from physical combat, but a rare few might relish it, striving to see if their superior speed is enough to best hardier warriors.

Reckless
You naturally sacrifice accuracy to put more power behind your blows.

Benefit
You gain a +1 bonus on damage rolls after successful melee attacks.

Drawback
You take a -1 penalty on melee attack rolls.

Roleplaying Ideas
Characters with this trait might be loudly passionate about entering combat and overcoming foes through strength of arms, or they might be quiet and so desperate to avoid confrontation that they put extra effort into every blow in an attempt to end the encounter more quickly.

Relentless
You don't know the meaning of the word "tired." You go all out until you simply can't continue.

Benefit
You gain a +2 bonus on Constitution checks and similar checks made to continue tiring activities or to resist fatigue. In cases of Level Drain, you are entitled to a separate Constitution check to avoid becoming fatigued from the level drain. The CL of this check is equal to the HD of the creature inflicting the level drain.

Drawback
Any effect or condition that would normally cause you to become fatigued instead causes you to become exhausted. See p. 167 for information regarding Fatigue and Exhaustion.

Roleplaying Ideas
Characters with this trait may see others as soft or weak, especially anyone who complains about being tired or fatigued. They might openly scoff at others' weaknesses or might quietly encourage them to "tough it out."

Saddleborn
You are a natural in the saddle, but you have little patience for handling animals when not riding them.

Benefit
You gain a +1 bonus on Dexterity checks to ride animals, including animals not normally thought of as mounts.

Drawback
You take a -1 penalty on Attribute checks to handle, train, or otherwise care for animals.

Roleplaying Ideas
Characters with this trait rarely bother to consider animals as good for anything other than mounts, but they are extremely confident about their riding abilities.

Skinny
You are exceptionally slender and scrawny.

Benefit
You gain a +1 bonus on Attribute checks made to escape from bonds such as rope or shackles. You also use your Dexterity rather than your Strength to attempt to escape from bonds. This trait stacks with appropriate class abilities.

Drawback
You take a -2 penalty on Strength checks to avoid overbearing.

Roleplaying Ideas
Skinny characters tend to be pushed around by tougher types, so those with this trait might be shy, or they might be very defensive when faced with such situations.

Slippery

You are less adept at grappling and wrestling than others of your size and strength, but you are adept at slipping out of another's hold.

Benefit

You gain a +1 bonus on checks to escape a grapple or avoid being grappled.

Drawback

You take a -1 penalty to attempt to grapple another.

Roleplaying Ideas

Characters with this trait might fear close combat, knowing they are less adept grapplers than most opponents. On the other hand, good escape artists with this trait might enjoy baiting larger foes into grappling them, knowing they can easily slip out of the grasp of most foes.

Slow

You are slow, but sturdier than other people.

Benefit

Add +2 to your hit points gained at each level.

Drawback

Your base movement is halved (round down to the nearest 5-foot interval).

Special

You must have a base land speed of at least 20 feet to select this trait.

Roleplaying Ideas

Characters with this trait tend to be relatively immobile in combat. They typically prefer to wear strong armor (or other protective devices), since it's hard for them to flee a fight.

Specialized

You have a knack for one kind of work or study, but other tasks are harder for you to accomplish.

Benefit

Choose one specific Background or Secondary Skill. You gain a +2 bonus on checks using the specified Background or skill.

Drawback

You take a -2 penalty on checks using all other Backgrounds or Secondary Skills.

Special

This Trait is only available in campaigns using Backgrounds or Secondary Skills.

Roleplaying Ideas

Characters with this trait often see themselves as elite artists or experts rather than mere professionals, and they might regard their chosen vocation or study as more useful or interesting than other tasks.

Spellgifted

You have a gift for casting spells of certain type. Although your spells in this area are more potent than those of other casters, you are not as effective at casting spells from other schools.

Benefit

Choose a type of magic from the following list: Conjuring/Summoning, Defensive, Divination, Elemental (choose an element), Enchantments/Charms, Illusion, Necromancy/Healing, Offensive (spells that cause direct damage), Transmutation/Alteration. Add 1 to your caster level when casting spells of this type. Some spells may be at the GM's discretion for the category under which they fall.

Drawback

Reduce your caster level by 1 whenever you cast a spell that is not from your chosen school.

Special

Not all spells on the Charisma spell list are considered Illusion spells. Color Spray, for example, is an Offensive spell, Fog Cloud could be Defensive or Conjuring/Summoning, and Light could be Enchant, Transmutation, or Conjuring, at the GM's discretion. The GM always has final ruling on what school a spell falls under.

Roleplaying Ideas

Characters with this trait might be loudly vocal about the merits of the school of magic that they understand most readily, or they might feel awkward and out of place around "normal" spell casters as a result of their unusual aptitude.

Stout

You are stocky and heavy.

Benefit

You gain a +2 bonus on Strength checks to avoid being bull rushed or overrun.

Drawback

You take a -1 penalty on Escape Artist checks.

Roleplaying Ideas

Overweight characters are often bullied, so those with this trait might be shy, or they might be very defensive when faced with such situations. Some turn to humor to defuse such situations, while others become bitter.

Suspicious

You are naturally suspicious of everyone and everything. While this trait makes you hard to fool, it makes others slightly less likely to agree with you or find you threatening.

Benefit

You gain a +1 bonus on Wisdom checks to detect lies, falsehoods, or ulterior motives in others.

Drawback

You take a -1 penalty on Charisma checks to be diplomatic or intimidate others.

Roleplaying Ideas

This trait might express itself as comic levels of paranoia, or it might make the character quietly cautious about others.

Torpid

You are sluggish and slow to react to danger, but also resistant to others' commands.

Benefit

You gain a +1 bonus on saves against enchantment (compulsion) effects.

Drawback

You take a -2 penalty on initiative checks.

Roleplaying Ideas

Torpid characters may be seen as lazy, or as methodical and measured in their actions.

Uncivilized

You relate better to animals than you do to people.

Benefit

You gain a +1 bonus on Charisma checks to handle animals. See p. 58 for animal handling.

Drawback

You take a -1 penalty on Charisma checks to bluff, gather information, or be diplomatic.

Roleplaying Ideas

Characters with this trait are likely to feel awkward in many social situations; that might be expressed as shyness and quiet behavior, or it might be expressed through an overly exuberant need to participate in conversations.

SANITY

This optional system allows you to introduce an element of dark horror into your game. In campaigns using these rules, characters gain a new attribute called Sanity. This statistic functions like an ability score in some ways, but it has its own unique mechanics that represent the character's descent from a stable and healthy mental state into confusion, dementia, and mental instability. As a character encounters monsters, witnesses horrible acts, masters forbidden knowledge, or casts spells, his Sanity score, and his corresponding ability to function as a normal member of humanity, deteriorates. This gradual descent is balanced in part by the powers that characters gain each time they overcome a horrific foe or grow in skill and expertise, but even as those characters grow in power, they know or fear that an even greater peril lies ahead—the threat of becoming permanently insane.

The rules for sanity are included herein due to the fact that they are most often associated with monsters and unnatural things, so they go hand-in-hand with the bestiary. They are completely optional, and are not recommended for Game Masters who desire their games to be of the heroic, two-gun, fast and furious style. Games that include sanity tend to be more nihilistic in tone and generally involve either inevitable slides into madness or raging against an equally inevitable dying of the light. There's rarely a light at the end of the tunnel in games that involve sanity, so think carefully before importing it into your game.

WHAT IS SANITY?

Sanity is the natural mental state of ordinary life. Normal mental balance is endangered when characters confront horrors, entities, or activities that are shocking, unnatural, and bewildering. Such encounters cause a character to lose points from his Sanity score, which in turn risks temporary, indefinite, or permanent insanity. Mental stability and lost Sanity points can be restored, up to a point, but psychological scars may remain.

Insanity occurs if too many Sanity points are lost in too short a time. Insanity does not necessarily occur if Sanity points are low, but a lower Sanity score makes some forms of insanity more likely to occur after a character experiences an emotional shock. The character's Sanity may be regained after a few minutes, recovered after a few months, or lost forever.

A character may regain Sanity points, and even increase her Sanity point maximum. However, increasing a character's ranks in the Forbidden Lore knowledge always lowers her maximum Sanity by an equal amount.

SANITY POINTS

Sanity points measure the stability of a character's mind. This attribute provides a way to define the sanity inherent in a character, the most stability a character can ever have, and the current level of sane rationality that a character preserves, even after numerous shocks and horrid revelations.

Sanity is measured in three ways: starting Sanity, current Sanity, and maximum Sanity. Starting and current Sanity cannot exceed maximum Sanity.

STARTING SANITY

A character's starting Sanity equals his Wisdom score multiplied by 5. After creation, a character's current Sanity often fluctuates considerably and might never again match starting Sanity. A change in a character's Wisdom score changes his starting Sanity in terms of what treatment with the Heal skill can restore. Current Sanity, however, does not change if Wisdom rises or falls.

CURRENT SANITY

A character's current Sanity score fluctuates almost as often as (and sometimes much more often than) his hit points.

MAXIMUM SANITY

A character's maximum Sanity score erodes as he gains exposure to all of the Things that Should Not Be which reside in the Deeper Dark between the planes of existence. Ranks in the Forbidden Lore Knowledge (see below) simulate a character's comprehension of aspects of the dark creatures at the edges of reality. Once gained, this horrible knowledge is never forgotten, and the character consequently surrenders mental equilibrium. A character's Sanity weakens as his comprehension of these hidden truths increases. Such is the way of the universe.

The first time a character gain Forbidden Knowledge, a character's maximum Sanity score is permanently reduced by 5 points. Thereafter, each improvement a character gains in this knowledge permanently reduces a character's maximum Sanity by 1 point: The more a character knows about the horrible truths underlying reality, the less capable a character is of leading a normal life. These total modifiers (an easy calculation is 4 + total Forbidden Lore levels) are called the Forbidden Lore Modifier.

A character's maximum Sanity can never be higher than 99 minus the character's total Forbidden Lore modifier.

MAKING A SANITY CHECK

When a character encounters a gruesome, unnatural, or supernatural situation, the GM may require the player to make a Sanity check. On a successful check, the character either loses no sanity, or a minimal amount. Potential sanity loss is usually shown as two numbers or die rolls separated by a slash, such as 1/1d4. The number before the slash indicates the number of sanity points lost if the sanity check succeeds (in this case, 1). The number after the check indicates the number of additional sanity points lost if the check fails (in this case, 1d4+1; 1d4 for failing, plus the 1 automatic loss if the check had succeeded).

This check is a Wisdom-based saving throw with a CL equal to 10 minus 10% of the character's current SAN score, rounded down. Thus, a character with SAN 90 makes a SAN check at CL 1 (10-9), while a character with SAN 50 makes a SAN check at CL 5 (10-5). SAN loss creates diminishing returns.

A character's current Sanity is also at risk when the character reads certain books, learns certain types of spells, and attempts to cast them. These Sanity losses are usually automatic (no Sanity check is allowed); the character who chooses to undertake the activity forfeits the indicated number of Sanity points.

In most cases, a new Sanity-shaking confrontation requires a new Sanity check. However, the GM always gets to decide when characters make Sanity checks. Confronting several horribly mangled corpses at one time or in rapid succession may call for just one Sanity check, while the same corpses encountered singly over the course of several game hours may require separate checks.

SIMPLER SANITY CHECKS

A simpler method for making Sanity Checks is to just have a player roll percentile dice against his character's existing Sanity score. A result under the character's current SAN is successful. This yields similar (though not mathematically identical) results to the Wisdom save, but does not require the GM to figure out the CL for the save. On the other hand, it is not a standard SIEGE method of resolution, so for players that insist upon standardized task resolution this method may not be ideal.

FORBIDDEN LORE

The Sanity rules assume that some knowledge is so alien to human understanding that simply learning of its existence can shatter the psyche. While magic and nonhuman races form an everyday part of an ***Amazing Adventures*** character's life, even a seasoned adventurer cannot conquer or understand some things. Knowledge of these secrets and creatures is represented by a new Knowledge skill that goes hand in hand with a character's Sanity score: Forbidden Lore. Even if the GM decides not to use Knowledge Skills or Backgrounds in game, if Sanity rules are adopted, this particular Knowledge should be included.

This type of knowledge permanently erodes a character's ability to maintain a stable and sane outlook, and a character's current Sanity can never be higher than 99 minus the modifier the character has in the Forbidden Lore skill. This number (99 minus Forbidden Lore) is the character's maximum Sanity. This score represents the upper limit of Sanity that can be restored by the Heal skill (see The Heal Skill and Mental Treatment, later in this section).

KNOWLEDGE SKILL: FORBIDDEN LORE

You know That Which Should Not Be Known. You have had horrible supernatural experiences and read forbidden tomes, learning truly dark secrets that have challenged everything

you thought you knew. Since these revelations defy logic or commonly accepted fact, it does not matter how intelligent or wise you are when using this skill—only how much exposure to these dark secrets themselves you have experienced.

FORBIDDEN LORE SIEGE CHECKS

The Forbidden Lore Knowledge works identically to other Knowledge Skills, which are included on page 64. In short, having a knowledge skill grants +3 to any SIEGE check when using that Knowledge. Unlike other knowledge skills, however, Forbidden Knowledge can be improved by future contacts with blasphemous horrors. Each "improvement" to the skill grants an additional +1 to checks.

Also unlike other SIEGE checks, the only characters who add their level to Forbidden Knowledge checks are Arcanists, who are already tuned into knowledge of Things that Should Not Be. Characters cannot gain this knowledge through normal experience advancement. They can only gain ranks by reading forbidden tomes or having experiences with horrible creatures.

Likewise, characters cannot take the Forbidden Lore knowledge during character creation as one of their starting Knowledge skills (p. 64). The GM will tell you when you gain an improvement in your Forbidden Lore knowledge.

The thing that makes Forbidden Lore dangerous is its utility; despite its devastating effects on Sanity, characters will likely want to learn more Forbidden Lore once they first access it.

Answering a question about the horrible deities and secrets that lurk at the edges of reality has a CL which will vary by difficulty:

CL of 3 (for really easy questions)

CL of 5 (for elementary questions)

CL of 10 to 20 (for difficult or really tough questions).

Unlike in other fields of study, there are exceedingly few really easy questions associated with this dark knowledge.

A character can use this skill to identify monsters and their special powers or vulnerabilities. In general, the CL of such a check equals the monster's HD. A successful check allows a character to remember a bit of useful information about that monster. For every 5 points by which a character's check result exceeds the DC, the GM can give another piece of useful information.

The GM can decide which monsters are subject to the Forbidden Lore knowledge and which monsters are subject to one of the standard Knowledge skills. For example, the GM may rule that Knowledge (folklore) is still the relevant skill for learning or knowing about vampires and werewolves, rather than allowing them to be identified by Forbidden Lore. There may, however, be a certain *species of werewolves* attached to the Great Old One Nyarlathotep, which are affected by gold rather than silver; in this case the GM may rule that Forbidden Lore is required to reveal this knowledge.

In most campaigns that use Sanity, such creatures as aberrations, oozes, demons and devils should be identified by Forbidden Lore. If the GM wants to make Forbidden Lore especially attractive, all monsters could be identified by this skill, while other knowledges grant limited information about specific creatures.

MADNESS AND MAGIC

To add a touch of the alien to your Arcanists, you can tie Sanity to spells, making magic an otherworldy energy that corrupts and drains the sanity of its user. In this system, any time an arcanist casts a spell, he must make a Sanity check. The CL of this check is modified by the spell's level. Thus, zero-level spells do not modify the CL, while 9th level spells increase the CL by +9. Failing this check costs the caster Sanity points equal to 1d6 plus the level of the spell being cast.

You can modify the chance of SAN loss from a spell by changing when checks are made. If every spell cast is too much, try requiring a roll when the caster rolls a 1 or otherwise fails a spell casting roll, or have the roll occur only the first time the Caster uses a spell on a given day, week, or month.

GOING INSANE

Losing more than a few Sanity points may cause a character to go insane, as described below. If a character's Sanity score drops to 0 or lower, she begins the quick slide into permanent insanity. Each round, the character loses another point of Sanity. Once a character's Sanity score reaches -10, she is hopelessly, incurably insane. The Heal skill can be used to stabilize a character on the threshold of permanent insanity; see The Heal Skill and Mental Treatment, below, for details.

A GM's description of a Sanity-shaking situation should always justify the threat to a character's well-being. Thus, a horde of frothing rats is horrifying, while a single ordinary rat usually is not (unless the character has an appropriate phobia, of course).

LOSS OF SANITY

Characters ordinarily lose Sanity in a few types of circumstances: when encountering something unimaginable, when suffering a severe shock, after casting a spell or when learning a new spell, when being affected by a certain type of magic or a particular spell, or when reading a forbidden tome.

ENCOUNTERING THE UNIMAGINABLE

When people perceive creatures and entities of unspeakable horror, this experience costs them some portion of their minds, since such creatures are intrinsically discomforting and repellent. We never lose awareness of their slimy, fetid, alien nature. This instinctive reaction is part and parcel of human nature. In this

category, we can include supernatural events or agents not always recognized as specifically devoted to these dark gods, such as hauntings, zombies, vampires, curses, and so on.

Sanity Loss from Creatures is generally based upon their size, perceived threat, and appearance. In general, small creatures such as rats (perhaps covered in viscera) net a Sanity loss of 0/1d4, while medium-sized creatures or swarms of smaller creatures may net 1d4/1d6. Large creatures can net anywhere from 1d6/1d8 to as much as 1d10/1d20 for colossal, monstrous creatures such as, for example, if the characters were to encounter an enormous, real, undead dragon. These are only suggestions–the GM can and should adjust individual monsters he deems more or less horrible than others of their size.

In addition, certain types of monstrous behavior might force additional Sanity checks, much like those described under Severe Shocks, below.

In most games, no character should need to make a Sanity check when encountering a normal human, or for encountering domesticated or otherwise commonplace animals. Of course, stumbling upon a group of otherwise normal humans performing unspeakable acts of torture and sacrifice is another issue, entirely...

SEVERE SHOCKS

A shocking sight of a more mundane nature can also cost Sanity points. Severe shocks include witnessing an untimely or violent death, experiencing personal mutilation, losing social position, being the victim of treachery, or whatever else the Game Master decides is sufficiently extreme. The following list gives some examples of severe shocks, and the Sanity loss each one provokes.

SANITY LOST[1]	SHOCKING SITUATION
Loss on a successful check/loss on a failed check.	
0/1d2	Surprised to find mangled animal carcass
0/1d3	Surprised to find human corpse
0/1d3	Surprised to find human body part
0/1d4	Finding a stream flowing with blood
1/1d4+1	Finding a mangled human corpse
0/1d6	Awakening trapped in a coffin
0/1d6	Witnessing a friend's violent death
1/1d6	Seeing a ghoul, zombie, or other human-shaped and -sized abomination
1/1d6+1	Meeting someone a character knows to be dead
0/1d10	Undergoing severe torture
1/d10	Seeing a corpse rise from its grave or encountering a large abomination
2/2d10+1	Seeing a gigantic severed head fall from the sky
1d10/d%	Seeing an Old One, Outer God, or other greater creature of the Deeper Dark

INSANE INSIGHT

At the GM's option, a character who has just gone insane may have an insight into the situation or entity that provoked the insanity. The player needs to make a CL 3 Wisdom check to gain the insight. Information provided by this sudden burst of awareness is up to the GM, but it may include something about a creature's origin or a fact about its nature (feeding habits, natural habitat, weakness), a clue to the identity of a murderer at a murder scene, or some hint at a location of great importance.

TYPES OF INSANITY

Character insanity is induced by a swift succession of shocking experiences or ghastly revelations, events usually connected with dark gods or creatures from the Outer Planes.

Horrifying encounters can result in one of three states of mental unbalance: temporary, indefinite, and permanent insanity. The first two, temporary insanity and indefinite insanity, can be cured. Permanent insanity results when a character's Sanity points are reduced to 0 or lower. This condition cannot be cured.

TEMPORARY INSANITY

Whenever a character loses Sanity points equal to or greater than one-half her Wisdom score from a single scene of game play, she has experienced enough of a shock that the GM must ask for a Sanity check. If the check fails, the character realizes the full significance of what she saw or experienced and goes temporarily insane. If the check succeeds, the character does not go insane, but she may not clearly remember what she experienced (a trick the mind plays to protect itself).

THE SCENE

A "scene" of game play is a nebulous element of time that is set by the GM. It generally represents a single combat or role playing encounter, or the time it takes to investigate a location or solve a puzzle. If you think of it in terms of a movie or television series, a scene would be the length of time that the camera focuses on one specific location and set of events before cutting away to the next. It's shorter than an "act," which would be a collection of inter-related scenes comprising one of (usually four) sections of an adventure scenario. For more on Acts and Scenes, see Book Five: Mysteries of the Dark.

Temporary insanity might last for a few minutes or a few days. Perhaps the character acquires a phobia or fetish befitting the situation, faints, becomes hysterical, or suffers nervous twitches, but she can still respond rationally enough to run away or hide from a threat.

A character suffering from temporary insanity remains in this state for either a number of rounds or a number of hours; roll d% and consult Table: Duration of Temporary Insanity to see whether the insanity is short-term or long-term. After determining the duration of the insanity, roll d% and consult either the Short Term or Long Term Temporary Insanity Effects tables to identify the specific effect of the insanity. The GM must describe the effect so that the player can roleplay it accordingly.

Successful application of the Heal skill (see The Heal Skill and Mental Treatment, below) may alleviate or erase temporary insanity.

Temporary insanity ends either when the duration rolled on Table 6-8 has elapsed, or earlier if the GM considers it appropriate to do so.

After an episode of temporary insanity ends, traces or even profound evidence of the experience should remain. No reason exists why, for instance, a phobia should depart from someone's mind as quickly as a warrior draws his sword. What remains behind after a brief episode of temporary insanity should exert a pervasive influence on the character. The character may still be a bit batty, but her conscious mind once again runs the show.

As a variant rule, if the amount of Sanity lost exceeds the character's current Wisdom score, consider the temporary insanity to always be of the long-term variety.

DURATION OF TEMPORARY INSANITY

d%	Temporary Insanity Type	Duration
01-80	Short-term	1d10+4 rounds
81-100	Long-term	1d10×10 hours

SHORT-TERM TEMPORARY INSANITY EFFECTS

d%	Effect
01-20	Character faints (can be awakened by vigorous action taking 1 round thereafter, character is shaken until duration expires).
21-30	Character has a screaming fit.
31-40	Character flees in panic.
41-50	Character shows physical hysterics or emotional outburst (laughing, crying, and so on).
51-55	Character babbles in incoherent rapid speech or in logorrhea (a torrent of coherent speech).
56-60	Character gripped by intense phobia, perhaps rooting her to the spot.
61-65	Character becomes homicidal, dealing harm to nearest person as efficiently as possible.
66-70	Character has hallucinations or delusions (details at the discretion of the GM).
71-75	Character gripped with echopraxia or echolalia (saying or doing whatever those nearby say or do).
76-80	Character gripped with strange or deviant eating desire (dirt, slime, cannibalism, and so on).
81-90	Character falls into a stupor (assumes fetal position, oblivious to events around her).
91-99	Character becomes catatonic (can stand but has no will or interest may be led or forced to simple actions but takes no independent action).
100	Roll on Table 2-5: Long-Term Temporary Insanity Effects.

LONG-TERM TEMPORARY INSANITY EFFECTS

d%	Effect
01-10	Character performs compulsive rituals (washing hands constantly, praying, walking in a particular rhythm, never stepping on cracks, constantly checking to see if crossbow is loaded, and so on).
11-20	Character has hallucinations or delusions (details at the discretion of the GM).
21-30	Character becomes paranoid.
31-40	Character gripped with severe phobia (refuses to approach object of phobia except on successful DC 20 Will save).
41-45	Character has aberrant sexual desires (exhibitionism, nymphomania or satyriasis, teratophilia, necrophilia, and so on).
46-55	Character develops an attachment to a "lucky charm" (embraces object, type of object, or person as a safety blanket) and cannot function without it.
56-65	Character develops psychosomatic blindness, deafness, or the loss of the use of a limb or limbs.
66-75	Character has uncontrollable tics or tremors (-4 penalty on all attack rolls, checks, and saves, except those purely mental in nature).
76-85	Character has amnesia (memories of intimates usually lost first, Knowledge skills useless).
86-90	Character has bouts of reactive psychosis (incoherence, delusions, aberrant behavior, and/or hallucinations).
91-95	Character loses ability to communicate via speech or writing.
96-100	Character becomes catatonic (can stand but has no will or interest, may be led or forced into simple actions but takes no independent action).

RANDOM INDEFINITE INSANITY

d%	Mental Disorder Type
01–15	Anxiety (includes severe phobias)
16–20	Dissociative (amnesia, multiple personalities)
21–25	Eating (anorexia, bulimia)
26–30	Impulse control (compulsions)
31–35	Mood (manic/depressive)
36–45	Personality (various neuroses)
46–50	Psychosexual (sadism, nymphomania)
51–55	Psychospecies (character falsely believes he is something other than human—vampire, werewolf, goblin, etc.)
56–70	Schizophrenia/psychotic (delusions, hallucinations, paranoia, catatonia)
71–80	Sleep (night terrors, sleepwalking)
81–85	Somatoform (psychosomatic conditions)
86–95	Substance abuse (alcoholic, drug addict)
96–100	Other (megalomania, quixotism, panzaism)

INDEFINITE INSANITY

If a character loses a significant amount of Sanity points in a short space of time (say, a few hours or so), she goes indefinitely insane. The GM judges when the impact of events calls for such a measure. Some GMs never apply the concept to more than the result of a single roll, since this state can remove characters from play for extended periods. An episode of indefinite insanity lasts for 1d6 game months (or as the GM dictates). Symptoms of

indefinite insanity may not be immediately apparent (which may give the GM additional time to decide what the effects of such a bout of insanity might be).

The Random Indefinite Insanity table is provided as an aid to selecting what form a character's indefinite insanity takes. Many GMs prefer to choose an appropriate way for the insanity to manifest, based on the circumstances that provoked it. These rules will not go into detailed breakdowns of all different kinds of insanity; this isn't a psychology textbook, and it is the author's feeling that overly detailed rules and strictures for portraying madness in a roleplaying game will interfere with the pulpy nature of these rules.

The state of indefinite insanity is encompassing and incapacitating. For instance, a schizophrenic may be able to walk the streets while babbling and gesticulating, find rudimentary shelter, and beg for enough food to survive, but most of the business of the mind has departed into itself: She cannot fully interact with friends, family, and acquaintances. Conversation, cooperation, and all sense of personal regard have vanished from her psyche.

As a general rule, a character suffering from indefinite insanity should be removed from active play until she recovers. At the GM's discretion, the player of the character might be allowed to use a temporary character until the end of the story. Whether this "stand-in" character is an incidental NPC in the adventure, a character of the same level as the rest of the group, one or two levels below the rest of the characters, or even a 1st-level character, is up to the GM. Different GMs have different ways of handling this transition.

If a character goes indefinitely insane near the end of an adventure, the GM may decide to set the next adventure to begin after the insane character has recovered.

After recovery, a victim retains definite traces of madness. For example, even though a character knows he is no longer insane, she might be deathly afraid of going to sleep if her insanity manifested itself in the form of terrifying nightmares. The character is in control of her actions, but the experience of insanity has changed her, perhaps forever.

PERMANENT INSANITY

A character whose Sanity score falls to 0 goes permanently insane. The character becomes an NPC under the control of the Game Master.

A character with permanent insanity may be reduced to a raving lunatic or may be outwardly indistinguishable from a normal person; either way, she is inwardly corrupted by the pursuit of knowledge and power. Some of the most dangerous cultists in the world are characters who have become permanently insane, been corrupted by forbidden knowledge, and "gone over to the other side."

A character might be driven permanently insane by forces other than dark gods or forbidden knowledge. In such cases, moral corruption need not necessarily occur. The GM might decide to consider different sorts of permanent insanity, rolling randomly or choosing from among the mental disorders on the Random Indefinite Insanity table, above.

A character who has gone permanently insane can never be normal again. She is forever lost in her own world. This need not mean a lifetime locked away from society, merely that the character has retreated so far from reality that normal mental functions can never be restored. She might be able to lead, within restricted bounds, a more or less normal life if kept away from the stimulus that triggers strong responses in her individual case. Yet a relapse may come quickly. Her calm facade can be destroyed in seconds if even the smallest reminder of what it was that drove her mad disturbs her fragile equilibrium. In any event, the eventual fate of a permanently insane character is a matter for individual Game Masters and players to decide.

GAINING OR RECOVERING SANITY

A character's Sanity score can increase during the events of a campaign. Although a character's Maximum Sanity score can never exceed 100 minus her Forbidden Lore bonus, her maximum Sanity and current Sanity can exceed her starting Sanity.

LEVEL ADVANCEMENT

A character's current Sanity can become higher than her starting Sanity as a result of gained levels: Whenever a character gains a new level, she rolls 1d6 and adds the result to her current Sanity. Some GMs may feel such self-improvement to be antithetical to this variant's dark tone, and thus may not allow it. Others may allow it if the player can roll over her character's current Sanity points after the character gains a level. Most Game Masters should find the question to be of no consequence, since characters continue to go insane regardless of how many Sanity points they gain. This is a point for players to be aware of, but not to worry about.

STORY AWARDS

The GM may decide to award increases in character's current Sanity if they foil a great horror, a demonic plan, or some other nefarious enterprise.

MENTAL TREATMENT

The Sanity rules presented here provide a new use for characters with a psychology background or knowledge, allowing trained alienists to help characters recover lost Sanity points. The CL and effect of a Siege check made to restore lost Sanity depend on whether the therapist is trying to offer immediate care or long-term care.

IMMEDIATE CARE

When someone suffers an episode of temporary insanity, a therapist can bring him out of it–calming his terror, snapping him out of his stupor, or doing whatever else is needed to restore the patient to the state she was in before the temporary insanity–by making a CL 3 Wisdom check. This check is the only thing the alienist can do for the entire round–no other action may be taken.

A therapist can also use immediate care to stabilize the Sanity score of a character whose current Sanity hits 0 or below. On a successful CL 5 Wisdom check, which takes the entire round and during which the therapist can take no other actions, the character's Sanity score improves to 1.

LONG-TERM CARE

Providing long-term care means treating a mentally disturbed person for a day or more in a place away from stress and distractions. A therapist must spend 1d4 hours per day doing nothing but talking to the patient. If the therapist makes a CL 10 Wisdom check at the end of this time, the patient recovers 1 Sanity point. A therapist can tend up to six patients at a time; each patient beyond the first adds 1 hour to the total time per day that must be devoted to therapy. The check must be made each day for each patient. A roll of 1 on any of these Wisdom checks indicates that the patient loses 1 point of Sanity that day, as she regresses mentally due to horrors suddenly remembered.

Recovery from indefinite insanity only comes with time (typically, 1d6 months). It is not dependent upon the character's Sanity points and is not connected to them. A character can be sane with 24 Sanity points and insane while possessing 77 Sanity points.

TREATMENT OF INSANITY

Temporary insanity ends so quickly that schedules of treatment are essentially pointless; it runs its course soon enough that one merely need protect a deranged character from further upset or harm. On the other hand, treatment of permanent insanity has no real meaning. By definition, a permanently insane character never recovers, no matter how good the therapist or the facility. Thus, indefinite insanity is the only form of mental illness that might be addressed by intervention and treatment.

After 1d6 months, if undisturbed by further trauma and with the agreement of the Game Master, an indefinitely insane character finds enough mental balance to reenter the world. Two kinds of care may help the character regain Sanity points during this recovery period. When choosing among them, the GM and player should consider the character's resources, her friends and relatives, and how wisely she has behaved in the past.

PRIVATE CARE

The best care available is at home or in some friendly place (perhaps a small church or the home of a wealthy friend) where nursing can be tender, considerate, and undistracted by the needs of competing patients. This can include outpatient therapy sessions with a skilled alienist (psychologist or psychiatrist) combined with rest, relaxation, and natural recovery.

If mental healing or medications are available, roll d% for each game month that one or the other is used. A result of 01-95 is a success: Add 1d3 Sanity points for either mental therapy or proper use of medications, whichever is used (a character can benefit from both used together, increasing gain to 1d6). On a result of 96-100, the healer fumbles the diagnosis or the character rejects the alchemical treatments. She loses 1d6 Sanity points, and no progress is made that month.

INSTITUTIONALIZATION

The next best alternative to private care is commitment to a good insane asylum. These institutions are of uneven quality, however, and some may be potentially harmful. Some are creative places of experiment and therapy, while others offer mere confinement. In any setting, concentrated and nourishing treatment by strangers is rare. Therapy using the psychology background or knowledge is usually the only treatment available, but in some cases, primitive institutions offer no treatment at all. Sometimes an institution can convey an uncaring sense that undermines the useful effects of alchemical medications, leaving the character with a sense of anger and loss. He is likely to be distrustful of the organization and its motives. Escape attempts are common by inmates, even in the most enlightened fantasy settings.

Roll d% for each game month a character is in the care of an institution. A result of 01-95 is a success; add 1d3 Sanity points if therapy with the Heal skill was available, or 1 Sanity point if no treatment was present. On a result of 96-100, the character rebels against the environment. He loses 1d6 Sanity points, and no progress can be made that month.

REPUTATION

As characters increase in level, their deeds tend to precede them as storytellers and socialites spread tales of their exploits. Any time there is a chance of a character being recognized, the GM makes a Reputation Check using the Intelligence bonus of the NPC, plus the level of the character being recognized. A separate check should be made for each character, unless the party is more important (i.e. a legendary group such as the Knights Templar). In the case of a party Reputation Check, use the average level of all characters in the party, +1 per party member present.

This Reputation check has a CL based on how far from their usual base of operations the party is, and whether or not the character(s) are actively trying to remain discreet. If the check succeeds, the character(s) is recognized, providing a +2 to efforts to be diplomatic, intimidating, or social, or in the cases of infamy, may result in the immediate notification of the proper authorities, or may cause all manner of other troubles for the group, at the GM's discretion.

Game Masters may also assign bonuses to reputation checks for characters who perform great or evil deeds. Players who receive these bonuses should note them on their character sheet, keeping track of bonuses for fame and bonuses for infamy.

TABLE: CL MODIFIERS FOR REPUTATION

Circumstance	CL Mod.
Less than a mile from normal base of operations	-5
Less than 10 miles from normal base of operations	-2
10-15 miles away from normal base of operations	+1
16-30 miles away from normal base of operations	+2
31-50 miles away from normal base of operations	+3
50-100 miles away from normal base of operations	+5
Over 100 miles away from normal base of operations	+10
Over 500 miles away from normal base of operations	+20
Over 1000 miles away from normal base of operations	+30
Characters are trying to remain discreet	+1 to +5*
Characters are actively calling attention to themselves	-1 to -10*

*depends on exactly what the characters are doing, at the GM's discretion.

WEALTH

The system for wealth in ***Amazing Adventures*** is fluid and freeform; that is, there is no tracking of specific funds, and in general, when a player wishes his or her character to purchase something, it's up to the GM to decide whether that's possible. For those who wish a more concrete method of purchasing and wealth, to represent the treasure-hunting mentality of some pulp heroes, we present this optional wealth system.

Rather than tracking every penny a character has, each character has a Wealth rating based upon their class, level, and any situational factors the GM deems appropriate. In this system, Wealth essentially becomes its own Ability Score, and certain classes treat Wealth as a Prime score, using a CB of 12 to calculate difficulty. It is important to note, however, that while Wealth works like an ability score, it does not count against the maximum of four Prime Attributes mentioned in the Generic Class Abilities on p. 57.

Whenever an expense is required, be it purchasing a car or bribing a prison guard, players make a SIEGE check using their level and Wealth Rating. The CL of this check is based upon the expense in question. In general, inexpensive mundane items like cigarettes or boots should not be subject to a Wealth check, unless the character is exceptionally poor (their Wealth rating is in the negatives). Only expensive and luxury items are normally subject to this check. In some cases, mundane items may become specialized enough to require a check. For example, if a character is in a foreign land and doesn't have easy access to all of her funds, a Wealth check may be required.

Most items in the Equipment section have listed dollar values. In general, every $50 of an item's worth equates to +1 to the Wealth Check CL. This CL tops out at +20. As such, low-level characters will have a tough time making the check to purchase really expensive items, making it an attractive prospect to have a Socialite handy who also has the Wealthy Generic Class Ability.

FLUCTUATING WEALTH RATING

It is possible for characters to see increases or decreases to their Wealth Rating based on in-game events. Indeed, this is recommended and should occur based on world events and the actions of the character. If a group, for example, the characters end up in the employ of a government agency, secret society, or adventuring guild, they might see their wealth rating increased by +1 or +2 as a result of their new resources. If the party discovers King Solomon's treasure, the GM may award them a permanent bonus of +4 or more to their Wealth Ratings (and Reputation, to boot) as they become fabulously wealthy and famous.

Conversely, in the case of games set in the Great Depression, even the wealthy saw their finances lowered; the GM may rule that all classes see their starting Wealth ratings reduced by 2 as a result, or in a game where the players run through the Black Tuesday Stock Market crash of 1929 may find themselves suddenly facing a -4 or more to their Wealth Ratings.

STARTING WEALTH RATING

Each character begins with a Wealth Rating based upon their character class. The table below outlines the class' starting Wealth Rating and whether or not the Wealth Score is Primary (P) or Secondary (S).

TABLE: WEALTH RATING BY CLASS

Class	Rating	P/S
Arcanist	+2	P
Gadgeteer	+2	P
Gumshoe	0	S
Hooligan	-1	S
Mentalist	0	S
Pugilist	-2	S
Raider	+1	S
Socialite	+3	P

"Hello ladies. Call me ... Jack"

BOOK THREE: MYSTERIES OF MAGIC AND MENTALISM

This book is most important for Game Masters and players running arcanist and mentalist characters, though it will also be useful for gadgeteers looking for new effects upon which to base their gadgets. Herein you will find rules for magic and psychic powers, and complete spell tables and lists.

PSIONIC POWERS

Psionic powers are abilities that impart great and broad power, but are far more focused than the magic wielded by that of arcanists. Mentalists may have far more control over one or two areas of power, but will never have the diversity of effects available to them that their more traditional magic-using counterparts have. Even still, psionics is a gateway to vast power that creates suspicion and jealousy in more traditional magic users.

Many games use psionics as not much more than another form of magic; psionic power accomplishes many of the same things that magic does, is broken down into spell-like lists of effects, and Mentalists resemble little more than arcanists or magi with a different flavor. Worse, systems that do this fail to present psychic powers that ring true of those we read about in many science fiction novels, and those that fall into the realm of what we grudgingly (and for lack of a better term) call "believability." We've all heard of clairvoyance, of E.S.P., of telekinesis, even of pyrokinesis. Outside of systems that are trying to do little more than simulate a different kind of magic, whoever heard of psychic teleportation, or psychic time travel? This system attempts to present a psychic powers system that not only is very different from magic, but that remains in the realm of "familiar" insofar as what psychic power is and what it can do.

USING PSIONIC POWERS

Like all abilities in the system, psionic powers work off of an attribute check and have a Challenge Base of 12 if the attribute upon which they are based is Prime or 18 if the Attribute is Secondary. For this reason, Wisdom-based psionic powers are the most commonly encountered ones (given that Wisdom is the Prime for the Mentalist class), though may Mentalists exhibit a range of powers dedicated across their Primary mental attributes. Unless otherwise noted, any psychic powers that can be used on others have a range of "line of sight."

Since the range of effects possible with many psionic powers is broad and varied, GM's and players are encouraged to invent new effects and manifestations of their powers, using those listed as examples. The CL to use these effects, as well as whether the power is activated by a simple Attribute check or a Psychic attack roll (see below) is always at the discretion of the GM.

PSYCHIC BACKLASH

Any time a mentalist attempts to use an ability beyond their current expertise, there is a chance of suffering psychic backlash, a sort of burnout for pushing their limits. If at any time a mentalist fails her roll to activate a psionic power, she suffers 1d4 points of subdual damage per CL of the power, and may not access that particular ability for 24 hours.

EXAMPLE: Clara, a third-level mentalist with 18 Wisdom, attempts to activate her pyrokinesis power to mimic a fireball spell.

Since fireball is a damaging spell, 3rd-level for arcanists, it has a CL of 6 (see Psionics and Magic, below). Pyrokinesis is a Wisdom-based ability, a Prime for mentalists. This sets the CB at 12. This means the CC to activate the power is 18 (base of 12, plus CL 6). She rolls and gets a 5. She adds her Wisdom modifier (+3) and her level (3) for a final total of only 11. The power fizzles. Clara suffers 6d4 points of subdual damage (CL 6 power; d4 per level) and may not use her pyrokinetic abilities for another day. Perhaps she would've been better off trying to mimic Burning Hands...

PSIONICS AND MAGIC

Despite our earlier assertion that psionics and magic should be distinct and separate, there are inevitably areas where the two will overlap (pyrokinesis, for example, will have the ability to create flame effects similar to Burning Hands and Fireball.) In general, a power that mimics an existing spell has a CL equal to the spell level +2 for non-damaging spells, and spell level +3 for combat-oriented spells. The power's effect then functions identically to the spell it is mimicking. If a spell appears on two different tables, the level for CL should always be based on the Wisdom table first; if the spell is not on the Wisdom table, then check the Charisma table, with the Intelligence table being lowest in the hierarchy.

PSYCHIC ATTACK ROLLS

In some cases, usually when a psychic power causes direct, physical harm to an opponent (such as hurling an object with Telekinesis, or using Pyrokinesis against a living opponent) a power will indicate the necessity for a psychic attack roll. In this case, rather than a standard Attribute check, treat the power's usage as an attack roll, substituting the power's associated attribute for strength. Thus, if a power is based upon Wisdom, a psychic attack roll for that power would be Wis Bonus + BtH + 1d20.

The AC of the target of a psionic attack, for attacks that create physical effects, such as telekinetic attacks, is standard, unless the effect mimics a spell, in which case the effect is subject to the same restrictions as the spell it is mimicking (fireball, for example, doesn't require a roll vs. AC to activate; it goes off based on the spell CL and is then subject to the same restrictions and effects as the spell). For effects such as Biokinetic Harm, which deals damage by manipulating the victim's biological processes, AC is determined by adding the victim's level and Wisdom bonus to 10; armor bonuses do not apply. As always, the GM is the final arbiter of the target's AC.

RESISTING PSIONIC POWERS

In most cases, an unwilling victim of a psychic power resists with a Wisdom-based saving throw. Generally, since the psychic is actively trying to force the power through, the CL for this save is equal to the psychic's level or hit dice. At the GM's discretion, in some cases the CL may also include the bonus for the attribute used to activate the power.

In cases where a psionic power mimics a magic spell effect, the power (once successfully activated via the appropriate Attribute check or Psychic Attack Roll) is subject to the same restrictions, limitations, and resistances as the spell.

BASIC PSIONIC POWERS

Listed below are descriptions of the Basic Psionic Powers. These abilities have no prerequisite, and a psionic character can select them any time a new power is available.

Biokinetic Healing (Cha)

Biokinetic healing allows a psychic, with a successful Charisma check, to heal injury or disease in another. So long as the patient is conscious and mobile (i.e. hit points are still above zero) this Charisma check is a standard Attribute check. The amount of damage that may be healed by this ability is 1d4 per every 2 Mentalist levels.

For patients who have been reduced below zero hit points, two Charisma checks must be made; the first, modified by the number of hit points below zero the patient is, stabilizes the patient. Thus, if the patient is currently at -5 hit points, the psychic suffers -5 on her Charisma check to stabilize. The second is a standard roll that restores hit points as standard. Once a patient is stabilized, no further stabilization checks need be made to heal additional hit points; all checks heal hit points as standard.

In addition, this ability can restore 1d4 points of attribute damage if the psychic makes a Charisma check with a penalty equal to the attribute damage suffered; if a patient has suffered 4 points of attribute damage, the Charisma check to attempt to restore is at -4.

Finally, Biokinetic Healing can cure diseases and purge the body of poisons in the same manner as the Cure Disease and Remove Poison arcanist spells, though the psionic version requires a Charisma check.

This ability requires a "laying on of hands"; in other words, the psychic must touch the patient to be healed. Note that Biokinetic healing only works on others, not on the psychic. Also, unlike Arcanistal healing, biokinetic healing has no appreciable effect on undead.

Clairaudience (Int)

Clairaudience is an ability that allows the psychic to hear things far away. Unlike most psychic powers, this ability and its cousin, clairvoyance, are designed to transcend normal senses and step outside of "line of sight." To use this ability, the psychic must know exactly where his target is, or be

intimately familiar with the target (family member, lover, very close friend, etc.), or must have some personal item of the target's to use as a psychic focus. This ability is focused upon a living creature, not upon a place, unless used in conjunction with a successful Clairvoyance attempt (see below). Using this ability requires an Intelligence check with a CL equal to 1 per 5 miles of the target. If successful, the psychic can hear as though she were in the room with the subject.

Clairvoyance (Int)

Also known as "remote viewing," clairvoyance allows the psychic to see people, places, and things far from his current location. The Challenge Level to use this ability is the same as Clairaudience (see above) but Clairvoyance may be focused upon a location or object as well as a person; the rules of familiarity still apply just as with Clairaudience, however. If a psychic makes a successful clairvoyance roll, he may use any psychic powers he possesses as though his target were in direct line of sight (including clairaudience, which requires only a basic (CL 0) Intelligence check to activate in this case).

Clairvoyance has another use as well, however; the psychic can use it to gain visions of the future. This ability works exactly as a Divination or Communion spell, but the answers come from within the arcanist, and require an Intelligence check to activate; simulating a Divination spell is CL 5; simulating a Communion spell is CL 8.

Combat Awareness (Int)

In many ways, Combat Awareness is an extension of the psychic's basic psionic senses, but geared specifically towards the dangers involved in battle. Activating the ability requires an Intelligence check with a CL equal to the highest level or hit dice from all attackers currently threatening the psychic. While this power is active, the psychic may substitute his Intelligence bonus for his Strength or Dexterity bonus during combat. This includes substituting Intelligence bonus for Dexterity bonus to Armor Class. Once activated, this power lasts for an entire scene.

Finally, any time a Hooligan attempts to Back Attack or Sneak Attack the psychic while this power is active, the psychic may make an Intelligence Check opposed by the Hooligan's Dexterity Check; if the psychic wins, he is not caught off guard and is thus immune to the extra effects of the Sneak Attack or Back Attack (but may still be struck as a regular attack, if the Hooligan's attack is otherwise successful).

Empathic Transmission (Cha)

Empathic Transmission lets you project an emotion at an opponent and cause them to feel it. For example, you could cause someone to feel afraid or hopeless, giving you an advantage in combat; alternately, you could cause that hot bar maid to be consumed with desire to guarantee a fun night (at least, until her father finds out).

Use of this ability requires a full round; it cannot be used while the psychic engages in combat, as it requires focused concentration. Once successfully invoked, the power lasts as long as the psychic concentrates on the victim or for 1D4 rounds per level of the psychic after concentration stops. The opponent resists with a Wisdom check.

Emotions that can be invoked with this power are divided into the groupings of Easy, Medium, and Hard. Easy emotions have a CL of 0 to invoke; medium emotions have a CL of 5, and hard emotions have a CL of 10. Some possible emotions are listed below; others may be devised by the player or GM as the game goes on. Note that the GM should always roll uses of this power in secret; unless he possesses the Empathy power (see below) the psychic has no way of knowing if he was successful in the use of this power until he observes the target's behavior.

Easy Emotions:

Antipathy: the target's attitude is worsened by one step.

Good Will: the target's attitude is improved by one step.

Trepidation: the target is shaken, suffering a -2 morale penalty on attack rolls, damage rolls, and saving throws.

Medium Emotions:

Amiability: the target's attitude is improved by two steps.

Discord: the target's attitude is worsened by two steps.

Fright: the target is frightened, fleeing as well as it can. If unable to flee, the target is shaken and will attempt to flee at the first opportunity.

Love/Lust: the target is charmed.

Rage: The target enters a blind rage and attacks the nearest creature immediately.

Weariness: the target feels fatigued.

Hard Emotions:

Hopelessness: The target loses all hope and submits to simple demands from opponents, such as to surrender or get out. If no foes are present to make demands, there is a 25% chance that the hopeless creature is unable to take any action except hold its ground. If the creature remains free to act, there is a 25% chance that it retreats at normal speed.

Nausea: The target is unable to attack, cast spells, concentrate, or do anything else requiring attention or concentration. The target can do nothing on his turn except move at standard speed.

Panic: The target becomes panicked and suffers a -2 morale penalty on all attack rolls, damage rolls, and saving throws, and must flee at the first opportunity. If cornered, the victim will simply cower. Generally, panic involves crying, screaming, begging, and other noisy factors.

Empathy (Cha)

Empathy allows you to detect the emotional state of a single creature, gaining insight into the target's mood and attitude. To perform this ability, you must spend an entire round concentrating on the target and make a Charisma Check with a CL equal to the target's Wisdom bonus. There is no way to actively resist this ability. If the roll succeeds, you receive a general description of the target's emotional state. This ability grants the user a +4 bonus on all attempts to bluff, intimidate, charm, or otherwise non-psychically influence the target (this bonus does not apply to the use of Empathic Transmission.)

Mental Stun (Cha)

By making a Charisma-based psychic attack roll, the character fires a blast of psychic energy at his opponent, causing nonlethal damage and potentially stunning his opponent. This ability deals 1d6 points of nonlethal damage, and requires the opponent to make a Wisdom-based save (CL 1) or be stunned, suffering a -2 to AC, losing his dexterity bonus to AC, and being unable to take any actions for 1d4 rounds. At the end of this d4 rounds, the victim may attempt another save; if successful, he shakes off the effects of the stun. If unsuccessful, he remains shaken for an additional 1d6 minutes, suffering -2 to all attack rolls, ability checks, and saving throws. Repeated uses of this ability against the same victim deal extra nonlethal damage, and require additional saving throws or the amount of time the victim remains stunned increases.

Mesmerism (Cha)

Mesmerism requires a Charisma check resisted by the target's Wisdom check. If successful, the psychic can create the effect of any of the following spells: Command (CL 1), Sleep (CL 1 and affects one creature only, but is not restricted by HD), Suggestion (CL 5), or Confusion (CL 7). The difficulty for the victim to resist this effect is equal to the result of the psychic's Wisdom Check, and the psychic must declare which effect he is trying to invoke before using this power.

Metabolic Control (Wis)

The basic use of Metabolic Control works in an identical fashion to Biokinetic Heal, but works on the psychic rather than on another.

A secondary, albeit just as important, use of this power is the classic "mind over matter." Any time a character with Metabolic Control fails a Constitution-based Save, he may immediately roll a second, Wisdom-based save against the same CC or target as the failed Con-based save, though the Wisdom save suffers a -4 penalty. If this second save is successful, treat the situation as though the Constitution save had succeeded.

Obfuscation (Cha)

Obfuscation is an ability that allows a psychic to move undetected, even when in plain sight or in the middle of a crowd. The psychic makes a Charisma check; this check is opposed by the Wisdom check of any who might spot the psychic. If the psychic wins the opposed roll, he is able to move completely undetected unless he does something to give himself away (such as attacking an opponent, moving an object in plain sight, etc.) It is possible to use this ability in combat, providing the psychic cover similar to that granted by an invisibility spell, though doing this after the first attack is made requires a Psychic Attack Roll based on Charisma each round in which the psychic remains in combat, and any attacks made while the psychic is obfuscated suffer a -4 penalty due to the concentration required to maintain the effect. Note that the psychic using this power is not actually invisible; she just telepathically convinces anyone looking at her that she isn't, in fact, there. Thus, she still may cast a shadow on a sunny day, giving herself away. On the other hand, since this invisibility is based on a form of mind control, successfully obfuscated Mentalists are invisible even to abilities that normally allow one to see the invisible.

Psychic Defense (Wis)

Psychic Defense is a powerful psionic ability that builds a mental wall up to protect the psychic's mind and emotions from intrusion. With this power, the psychic may substitute a Wisdom check for any attribute saving throw that would normally require Intelligence, Charisma, or Wisdom. Note this ability only works for saving throws, not for other kinds of attribute checks. This ability stacks with the standard Mental Resistance ability granted by the Mentalist character class.

Psychometry (Int)

Psychometry is also often known as Object Reading. This ability allows a psionic to detect properties, history, and abilities (if any) of any inanimate, nonliving object she touches. In a fantasy game, its most common use is to mimic the first-level spell identify. Identifying the properties of a magic item requires an Intelligence check at a CL of 3; success indicates the Mentalist divines 1d4 properties of the object in question. The read can be repeated to learn more, though each subsequent attempt adds 1 to the CL of the test.

Another use of psychometry is to discover secrets about the item's past. With an Intelligence check, the Mentalist can divine where the item has been, the ways in which it has used, or even facts about its previous owners. The CL for this test is 1 per five years in the past the Mentalist attempts to look. Thus, attempting to divine information about someone who owned the object a century ago is a CL 20 challenge. Each successful psychometry check will divine 1d4 pieces of information about the item's past or about a past owner.

Pyrokinesis (Wis)

Pyrokinesis is the destructive ability to control heat and fire. Using this ability requires a Wisdom check; the CL depends upon the effect the Mentalist is trying to generate. Generally, using this power offensively to cause direct damage to another in combat uses a Wisdom-based psychic attack roll and allows a Dexterity save for half damage by the opponent; the CL of this save is equal to the level (or hit dice, in the case of monsters) of the Mentalist.

The effects of any fire-based arcane magical spell can be duplicated by this ability; the CL of these effects are equal to the spell's level plus 3. Thus, to mimic Burning Hands, a first-level spell, has a CL of 4. Mimicking Fireball, a third-level spell, has a CL of 6. In addition, both of these effects, since they are offensive in nature, would use a Wisdom-based psychic attack roll instead of a standard Wisdom check.

Controlling fire in other ways is also possible. Simple effects, such as creating a spark to ignite kindling for a campfire in dry conditions, or lighting a lamp or pipe, have a CL of 0. Moderately difficult effects (the kindling is soaked; a small bonfire needs to be staunched) have a CL of 2. More difficult effects can have a CL of anywhere from 10 (engulfing a carriage in flames) to 50 (engulfing an entire building in flames) or greater, at the GM's discretion.

It gets worse; this power is as dangerous to the Mentalist as it is to the target. Any time a Mentalist fails a roll to activate a power, the ability turns back upon him, dealing 1d6 damage per CL of the attempt (CL 0 effects deal no damage; the backlash just causes a minor, small, but painful burn). The Mentalist may make a Constitution save against a CL equal to that of the effect he tried to create, for half-damage.

Telekinesis (Int)

Telekinesis, as most everyone knows, is the ability to move objects with the mind. The basic functionality of TK is one of the simpler psionic manifestations. The Mentalist makes a standard Intelligence check; the result is his telekinetic strength, functioning exactly as though it were the character's Strength attribute for purposes of using his Telekinesis. Thus, a character who rolls d20 + Int bonus + level and achieves a result of 15 can with his TK move any object that could be moved by a character with a strength of 15. It is possible for a character to use Telekinesis to wield a weapon in combat; however, use of this ability requires constant concentration and doing so robs the Mentalist of his dexterity bonus to AC, as well as imposing an additional -2 penalty to AC. For this reason, telekinetic combat is generally performed from a distance.

If the telekinetic character suffers damage or has his concentration interrupted in any way, the ability ends. Treat these conditions exactly as the interruption of an arcanist's spell.

Telepathic Communication (Int)

This ability allows the Mentalist to send messages via telepathy. It does not allow the reception of return messages. Sending a message requires nothing more than an Intelligence check; unwilling recipients resist with a Wisdom save having a CL equal to the Mentalist's level (or hit dice, if a monster).

Telepathic Probe (Wis)

Telepathic Probe is, quite simply, mind reading. It is this ability, in conjunction with Telepathic Communication, that allows a Mentalist to conduct two-way psychic conversations; using this ability to receive thoughts projected from friends requires concentration and a Wisdom check with a CL of 1 per willing mind.

It is also possible to read unwilling or unsuspecting minds with this power, though this is a bit more difficult. Gleaning immediate surface thoughts are the easiest; this requires a Wisdom check with a CL equal to the level (or hit dice, if a monster) of the target. Attempting to go deeper is more difficult; attempting to read the mind of a target in order to learn secrets requires a Wisdom check as described above, but also grants the target a saving throw with a CL equal to the Mentalist's level (or hit dice, if a monster). Going even deeper, to probe for the roots of phobias, childhood trauma, or similarly blocked memories might impose even greater CLs, at the GM's discretion.

ADVANCED PSIONIC POWERS

The abilities below may not be selected before the Mentalist reaches ninth level. In addition, each ability has prerequisite powers that must first be possessed before the advanced version is selected.

Biokinetic Harm (Cha)

Prerequisites: Mental Stun, Biokinetic Heal

Biokinetic Harm is, quite simply, the ability to hurt someone through manipulating their body. Heart attacks, hemorrhages, lesions, contusions, all of these can be accomplished by the psychic with this brutal power. All uses of this ability are performed with a Charisma-based psychic attack roll. This psychic attack roll bypasses AC granted by armor; the victim's mental AC is equal to 10 + Wisdom Bonus. If Wisdom is a Prime for the victim, the victim adds half his or her level to the mental AC. The basic game effects of this power cause the victim to suffer 1d6 points of damage per level of the Mentalist.

Another use of this power is to cause temporary ability damage to a victim, though this is more difficult. In this case, the victim's AC is equal to 10 + level (or Hit Dice) + Wisdom bonus. In this case, if Wisdom is a Prime, increase mental AC by an additional +3. A successful attack deals 1d4 damage to an attribute of the psychic's choosing.

More powerful effects may be possible, but the consequences and CL of such uses are always at the discretion of the GM.

Empathic Bond (Cha)

Prerequisites: Empathy, Empathic Transmission

This ability allows you to establish an empathic rapport between yourself and another thinking creature. Establishing this rapport requires ten minutes of total concentration from both the psychic and the recipient of the bond. At the end of ten minutes, the psychic makes a Charisma check with a CL of 10. If successful, the bond is created for a duration of 2d4 + the psychic's Charisma modifier in hours. It has no maximum range; the shared bond can be felt across opposite ends of the world.

It is possible to create a bond with more than one person simultaneously; for each person after the first added, the CL increases by 2.

While the bond is in effect, the joined parties can sense each other's emotional state, and general direction towards one another, as well as perceive the general distance separating you (very near, far, hundreds of miles, thousands of miles, etc.).

It is also possible to establish a permanent rapport between two individuals. This requires a full day's concentration, a successful Wisdom check with CL 15, and the expenditure of 500 XP by both the psychic and the target.

Mind Control (Cha)

Prerequisites: Mesmerism, Empathic Transmission

By making a Charisma-based Psychic Attack Roll, the psionic can control the actions of any single intelligent, humanoid creature through a telepathic link that she establishes with the subject's mind. If the Mentalist and the subject have a common language, the Mentalist can generally force the subject to perform as the Mentalist desires, within the limits of its abilities. If no common language exists, the Mentalist can communicate only basic commands, such as "Come here," "Go there," "Fight," and "Stand still." The Mentalist knows what the subject is experiencing, but does not receive direct sensory input from it, nor can it communicate with the Mentalist telepathically (unless an empathic or telepathic bond has been established with the creature–see those abilities for details).

Once the Mentalist has given a dominated creature a command, it continues to attempt to carry out that command to the exclusion of all other activities except those necessary for day-to-day survival (such as sleeping, eating, and so forth). Because of this limited range of activity, an observer making a Wisdom check at CL 5 can determine that the subject's behavior is being influenced by an enchantment effect.

This ability lasts for one day per level of the Mentalist, and is resisted by the creature's Wisdom-based save. If the creature is ever mistreated or is routinely placed in danger or forced to do anything outside its nature, it is entitled to a new save. An order to commit suicide or engage in blatantly suicidal behavior entitles the victim to a new save at +10.

Telepathic Bond (Wis)

Prerequisites: Telepathic Communication, Telepathic Probe

As Empathic Bond is with emotions, this ability is with thoughts. The requirements are identical, but all rolls are based on Wisdom, rather than Charisma, and as long as the characters are bound, they know everything there is to know about one another, including one's deepest, darkest secrets. This is an extremely personal ability, and most Mentalists only use it upon those they trust and care for the most. Characters bound by this ability are constantly and continually aware of what each other is thinking, no matter how far apart they are, so they generally know exactly what is going on with each other at any given time; however, without a shared empathic bond (see that power for details) they don't experience the emotions of one another.

Two characters bound in this manner can call upon the knowledge and experience of one another, allowing each other to mimic intuition-based class abilities possessed by either, though any class abilities not possessed by the user are performed at half usual proficiency, using the level of the character who knows the ability. Magical and spell knowledge is never shared in this manner, however, as calling upon the spells of a friend would deplete that friend's reserves for the day. In general, any abilities that are based on physical attributes (Strength, Dexterity, or Constitution) are not transferred, as these require muscle memory as much as they do knowledge. Any non-magical abilities based upon Intelligence, Wisdom, or Charisma can be shared.

For example, James is joined to his raider friend, Alex, who is not currently with the party. The party needs to attempt to track a bugbear through the wilderness. James can call upon Alex's Raider Tracking ability, using his own Wisdom, but adding only half Alex's class level to the roll.

A side effect of this ability, however, allows the Mentalist to use Telepathic Communication as a 2-way power, both transmitting and receiving telepathic communication with anyone within line of sight.

Telekinetic Defense (Int)

Prerequisites: Telekinesis, Psychic Defense

Telekinetic Defense allows the user to manipulate the kinetic energy in the air surrounding himself or another, to the end of making the target harder to hit in combat. In effect, he creates an area of mild chaos in the air surrounding his body, making

weapons go astray as they target him. In game terms, the character declares the AC bonus he wishes to add to a target; double this bonus to determine the CL of the Intelligence roll. The ability isn't quite as taxing as other concentration-based psychic powers, but does require a degree of attention, so all actions performed while the psychic maintains the shield are at -2. If the psychic creates more than one telekinetic defense field, penalties are cumulative; -2 per shield being maintained.

Another use of this power, albeit a far more difficult one, is that of creating a telekinetic barrier. By making an Intelligence Check at CL 10, the psychic creates an immobile wall of force that covers a 10'x10' area, providing 9/10 cover from attacks coming from the direction of the wall. Any creatures attempting to move through the wall must make a Strength Check with a CL equal to the psychic's level + Wisdom modifier. Failure indicates they have been repulsed. This ability requires a full round to enact, and constant concentration to maintain, meaning the psychic loses all actions, loses Dex bonus to AC, and suffers an additional -2 to AC.

Telemagry (Cha)

Prerequisites: Obfuscation, Mesmerism

This ability, an advanced form of Obfuscation, allows the Mentalist to create illusions in the minds of her victims, so that she can appear as someone else, or fool the senses of the onlooker in another way. In this manner, the psychic can, with a Charisma-based Psychic Attack Roll, mimic the effects of the spell Alter Self. Alternately, she can choose to make the victim believe something that isn't quite true; i.e. a quarter is actually a dollar. Telemagry allows most types of illusory powers to be used by the psychic. In general, and at the GM's option, any spell with the "illusion" descriptor can be mimicked; the CL for doing so is equal to the spell level (using the Arcanist spell list) plus 3. If a spell wishing to be mimicked appears on more than one list, the Charisma list is checked first, followed by Intelligence, then Wisdom.

MAGIC AND SPELL CASTING

MANA AND DIVINE ENERGY

Mana is the mystic energy that all spell casters draw upon to create magical effects. It is a natural force that permeates the world, created by living things, and by the world itself. Mana circles the world in dragon lines, or lines of magical power. At places where dragon lines intersect, there are nexus points possessed of vast mystical energy. Effects of dragon line nexus points will be discussed later.

MANA ENERGY POINTS

All magic using characters have a pool of Mana Energy Points (MEP) from which they draw the energy to cast spells. Every time a magical character casts a spell, subtract the appropriate number of points from the character's MEP pool; casters can continue to cast spells until their MEP reaches zero, at which point they are fatigued and cannot under normal circumstances perform any further magical feats. In addition, any character with an MEP of zero or below (see emergency spells, later) is considered fatigued, and suffers a -2 to Strength and Dexterity as per the standard rules, until his MEP again reaches 1 or better. All spells are still subject to the listed casting times and components.

REGAINING MEP

MEP is regained through meditation or (preferably) sleep. Each hour of meditation restores MEP at the rate of the caster's level plus his primary spell casting attribute bonus, be it Int, Wis, or Cha (see the Arcanist class for more on primary spell casting attributes). Meditation restores half this amount, and each hour of meditation requires a successful Spellcraft check at CL 5.

This process is the same for all casters regardless of Primary Spell casting Ability, as during these quiet periods, the body gradually opens itself back up to the return of magical energies.

STARTING AND INCREASING MEP

Arcanists start play with d4 + Con bonus + Primary Spell casting Attribute bonus.

At each additional Arcanist class level, a character in a spell casting class gains 1d10 additional MEP. Multiclass characters only gain MEP when they advance in the Arcanist class, not in their non-spell casting class.

CASTING SPELLS

Spells are organized into levels based upon their basic power. All spells of a given level are considered and assumed to be of equal power to all other spells of that same level. Thus, each spell of a given level costs the same number of MEP to cast. Spells cost a number of MEP equal to the spell's level + 1. 0-level spells cost 1 MEP, 1st level spells cost 2, etc.

There is no limit to how many times a magic using character can cast a given spell on his or her list, so long as she has enough Mana Energy Points left in her pool to cast the spell. However, spell casting is a complex business, and as such, arcanists must still refresh their knowledge and prepare spells each day by studying their spell book, according to the table for their character class. Preparing spells is more than simply reading and memorizing arcane formulae. Spell casting is a ritual business, and thus to be able to quickly cast spells, the arcanist must daily begin the rituals for every spell she feels she may need that day, consuming spell components, and leaving only the briefest of incantations unsaid. In this

manner, the spells in her repertoire are ready to be launched at a moment's notice. However, magic energy fades with the passing hours, and thus, the arcanist much prepare her arsenal daily.

So, while a character does not need to prepare Arcane Bolt, for example, multiple times if she feels she might need to cast the spell more than once, she will still not have access to all of her spell knowledge at all times. Rather, the first level arcanist character can now prepare four completely different zero level spells, and two first level spells, and may cast among those spells with impunity, so long as she has the MEP to spend on powering the spells.

Finally, MEP is only spent upon completion of spell casting; not during daily preparation. So the two MEP spent on a casting of Arcane Bolt is only expended when the arcanist attempts to use the spell against a foe or target, not in the morning when she prepares it.

THE SPELLCRAFT CHECK

The next step in casting a spell is to make a spellcraft check, representing the caster's skill at crafting his magic. This check has a CL equal to the level of the spell being cast. If the check is successful, the MEP is spent and the spell goes off. The result of the Spellcraft check, minus the Challenge Base, is also the CC of any saving throws allowed by the spell.

For Example: A sixth-level Intelligence-based arcanist casts Lightning Bolt, a third-level spell. This requires the expenditure of four MEP, and a spellcraft check at a CL of 3 for the spell level. Since Intelligence is a Prime for the arcanist, his CC for the check is 15. The player rolls and gets a 20 on his spellcraft check. The spell goes off, and Dexterity saves for half damage are rolling against a CL of 8 (Total roll of 20, minus the CB of 12).

If the check fails, on the other hand, the spell fails. The MEP is still lost, and the caster suffers spell burn for his troubles. Spell burn is equal to 1d4 points of subdual damage per level of the spell that was attempted and failed.

Spell burn can also be applied to casters who fail spell casting based on interference from another caster (see Counter Spells).

MEP AND SPELL-LIKE ABILITIES

Spell-like abilities for monsters, spells granted as "per day" features, and similar magical effects are not governed by MEP and function exactly as outlined for a given creature or item.

BONUS SPELLS

As stated in the arcanist character class description, any time a character would receive bonus spells for high attributes, he receives extra spells on his daily list, as well as bonus MEP equal to that needed to cast each extra spell one time. This bonus MEP is gained at the level in which the character gains the bonus spell.

For Example: An arcanist with an Intelligence of 18 receives a bonus spell to his daily list, plus 2 MEP at first level. He then receives a second level spell plus 3 MEP at fourth level, and an extra third level spell plus 4 MEP at sixth level. By fifth level, he has received a total of 9 bonus MEP, as well as three extra spells per day (one first, one second, and one third level).

Bonus MEP is added to the character's base just as though he had gained MEP through a normal level advancement. This bonus MEP may be used to cast any spell in the character's repertoire; it is not restricted to the casting of bonus spells.

EMERGENCY SPELLS

Sometimes things get desperate. You're up against the wall, and the mummy is closing in. Your gunslinger is down, your psychic is reeling from backlash. You've got a perfect cover spell prepared, but damn it all, you're out of MEP and fatigued. Maybe, just maybe, if you put enough willpower and faith into the casting, you can still...

Emergency spells are for just these kinds of instances. When a spell caster is at zero MEP, sometimes it's possible to channel his very life energy into the casting of one last spell, to (hopefully) save the day. Casting an emergency spell is only possible in the most dire of circumstances, and results in severe and permanent consequences to the caster. To cast an emergency spell, the caster must first make a Wisdom check with a CL equal to the level of the spell being attempted. If this check is successful, he may use his own life energy to cast the spell. The caster takes temporary Constitution damage equal to half the MEP cost of the spell being cast; this energy replaces MEP in the cost of casting the spell (each point of Constitution spent is equal to 2 MEP), and the spell goes off as normal. This ability damage returns as normal at the rate of 1 point per day.

However, the end result of this casting is that the caster suffers 1d4 points of semi-permanent ability loss divided as the player chooses between Constitution and his primary spell casting attribute. Also, the moment the spell goes off, the character is reduced to -1 hit points and is unconscious (but automatically stabilizes). This "permanent" ability loss can only be recovered by resting for days at a Site of Power (see below). If the spell requires the caster to remain conscious for the duration, unconsciousness sets in immediately after the spell has completed its intended function. The experience is quite harrowing for the caster, and is not something to be undertaken lightly. Still, there are times when it can save the day.

COUNTER SPELLS

In this system it is also possible for an arcanist to interfere with another spell caster by channeling personal MEP. The process of counter-spelling must be undertaken before the results of a spell casting roll are known. If the original caster successfully casts a spell, it cannot be interfered with. If, however, the GM has not yet announced the result of the casting, the interfering character can still attempt to counter the spell.

The process for this is simple: the caster attempting to interfere first makes a spellcraft check, using his primary spell casting attribute (CL = the level of spell being cast). If the targeted spell caster happens to be using the same primary spell casting attribute, the character gains a +2 to all related spellcraft checks.

If successful, the interfering caster knows the level of the spell being cast, and may devote a number of MEP up to his primary attribute bonus + arcanist class level to interfering with the spell, making it more taxing on the original caster. The CL for the original caster to successfully fire off the spell is then increased by ½ the MEP spent to interfere, rounded down. If he is unable or unwilling to make the check, his spell simply fails.

For example: Marie Laveau finds herself and her comrades in battle with a horde of skeletons led by an evil Nazi necromancer. The necromancer begins to cast a spell, and Marie makes a spellcraft check. The GM secretly sets the CL at 5 (the necromancer, with primary spell casting attribute Wisdom is casting a 5th-level spell), and Marie, whose primary spell casting attribute is also Wisdom, rolls a 16. However, since she shares the same primary casting attribute as the necromancer, she gains +2 to her spellcraft check, raising the result to 18. Since her CC was 17 (CB 12 + CL 5) The GM says, "the evil sorcerer is casting a 5th-level spell."

Marie, being an eighth-level arcanist with a Wisdom score of 18, can devote up to 11 MEP to interfere with this spell. Since counter spell interference is rounded down, spending 11 is pointless; Marie decides to spend 10. The necromancer is caught off guard by Marie's expenditure of power; his Wisdom check is only a 16, and he needed a 22 (his original 5th level spell was at a CL 5, augmented by 5 for half Marie's MEP expenditure, for a total CL of 10). His spell fails, but Martie is now down 10 MEP for her trouble. Combat continues...

DRAGON LINES

Magic energy is created by everything in the world, from the smallest blade of grass to a rock to a human being. It is a cosmic force generated by all matter. Dragon Lines are lines of mystic energy that crisscross the world. It is from these lines of magical energy that arcane casters draw their power. Dragon lines are invisible to the naked eye, and can only be detected by arcane spell casters who pass an Intelligence check with a CL of 0. While standing directly on a Dragon Line, an arcane spell caster sees the MEP cost of all spells reduced by one. Some of the more powerful Dragon Lines may even reduce the cost of spell casting by two, though these are rare indeed. Regardless, however, the cost of casting a spell can never be reduced below one point by a Dragon Line. It should be noted that Dragon Lines only exist in areas where the mystical energy of the world is particularly strong, and they are not incredibly common. They are like eddies and currents, streams or rivers of magical energy. Direct encounters with Dragon Lines are always at the discretion of the GM.

Where Dragon Lines intersect, places of magical power, much revered to sorcerous types, exist. These places are commonly known as Sites of Power, or Nexus Points. Places such as this are rare indeed, with perhaps five on the continent, and an estimated twenty to thirty existing throughout the entire world. Nexus Points are sanctuaries for arcane and natural magic users of all types, and provide a number of tangible benefits. First, when at a nexus, spell casters may cast zero level spells without expending any magic energy whatsoever. Spells of first level and up see their costs reduced by a full five MEP, to a minimum of one, always see all variable, numeric effects increased by ½, and are cast as though the caster were two levels higher. These effects are at no additional MEP cost, and since the effects are constant, magi must be extremely careful about casting spells on nexus points. With such power at their disposal, magic users have in ancient times gone to open war over control of a nexus point, until finally at a Grand Conclave of magic users, it was decreed that no arcane or natural user of magic would be allowed to create a domicile or exercise sole control over one of these sites. Rather, it fell to the druids to maintain groves near (but not on) Sites of Power and protect them from interlopers. In the modern era, this convention nominally remains, though political maneuvering and wealth often lead to some powerful and rich arcanist owning a Site of Power on his or her estate. With magic being the secret that it is, it's difficult to enforce the "no sole control" law in the face of real, human property laws and the battle for nexus points rages again. Often, secret societies such as the Templars or Brotherhood of the Rose Cross make arrangements to purchase the land upon which Sites of Power rest, ostensibly to maintain the neutrality of the site, but the real-world advantage of a group owning such a site cannot be overstated.

Again, nominally, Sites of Power are considered neutral ground, where sorcerers can meet without fear of violence, and sometimes are the subject of permanent Sanctuary spells, to ensure that no violence occurs within. All arcane or natural magicians resting at a Site of Power regain MEP at double their normal rate, and it is only at a Site of Power that permanent ability loss from the casting of emergency spells can be healed (at a rate of one point per day, as though it were ability damage).

SPELL TABLES

INT-BASED CASTERS

0-Level	
Arcane Mark	101
Dancing Lights	110
Detect Magic	111
Detect Poison	112
Endure Elements	115
Ghost Sound	121
Light	129
Mage Hand	129
Mending	132
Message	132
Open/Close	135
Prestidigitation	139
System Shock	154
1st-Level	
Alter Size	98
Arcane Bolt	101
Burning Hands	105
Change Self	105
Charm Person	105
Comprehend Languages	107
Erase	116
Feather Fall	117
Floating Disk	119
Hold Portal	124
Identify	125
Jump	128
Protection from Alignment	140
Read Magic	142
Shield	147
Shocking Grasp	147
Sleep	148
Spider Climb	149
Summon Familiar	150
Unseen Servant	158
2nd-Level	
Acid Arrow	97
Bulletproof	104
Continual Flame	108
Darkness	110
Detect Thoughts	113
Enhance Attribute	115
Fog Cloud	119
Invisibility	127
Knock	128
Levitate	129
Locate Object	129
Magic Mouth	131
Mirror Image	134
Pyrotechnics	141
Ray of Enfeeblement	142
Rope Trick	144
Scare	144
See Invisibility	145
Shatter	147
Web	161
3rd-Level	
Blink	104
Clairaudience/Clairvoyance	105
Dispel Magic	114
Explosive Runes	116
Fly	119
Gaseous Form	119
Glyph of Warding	121
Gust of Wind	123
Haste	123
Hold Person	124
Invisibility Sphere	127
Lightning Bolt	129
Magic Circle	130
Nondetection	135
Stinking Cloud	149
Suggestion	150
Summon Lesser Monster	153
Tiny Hut	157
Tongues	157
Water Breathing	161
4th-Level	
Arcane Eye	101
Charm Monster	105
Confusion	107
Detect Scrying	112
Dimension Door	113
Fear	117
Fire Shield	118
Fire Trap	118
Hallucinatory Terrain	123
Ice Storm	125
Locate Creature	129
Minor Globe of Invulnerability	133
Mnemonic Enhancer	134
Polymorph Self/Other	137
Remove Curse	142
Resilient Sphere	143
Scrying	144
Shout	147
Wall of Fire	159
Wall of Ice	160
5th-Level	
Animate Dead	99
Bind Elemental	103
Cloudkill	106
Cone of Cold	107
Contact Other Plane	107
Faithful Hound	117

BOOK THREE:

CHA-BASED CASTERS

BOOK THREE:

SPELL DESCRIPTIONS

SPELL DESCRIPTION FORMAT

As mentioned, each spell is defined by a description of the effect it causes and a set of terms necessary for game play. The spell descriptions appear after the class spell lists. A summary reminder on spell format and terms appears prior to the spell descriptions, but the following provides more detail and information on spell terms.

Any spell whose name is followed by an asterisk (*) means that the spell is reversible. Effects of the reversed spell are explained in the spell's description. Arcanists need not memorize a reversed spell separately–they can choose to reverse the spell at the time of casting. Thus, an Arcanist who has memorized Cure Light Wounds can choose upon any casting to Cause Light Wounds instead.

CASTING TIME (CT)

Most spells take one round to cast. A spell that takes one round (CT 1) to cast comes into effect during the caster's initiative turn for that round. Complex spells may take more time to cast, and such casting times are expressed in rounds (rd), minutes (min), hours (hr) or days. For relative understanding of casting time, a round is 10 seconds.

Spells that take more than one round to cast come into effect during the caster's initiative turn on the last round of the casting time for the spell.

Most Game Masters's make you announce at the beginning of the round whether you are going to cast a spell. If so, and you roll a low initiative roll, then you have a chance of being struck before the spell goes off. For those Game Master's who do not require announcement, some disallow any spell in the same round in which you were hit before your initiative turn. For Game Master's who do neither of the above, it would be more a situation of simultaneous swings with an enemy or some sort of environmental or magical effect situation disrupting the spell.

For example, Cardom the Chromatic rolls a 6 for initiative and he acts third in that round after his fighting companion, Quinn, and the giant ape they are fighting. Cardom casts a spell with a casting time of one round. The spell takes effect that round. If Cardom chose to cast a spell with a casting time of two, then the spell would take effect in the next round of combat during Cardom's turn for the next round. So, if Cardom acted first in next round the spell would take effect then, but if he acted last, then it would take effect after all others had taken their action.

RANGE (R)

A spell's range is the maximum distance from the character that the spell's effect can occur, as well as the maximum distance at which the character can designate the spell's point of origin. The character aims a spell by making some choice about whom the spell is to affect or where the effect is to originate, depending on the type of spell. If any portion of the spell's area extends beyond the range, that area is wasted.

Sometimes the range of a spell is only personal (affecting only the caster) or touch (the caster must touch a creature or object to affect it), as noted in the spell description. There are also four distance ranges in Castle & Crusades: 50 feet (close), 150 feet (medium), 450 feet (long), and unlimited (reaching anywhere on the plane of existence). Some rare spells have no standard range category, just a range expressed in feet.

Some spells create or summon things rather than affecting things that are already present. The character must designate the location where these things are to appear, either by seeing it or defining it. Range determines how far away an effect can appear, but if the effect is mobile it can move without regard to the spell's range.

TARGET OR AREA OF EFFECT (T) OR (AOE)

Spells that do not affect the caster personally generally have a target or affect a certain area. This part of a spell decription defines the number of creatures, dimensions, volume, weight and so on that the spell affects, if it is not otherwise obvious from the spell's description.

TARGETED SPELLS: Targeted spells are cast directly on creatures or objects, as defined by the spell itself. In most cases, the character must be able to see or touch the target, and the character must specifically choose that target. If the character casts a targeted spell on the wrong sort of target, the spell has no effect. If the target of a spell is the caster, the caster does not receive a saving throw, and spell resistance does not apply.

AREA SPELLS: Some spells affect an area. The character selects where the spell originates, but otherwise does not control which creatures or objects the spell will effect. Sometimes a spell describes a specially defined area, but usually an area falls into one of several categories:

BURST: The character selects the spell's point of origin, and the spell bursts out from this point, affecting whatever it catches in its area.

CONE: The cone shoots away from the character in the direction the character designates, starting directly before the character and widening out as it goes, though some spells affect all creatures in an area rather than individual creatures.

CYLINDER: The character selects the center of a horizontal circle as the spell's point of origin; the spell shoots down from the circle, filling a cylinder.

EMANATION: Some spells have an area like a burst but the effect continues to radiate from the point of origin for the

duration of the spell. Some spells affect objects within an area the caster selects, Some spells spread out like a burst, but can turn corners; the caster selects the point of origin, and the spell spreads out for a given distance in all directions.

OBSTACLES: Some spell effects likes rays, spreads, and cones are affected by obstacles. The character must have a clear line of effect to any target that the character casts a spell upon or to any space in which the character wishes to create an effect. The character must have a clear line of effect to the point of origin of any spell the character casts. For bursts, cones, cylinders, and emanating spells, the spell only affects areas, creatures, or objects to which it has line of effect from its origin (a burst's point, a cone's starting point, a cylinder's circle, or an emanating spell's point of origin). An otherwise solid barrier with a hole of at least 1 square foot through it does not block a spell's line of effect.

A caster aims a ray as if using a ranged weapon, though typically the character makes a ranged touch attack rather than a normal ranged attack. As with a ranged weapon, the character can fire into the dark or at an invisible creature and hope to hit something. The character doesn't have to see the creature he or she is trying to hit, as the character does with a targeted spell. Intervening creatures and obstacles, however, can block the character's line of sight or provide cover for the creature the character is aiming at. If a ray spell has a duration, the duration refers to the effect that the ray causes, not to the length of time the ray itself persists.

Spreads and cones spread out from a point of origin to a distance described in the spell. The effect can extend around corners and into areas that the caster cannot see. The caster must designate the point of origin for such an effect if the spell description does not specify one.

DURATION (D)

Duration measures how long a spell's effect lasts. Many durations are measured in rounds, minutes, hours or some other increment. When the time is up, the magic goes away and the spell ends. Some spells have a permanent duration, and some require the caster to concentrate in order to maintain the spell's effect. A character can typically dismiss personal spells at will before the duration ends, or if the spell description so states. A spell that requires concentration is dismissible by its very nature.

Sometimes a spell lasts for a short time after the character ceases concentrating. In these cases, the spell effects continue for the stated length of time after the character stops concentrating. Otherwise, the character must concentrate to maintain the spell, but the character cannot maintain it for more than the stated duration in any event.

If a spell affects creatures directly, the effects travel with the subject for the spell's duration. If the spell creates an effect, the effect lasts for the duration. The effect might move or remain still. Such effects can be destroyed prior to their durations end. If the spell affects an area, then the spell stays with that area for the spell's duration. Creatures become subject to the spell when they enter the area and become free of it when they leave. Certain spells last for a set duration, or until triggered or discharged.

SAVING THROW (SV)

Most harmful spells allow an affected creature to make a saving throw in order to avoid some or all of the spells effect. The spell description details whether the spell allows a saving throw, what type of saving throw is made and the effect of a successful save. If a spell does not include a saving throw entry, then assume no saving throw is allowed.

A creature that successfully saves against a spell without obvious physical effects feels a hostile force or a tingle, but cannot deduce the exact nature of the attack. Likewise, if a creature's saving throw succeeds against a targeted spell, the caster senses that the spell has failed. The caster does not sense when creatures succeed at saving throws against effect and area spells.

SAVING THROW CHALLENGE CLASS: A spell's challenge class is always equal to its caster's Spellcraft check to cast, unless otherwise specified.

NEGATES: This term means that the spell has no effect on an affected creature that makes a successful saving throw.

PARTIAL: The spell causes an effect on its subject, but a successful saving throw means some lesser effect occurs.

HALF: The spell deals damage, and a successful saving throw halves the damage taken (round down).

NONE: No saving throw is allowed.

DISBELIEF: A successful save lets the subject ignore the effect.

OBJECT: The spell can be cast on objects, which receive saving throws only if they are magical or if the spell specifies otherwise.

HARMLESS: A parenthetical (h) indicates a harmless spell. The spell is usually not harmful, but a targeted creature can attempt a saving throw if it wishes.

VOLUNTARILY GIVING UP A SAVING THROW: A creature can voluntarily forego a saving throw and willingly accept a spell's result. Even a character with a special resistance to magic can suppress this if he or she wants to.

ITEMS SURVIVING AFTER A SAVING THROW: Sometimes a spell specifies whether items in the area of effect for the spell are potentially damaged. These items are required to make a saving throw or are destroyed.

SPELL RESISTANCE (SR)

Spell resistance is a special defensive ability. A defender's spell resistance is like an armor class against magical attacks. If a spell is being resisted by a defender with spell resistance, the caster of the spell must roll 1d20. The result of that roll must be equal to or greater than the spell resistance of the target for the spell to take effect. This roll is modified by the intelligence of the caster, and the Prime bonus does apply. The spell resistance line and/or the descriptive text of a spell description explains whether or not the spell resistance applies, as some spells are not effected by a target creature's spell resistance.

Spell resistance applies even if a given spell also allows the target creature a saving throw. The effects of spell resistance, if any, are applied first, and then the creature may also make a saving throw. In most cases, spell resistance applies only when a resistant creature is targeted by the spell, not when a resistant creature encounters a spell that is already in place, such as a wall of iron.

The terms 'object' and 'harmless' mean the same thing for saving throws. A creature with spell resistance must voluntarily drop the resistance in order to receive the effects of a spell noted as 'harmless' without the check described above. If a spell does not include a spell resistance entry, then assume no spell resistance check is allowed.

COMPONENTS (C)

A spell's components line includes abbreviations for the components required to cast the spell. Spells can have verbal (V), somatic (S), material (M), focus (F), divine focus (DF) components, any combination thereof, or any other special components. If the components line includes F/DF or M/DF, the arcane version of the spell has a focus component or a material component and the divine version has a divine focus component. If the necessary components are not used, the casting fails. If a material component, focus or define focus has a monetary cost, the cost is listed; otherwise the character can assume that the actual materials involved have no significant monetary value, unless the Game Master rules otherwise. Material components are always consumed during the casting of a spell; a focus or divine focus is not. If a special focus or divine focus is required, it is unique to the spell and cannot be used as the focus for other spells.

That being said, pulp is a visceral genre of play, and having fantasy-style spell slingers running around can change the entire feel of the game. We recommend that arcanist characters be required to keep careful track of all spell components—even things as seemingly mundane as salt or odd as fecal matter—for purposes of having what they need to cast spells. Given the powerful nature of some of the spells herein, this will put a cap on the potential imbalance and altered feel magic can bring to a two-fisted pulp action game. When required to keep track of what components they have handy, and to describe what they're doing to cast their spells, arcanists will become much more mysterious and focused, and will play out as the strange outcasts they are intended to be.

V (VERBAL): A verbal component is a spoken incantation. To provide a verbal component, the character must be able to speak in a strong voice. A silence spell or a gag spoils the incantation.

SOMATIC (S): A somatic component is a measured and precise movement of the hand or some other part of the body. The character must have at least one hand free to provide a somatic component.

MATERIAL (M): A material component is a physical substance or object that focuses a spell casters energies during casting process. The component is generally destroyed in the process of casting the spell.

F (FOCUS): A focus component is a prop of some sort. Unlike a material component, a focus is not consumed when the spell is cast and can be reused. As with material components, the cost for a focus is negligible unless a specific price is listed.

DF (DIVINE FOCUS): A divine focus component is an item of spiritual significance. The divine focus for a faith-based arcanist is a holy symbol appropriate to the character's faith. For an evil arcanist, the divine focus is an unholy symbol.

THE GRIMOIRE

A

ACID ARROW, Level 2 Int

CT 1 **R** 450 ft. **D** 1 rd.+1 rd./2 lvl.
SV none **SR** yes **Comp** V, S, M

A magical arrow of acid springs from the caster's hand and speeds toward a single target. The caster must succeed with a ranged touch attack to hit the target. The acid arrow deals 2d4 points of acid damage if it hits. For every two caster levels, the acid, unless somehow neutralized, lasts an additional round and deals another 2d4 points each round (2 rounds at 3rd to 4th level; 3 rounds at 5th to 6th level; etc.). The material components of this spell are a drop of acid or corrosive substance.

AID, Level 2 Wis, Level 3 Cha

CT 1 **R** touch **D** 1 tn./lvl.
SV none **SR** yes (h) **Comp** V, S, DF

This spell allows the arcanist to heal, inspire, and raise the morale of one creature. The subject gains 1d8 temporary HP, +1 to hit, and +1 on saving throws against fear.

AIR/WATER WALK, Level 4 Wis
CT 1 **R** touch **D** 10 tn./lvl.
SV wisdom negates (h) **SR** yes (h) **Comp** V, S, DF

This spell allows a single target creature to tread on air or liquid as if walking on solid ground. The caster must choose the version of the spell desired upon the initial casting of the spell.

AIR WALK: The maximum upward or downward angle possible is 45 degrees, at a rate equal to one-half the creature's normal movement. A strong wind (21+ mph) can push an air walker along or hold the walker back. Each round at the end of the walker's turn, the wind blows the walker 5 feet for each 5 miles per hour of wind speed.

WATER WALK: The creature's feet hover an inch above the surface. Any liquid may be traversed, including mud, oil, snow, quicksand, running water, ice, and even lava (although creatures crossing molten lava or other harmful surfaces still take damage from the heat or other harm). The creature can walk, run, charge, or otherwise move across the surface as if it were normal ground. If the spell is cast underwater (or while the subject is partially submerged), the subject is borne toward the surface at 60 feet per round until they can stand on it.

ALARM, Level 1 Wis
CT 1 **R** 50 ft. **D** 2 hrs./lvl.
SV none **SR** N/A **Comp** V, S, F/DF

The caster summons a small animal to watch over an area. Each time a creature enters the warded area, a mental or audible alarm is triggered. Whether the alarm is mental or audible is left up to the caster but must be decided upon at the moment the spell is cast. A creature who speaks the password, also determined at the time of casting, does not set off the alarm. The caster may elect to have small animals not set off the alarm. Ethereal or astral creatures do not trigger the alarm unless the intruder becomes material while in the warded area. The spells area of affect is a 50 ft. diameter circle and reequires a small bell to activate.

MENTAL ALARM: A mental alarm alerts the caster so long as the character remains within a mile of the warded area. It will also awaken the caster from normal sleep, but does not otherwise disturb concentration. A silence spell has no effect on a mental alarm.

AUDIBLE ALARM: An audible alarm produces the sound of a bell, and anyone within 60 feet of the warded area can hear it clearly. Doors and walls will reduce the distance by 10 to 20 feet. In quiet conditions, the ringing can be heard faintly up to 180 feet. The ringing lasts for 1 round. Creatures within a silence spell cannot hear the ringing.

ALTER SELF, Level 2 Cha
CT 1 **R** person **D** 10 min./lvl.
SV none **SR** none **Comp** V,S

This is a more powerful version of Change Self. As with Change Self, the caster can assume the form of a creature of the same type as the caster's form. However, the caster also gains extraordinary special attacks and qualities, such as darkvision, low-light vision and so on. The caster does not gain any supernatural abilities though.

ALTER SIZE*, Level 1 Int
CT 1 **R** 50 ft. **D** 1 tn./lvl.
SV constitution negates **SR** yes **Comp** V, S

This spell allows the caster to enlarge or reduce a creature or object, increasing/decreasing both size and weight. The subject may be altered by up to 10% per caster level, increasing by this amount in height, width and depth (to a maximum of 50%). Alter size affects one creature or one object of up to 10 cubic ft/lvl in volume.

Weight increases by approximately the cube of the size increase, as follows:

HEIGHT	WEIGHT
+10%	(X 1.1)
+30%	(X 1.3)
+20%	(X 1.2)
+70%	(X 1.7)
+30%	(X 1.3)
+40%	(X 1.4)
+50%	(X 1.5)
+120%	(X 2.2)
+170%	(X 2.7)
+240%	(X 3.4)

Weight decreases proportional to the cube of the new height, as follows:

HEIGHT	WEIGHT
10%	(X 0.9)
20%	(X 0.8)
30%	(X 0.7)
40%	(X 0.6)
50%	(X 0.5)
60%	(X 0.4)
80%	(X 0.2)
90%	(X 0.1)

All equipment worn or carried by a creature is also changed by the spell. If insufficient room is available for the desired growth or reduction, the creature or object attains the maximum possible size, bursting weak enclosures in the process. However, it is constrained without harm by stronger materials: the spell cannot be used to crush a creature by its own growth.

Magical properties are not increased by this spell. Weight, mass, and strength are affected though. A creature's hit points, armor class, and base attack bonus do not change, but strength increases along with size. For every 20% of enlargement, the creature gains a +1 bonus to strength.

ANIMAL GROWTH, Level 5 Wis
CT 1 **R** 150 ft. **D** 1 tn./lvl.
SV none **SR** yes **Comp** V, S

The caster causes up to a maximum of eight animals to grow to twice their normal size. This doubles each animal's height, length, and width, increasing its weight by a factor of eight. The increase in size has a number of effects. The animal's HD doubles, increasing the animal's bonus to hit and saving throws accordingly. The increase in size increase the damage the animal delivers by one-third. It also doubles the animal's constitution bonus. When the spell ends, the animal's HP return to normal, and all damage taken while enlarged is divided by 2. The spell gives the character no special means of command or influence over the enlarged animals. Thus, the spell is often combined with speak with animals and a charm spell. Animal growth has a 25 x 25 foot area of effect.

ANIMAL MESSENGER, Level 2 Wis, Level 2 Cha
CT 1 **R** 50 ft. **D** 1 day/lvl.
SV none **SR** yes **Comp** V, S, M (food)

Using food to initiate the spell the caster compels a small animal to go to a spot the caster designates. The spell has no effect on an animal tamed, trained or under the influence of someone else. The caster can mentally impress on the animal a certain place well known to the caster or an obvious landmark. The directions must be simple, as the animal depends on the caster's knowledge and can't find a destination on its own. The caster can attach a small item or note to the messenger. The animal travels to the location and waits there until the spell expires. During the period of waiting, the animal allows others to approach it and remove any scroll or token it carries. The intended recipient of a message gains no special ability to communicate with the animal or read any attached message.

ANIMAL SHAPES, Level 8 Wis
CT 1 **R** 50 ft. **D** 1 hr./lvl.
SV none **SR** yes (h) **Comp** V, S, DF

The caster polymorphs up to one willing creature per level, in a 25 x 25 foot area, into a small or medium animal of the caster's choice. Recipients remain in the animal form until the spell expires or the caster dismisses the spell. The caster can designate the new form's physical qualities (such as hair color, hair texture, skin color, height, weight and gender), but all must fall within the norms for the species.

Upon changing into an animal, a subject regains lost hit points as if having rested for a day (though this healing does not restore temporary ability damage or provide other benefits of resting for a day). Further, the polymorphed subject acquires the physical and natural abilities of the animal while retaining its own mind. In general, the subject's new scores and faculties are average ones for the species into which it has been transformed. Natural abilities include armor class (if better), attack routines and damage, movement capabilities such as walking, swimming and flight, and extraordinary vision. The subject does not gain any extraordinary abilities of the animal.

The subject retains its Prime attributes, intelligence, wisdom and charisma scores, level and class, hit points (despite any change in its constitution modifier), alignment and attack bonus. The subject can cast spells for which it has components. When the polymorph occurs, however, the subject's equipment, if any, melds into the new form and becomes nonfunctional; material components and focuses melded in this way cannot be used to cast spells. A humanlike voice is required for verbal components, and humanlike hands are required for somatic components.

ANIMATE DEAD*, Level 3 Wis, Level 4 Cha, Level 5 Int
CT 1 **R** 50 ft. **D** n/a
SV none **SR** none **Comp** V, S, M

This spell turns the bones or bodies of dead creatures in a 25 x 25 feet area into undead skeletons or zombies that follow the caster's spoken commands. The undead can follow the caster, or can remain in an area and attack any creature or specific type of creature entering the area. The undead remain animated until they are destroyed. Destroyed undead can't be animated again. Regardless of the type of undead, the caster can't, in any single casting of the spell, create more HD of undead than the caster has levels.

The undead remain under the caster's control indefinitely. No matter how many times the caster uses this spell, however, the character can only control 2 HD worth of undead creatures per caster level. If the caster exceeds this number, all the newly created creatures fall under the caster's control, and any excess undead from previous castings become uncontrolled (the character chooses which creatures are released). If the caster is a arcanist, any undead the character might command by virtue of the caster's power to command or rebuke undead do not count toward the spell's limits.

A skeleton can be created only from a mostly intact corpse or skeleton. The corpse must have bones. If a skeleton is made from a corpse, the flesh falls off the bones. A zombie, however, can be created only from a mostly intact corpse. The statistics for skeletons and zombies are detailed in Monsters & Treasures; undead created with this spell do not return any abilities the creature may have had while alive.

PRESERVE DEAD: This reverse version has two effects. First, the caster preserves the remains of the target corpses

so that they do not decay, for one day per level of the caster. Doing so extends the time limit on raising that creature from the dead. The spell works on severed body parts and the like. Second, the spell permanently prevents the target corpses from being animated by an animate dead spell. If a target corpse is preserved, and then raised from the dead or resurrected, the spell ends.

ANTI-ILLUSION SHELL, Level 6 Cha
CT 1 **R** person **D** 1 tn./lvl.
SV none **SR** see text **Comp** V, S.

This spell creates an invisible, mobile, 20 ft. diameter sphere of energy around the caster that affects all illusions, whether created by spell, spell-like ability, device, or supernatural ability. It suppresses any illusion used within, passing into, or cast into the area, but does not dispel it. Time spent within an antimagic shell counts against the suppressed spell's duration. The shell prevents the entrance of illusory creatures; if the caster casts anti-illusion shell in an area occupied by such a creature, the creature is forced away. Should the character be larger than the area enclosed by the shell, any part of the character's person that lies outside the barrier is unaffected by the field. Illusions created by creatures of demigod or higher status may be unaffected.

ANTILIFE SHELL, Level 5 Cha
CT 1 **R** person **D** 1 tn./lvl.
SV none **SR** y **Comp** V, S, DF

This spell creates a mobile, 20 ft. diameter, sphere of energy around the caster that prevents the entrance of all living creatures, but not constructs, elementals, outsiders or undead. The shell is transparent, but it is not invisible. It moves with the caster. This spell may be used only defensively, not aggressively; an attempt to force the shell against a creature normally kept at bay causes the shell to collapse.

ANTIMAGIC SHELL, Level 6 Int
CT 1 **R** person **D** 1 tn./lvl.
SV none **SR** see text **Comp** V, S

This spell creates a mobile, 20 ft. diameter, sphere of energy around the caster that is impervious to most magical effects, including spells, spell-like abilities and supernatural abilities. An antimagic shell suppresses any spell or magical effect used within, brought into or cast into the area, but does not dispel it. Time spent within an antimagic shell counts against the suppressed spell's duration. Likewise, the shell prevents the functioning of any magic items or spells within its confines. The shell prevents the entrance of summoned or conjured creatures and incorporeal undead; if the caster casts antimagic shell in an area occupied by such a creature which has spell resistance, the caster must make a check against the creature's SR or the spell fails.

Normal creatures can enter the area, as can normal missiles. Unless they are summoned, golems and other magical constructs, elementals, outsiders, and corporeal undead may enter in an antimagic area, but the antimagic area temporarily nullifies their spell-casting supernatural, spell-like, and other magic abilities.

The shell is transparent, but it is not invisible. Should the character be larger than the area enclosed by the shell, any part of the character's person that lies outside the barrier is unaffected by the field.

Dispel magic does not affect an antimagic shell. Certain spells remain unaffected by an antimagic field, as detailed in their descriptions. Artifacts and creatures of demigod or higher status are unaffected. Two or more antimagic shells sharing any of the same space have no effect on each other.

ANTIPATHY*, Level 7 Int, Level 8 Cha, Level 9 Wis
CT 1 hr. **R** 50 ft. **D** 2 hr./lvl.
SV Cha (see text) **SR** yes **Comp** V, S, M, DF

By means of this spell or its reverse variation, the caster causes one location or one object to emanate magical vibrations that repel or attract a specific order of intelligent creature or creatures of a particular alignment. The creature to be affected must be named specifically and defined by the caster during the casting of the spell; larger groups, such as a type or subtype, are not specific enough. Alternatively, a specific alignment can be named. For example, the caster could specify zombies, but not undead; alternatively, the caster could specify neutral evil creatures. This spell cannot be cast upon living creatures.

If the spell is cast upon a location, the area affected is a 10 foot square area per level of the caster. If the spell is cast upon an object, only the object is affected. Casting the spell requires at least $150 worth of gems or jewelry.

ANTIPATHY: The spell emanates eldritch vibrations that repel specified creatures, forcing them to abandon the area or item. The creatures will not willingly return while the spell is in effect. A creature which makes a successful saving throw can stay in the area or touch the item, but feels very uncomfortable doing so. This discomfort, while in effect, reduces the creature's charisma by 4 points. Antipathy counters and dispels sympathy.

SYMPATHY: The reverse of the spell causes designated creatures to feel elated and pleased to be in the area, or desire to touch or to possess the object. The compulsion is overpowering. If the save is successful, the creature is released from the enchantment, but a subsequent save must be made every hour if the creature remains in the area or within the presence of the item (within 10 feet per level of the caster). If a subsequent save fails, the affected creature attempts to return to the area or object. Sympathy counters and dispels antipathy.

ARCANE BOLT, LEVEL 1 INT
CT 1 **R** 150 ft. **D** n/a
SV none **SR** yes **COMP** V, S

A missile of magical energy flies from the caster's hand and unerringly strikes its target. The missile deals 1d4+1 points of damage. As long as the caster can see the target and all the targets are in a 25 foot diameter area, the missile will hit. Specific parts of a creature cannot be singled out.

For every two levels of experience past first level, the caster gains an additional missile. The caster has two at 3rd level, three at 5th level, four at 7th level, and so on. If the caster shoots multiple missiles, the caster can have them strike a single creature or several different creatures. The caster must designate targets before rolling for damage or SR.

ARCANE EYE, LEVEL 4 INT
CT 1 tn. **R** unlimited **D** 1 tn./lvl.
SV none **SR** none **COMP** V, S, M

The caster creates an invisible magical eye that sends the caster visual information. The material component for the spell is an eye. The arcane eye travels at 30 feet per round, and sees exactly as the caster would see if the caster were there. If the eye examines walls or ceilings, it moves at 10 feet per round. Solid barriers prevent the passage of an arcane eye, although it can pass through a space no smaller than a small mouse hole (one inch in diameter). The caster must concentrate to use the eye. If the caster does not concentrate, the eye becomes inert until the caster again concentrates.

The powers of the eye cannot be enhanced by other spells or items (though the caster can use magic to improve the caster's own eyesight). The caster is subject to any gaze attack the eye encounters. A successful dispel magic cast on the caster or the eye ends the spell. With respect to blindness, magical darkness and other phenomena that affect vision, the arcane eye is considered an independent sensory organ of the caster (including a creature). Creatures with intelligence 12 or higher can sense the arcane eye by making an intelligence check. Spells such as detect scrying can also detect the eye.

ARCANE MARK, LEVEL 0 INT, 0 CHA
CT 1 **R** touch **D** permanent
SV charisma negates (h) **SR** yes **COMP** V, S

This spell allows the caster to inscribe a rune or mark, which can be no taller than six inches in height and consist of no more than six characters. The writing can be visible or invisible. The caster can etch the rune upon any substance without harm to the material upon which it is placed.

If an invisible mark is made, a detect magic spell causes it to glow and be visible. See invisibility, true seeing and the like allow their users to see an invisible arcane mark. A read magic spell reveals the words, if any. The mark cannot be dispelled, but it can be removed by the caster or by an erase spell.

Creatures and items with charisma receive a charisma saving throw to prevent the inscription of the mark. If cast on a creature, normal wear gradually causes the mark to fade in about a month.

ARMOR, LEVEL 2 WIS
CT 1 **R** touch **D** 10 tn./lvl.
SV none **SR** yes (h) **COMP** V, S, M , DF

The caster needs a piece of bark to cast the spell, which grants a +4 bonus to AC due to the toughening of the caster's skin. This bonus increases to +5 at 6th level and to +6 at 12th level and higher.

ASTRAL PROJECTION, LEVEL 9 ALL
CT 30 min. **R** touch **D** see below
SV none **SR** yes (h) **COMP** V, S

This spell frees the spirit from the body, allowing the caster to project an astral body into another plane. The caster can bring the astral forms of other creatures as well, provided the creatures are linked in a circle with the caster at the time of the casting. These fellow travelers must accompany the caster at all times to remain in an astral state. If something happens to the caster during the journey, the companions are stranded wherever the caster left them. The caster can bring one additional creature for every two levels of experience.

The bodies of the caster and companions are left behind, in a state of suspended animation. The spell projects an astral copy of them and all they wear or carry onto the astral plane. Because the astral plane touches upon other planes, the caster can travel astrally to any of these other planes as the caster wishes. The caster then leaves the astral plane, forming a new physical body (and equipment) on the plane of existence the caster has chosen to enter.

When on the astral plane or another plane, the caster's astral body is connected at all times to the caster's material body by a silvery cord. If the cord is broken, the caster is killed both astrally and materially. Very few things can destroy a silver cord. When a second body is formed on a different plane, the incorporeal silvery cord remains invisibly attached to the new body. If the second body or the astral form is slain, the cord simply returns to the caster's original body, reviving it from its state of suspended animation. Although astral projections are able to function on the astral plane, their actions affect only creatures existing on the astral plane.

The caster and the caster's companions may travel through the astral plane indefinitely. The spell lasts until the caster desires to end it, or until it is terminated by some outside means, such as dispel magic cast upon either the physical body or the astral form, or the destruction of the caster's body (which kills the caster).

ATONEMENT, Level 5 Wis
CT 1 hr. + 1 hr./lvl. of recip. **R** touch **D**
SV none **SR** yes (h) **Comp** V, S, F DF

This spell removes the burden of evil acts or misdeeds from the subject. The creature seeking atonement must be truly repentant and desirous of setting right its misdeeds. The spell removes the burden from a creature who committed the evil act unwittingly or under some form of compulsion. A suitable focus worth at least $50 and ceremonial components totaling $10 in cost are needed to cast the spell.

It may also be used to atone a creature who committed deliberate misdeeds and acts of a knowing and willful nature. In such cases, the caster's deity becomes directly involved in the atonement. Such intercession has a debilitating effect on the caster. Upon completion of the spell, the caster loses all spell casting ability for one week and must rest for one day before resuming normal, daily activity. Many casters first assign the atoning subject a quest or similar penance before casting the atonement spell on their behalf.

Atonement may be cast for one of several purposes:

REVERSE MAGICAL ALIGNMENT CHANGE: If a creature has had its alignment magically changed, atonement returns its alignment to its original status.

REDEMPTION OR TEMPTATION: The caster may cast this spell upon a creature of an opposing alignment in order to offer it a chance to change its alignment to match the caster's. The prospective subject must be present for the entire casting process. Upon completion of the spell, the subject freely chooses whether it retains its original alignment or changes to the caster's alignment. No duress, compulsion or magical influence can force the subject to take advantage of the opportunity offered if it is unwilling to abandon its old alignment. This use of the spell does not work on outsiders (or any creature incapable of changing its alignment naturally).

AUGURY, Level 2 Wis, Level 3 Cha
CT 1 **R** person **D** see below
SV n/a **SR** n/a **Comp** V, S, F, DF

By using a suitable focus worth at least $12 an augury can tell the caster whether a particular action will bring good or bad results for the caster in the immediate future. The base chance for receiving a meaningful reply is 70% + 1% per caster level; the Game Master makes the roll secretly. The Game Master may determine that the question is so straightforward that a successful result is automatic, or so vague as to have no chance of success. If the augury succeeds, the caster gets one of four results: (1) Weal (if the action will probably bring good results), (2) Woe (for bad results), (3) Weal and woe (for both), or (4) Nothing (for actions that don't have especially good or bad results). If the spell fails, the caster gets the nothing result. A arcanist who gets the nothing result has no way to tell whether it resulted from a failed or successful augury.

The augury can see into the future only about half an hour, so anything that might happen after that does not affect the augury. Thus, it might miss the long-term consequences of the contemplated action. All auguries cast by the same person upon the same topic use the same dice result as the first augury.

AWAKEN, Level 5 Wis
CT 1 day **R** touch **D** permanent
SV wisdom negates **SR** yes **Comp** V, S, DF

The caster awakens a tree or animal to humanlike sentience. To succeed, the caster must make a wisdom save, with the target's hit dice constituting the challenge level. The awakened animal or tree is friendly toward the caster. The caster has no special empathy or connection with the awakened creature, although it serves the caster in specific tasks or endeavors if the caster can communicate their desires to it. An awakened tree has characteristics of an animated object. Awakened trees gain the ability to move their limbs, roots, vines, creepers, etc., and have senses similar to a human's. An awakened animal gets 3d6 intelligence, a +1 charisma bonus, and +2 hit dice. An awakened tree or animal can speak one language that the caster knows.

B

BANISHMENT, Level 6 Wis
CT 1 **R** 50 ft. **D** permanent
SV charisma negates **SR** yes **Comp** V, S, F

Banishment enables the caster to force extraplanar creatures within a 25 x 25 foot area, back to their home plane. Up to 2 hit dice of creatures per caster level can be banished. To target a creature, the character must present at least one object or substance that it hates, fears or otherwise opposes. For each such object or substance, the creature suffers a -2 penalty on its saving throw, and the caster gains +1 bonus on the check to overcome the target's SR (if any).

BIND ELEMENTAL, Level 5 Int
CT 10 min. **R** 50 ft. **D** 10 min./lvl.
SV n/a **SR** n/a **Comp** V, S, M

Upon casting this spell, the sorcerer forcibly transports a powerful elemental from one of the elemental planes to the plane in which the caster is located. The type of elemental summoned must be designated by the caster before the spell is begun. This elemental has 12d8 HD, Physical Primes, a slam attack dealing 3D6 damage, and is capable of casting any spell from any list that could be directly associated with its element. As the elemental will be a large specimen, fire and water elementals will require a large source of either element in order to be able to take shape. Earth and air are typically present in abundance. The caster can use any item which can reasonably be associated with the element being summoned.

The elemental does not come willingly, nor will it do the caster's bidding without a struggle. The caster must maintain concentration upon the elemental to force it to serve. If the caster moves, speaks, takes damage, or performs any other action other than concentrating on forcing the elemental to do his or her bidding, the elemental attacks the caster immediately, and will not stop until destroyed. Control over the elemental cannot be regained. It will ignore any and all opponents save for the sorcerer who summoned it. The caster may release the elemental at any time.

BINDING*, Level 8 Int, Level 9 Cha
CT 1 tn. **R** 50 ft. **D** see below
SV charisma negates **SR** yes **Comp** V, S, M

A binding spell creates a magical restraint to hold a creature. The target only gets an initial saving throw if its HD is equal to at least half the caster's level. The caster may employ up to six assistants with the spell. For each assistant who casts suggestion, the caster's effective caster level increases by +1. For each assistant who casts a charm or other appropriate spell, the caster's effective level increases by +2 (provided the target is appropriate for the spell). All the assistants must join in chanting the spell as detailed below.

The binding spell has six versions. The caster chooses one when the spell is cast. Regardless of the version cast, the caster can specify triggering conditions that end the spell and release the creature whenever they occur. These can be as simple or elaborate as the caster desires (subject to the Game Master agreeing that the condition is reasonable and has a likelihood of coming to pass). The conditions can be based on a creature's name, identity or alignment, but otherwise must be based on observable actions or qualities. Intangibles such as level, class, HD or HPs do not qualify. Once the spell is cast, its triggering conditions cannot be changed. Setting a release condition results in a saving throw penalty of -2, if the subject gets a saving throw.

A creature may only be subject to one binding spell at a time. Additional binding spells cast on a subject already bound have no effect.

CHAINING: The subject is confined by restraints that generate an antipathy spell affecting all creatures who approach the subject except the caster. Duration is one year per caster level. The subject is confined to the spot it occupied when it became subject to the spell's effect.

SLUMBER: Imposes a comatose sleep upon the subject for up to one year per caster level. The subject does not need to eat or drink while slumbering, nor does it age. Saves are made at +1.

BOUND SLUMBER: A combination of chaining and slumber that lasts for up to one month per caster level. Saves are made at +3, if the subject gets a saving throw.

HEDGED PRISON: The subject is transported to or otherwise brought within a confined area from which it cannot wander by any means. The spell is permanent. Saves are made at +4, if the subject gets a saving throw.

METAMORPHOSIS: The subject assumes gaseous form, except for its head or face. It is held harmless in a jar or other container, which may be transparent. The creature remains aware of its surroundings and can speak, but cannot leave the container, attack or use any of its powers or abilities. The binding is permanent. The subject does not need to breathe, eat or drink while metamorphosed, nor does it age. Saves are made at +5, if the subject gets a saving throw.

MINIMUS CONTAINMENT: The subject is shrunk to a height of one inch or less and held within some gem or similar object or jar. The binding is permanent. The subject does not need to breathe, eat or drink while contained, nor does it age. Saves are made at +4, if the subject gets a saving throw.

FREEDOM: The reverse of this spell, Freedom, simply cancels the effect of any Binding spell cast by an arcanist of equal or lower level.

BLADE BARRIER, Level 6 Wis

CT 1 **R** 150 ft. **D** 3 rd./lvl.
SV dexterity negates **SR** yes **Comp** V, S

This spell creates a wall of whirling blades. The wall is immobile, standing 30 feet tall, 60 feet long and 5 feet thick. Any creature passing through the blade barrier takes 12d6 points of damage. Creatures within the blade barrier when it is invoked take the damage as well, but they can avoid the damage with a successful dexterity check, provided they can and do physically leave the area of the blades by the shortest possible route. Once the barrier is in place, anything entering or passing through the blades automatically takes damage.

BLESS*, Level 1 Wis

CT 1 **R** 50 ft. **D** 1 tn./lvl.
SV none **SR** yes (h) **Comp** V, S, DF.

The caster's allies gain +1 to hit, and a + 1 on saving throws against fear. The reverse spell, bane, causes the caster's enemies a -1 to hit and saving throws against fear.

BLESS WATER*, Level 1 Wis

CT 1 tn. **R** touch **D** permanent
SV n/a **SR** yes (object) **Comp** V, S, DF

This spell turns a flask (one pint) of water into holy water or unholy water. Holy water and unholy water have special effects on certain creatures, such as undead and evil outsiders, upon which a flask deals 1d8 points of acid damage. The reverse is called curse water, and has a similar effect on holy creatures and good outsiders.

BLINDING FLASH, Level 0 Wis

CT 1 **R** 10 ft./lvl **D** instant
SV Neg. **SR** no **Comp** V,S

This spell creates a blinding flash of light within ten feet per level of the caster. All characters within ten feet of the burst (including the caster and his allies) make a Constitution-based saving throw with a CL equal to the caster level plus one or are blinded and disoriented for one round, suffering -6 to all actions. If a target (ally or enemy) is aware the attack is coming and knows to close or avert their eyes, they are assumed to automatically save.

BLINK, Level 3 Int, Level 3 Cha

CT 1 **R** n/a **D** 1 rd./lvl.
SV n/a **SR** n/a **Comp** V, S

This spell rapidly cycles the caster in and out of existence (into the ethereal plane). Blinking has several effects. Attacks against the caster are made at -10. If the attacker, however, is capable of striking ethereal or incorporeal creatures, or is able to see invisible creatures, then attacks are made at only -2. If the attacker can both see and strike ethereal creatures, the attacker suffers no penalty. Individually targeted spells have a 50% chance to fail against the character while blinking unless the attacker can target invisible or ethereal creatures. Area attacks, such as fireball or a burst of bullets from an automatic firearm, cause full damage.

The caster's own attacks are made at -2. Likewise, the caster's own spells have a 50% chance to activate just as the character goes ethereal, in which case they take effect on the ethereal plane. Since the character spends about half the character's time on the ethereal plane, the character can see and even attack ethereal creatures. The character interacts with ethereal creatures roughly the same way the character interacts with material ones.

While blinking, the character can step through, but not see through, solid objects no more than 5 feet thick. If the caster attempts to walk through material thicker than 5 feet, they blink into the solid object, the spell ends, and they are shunted off to the nearest open space, suffering 1d6 points of damage per 5 feet traveled through solid matter.

BLUR, Level 2 Cha

CT 1 **R** touch (one) **D** 1 tn./lvl.
SV wisdom negates (h) **SR** yes **Comp** V

The subject's outline appears distorted, granting a +2 bonus to armor class. A see invisibility spell does not counteract the blur effect, but a true seeing spell does. Opponents who cannot see the subject ignore the spell's effect. This spell's effect does combine/stack with the Armor spell.

BULLETPROOF, Level 2 Int

CT 1 **R** touch **D** 10 min./lvl.
SV none **SR** yes **Comp** V, S, F

This spell shields the recipient against attacks from normal missiles and ranged weapons for the duration of the spell. This protection also shields the recipient from one attack by a large missile such as a catapult or hurled boulder, though such a powerful attack causes the magic of the spell to be consumed after the first deflected strike. The material component of this spell is a pendant shaped like a shield.

BURNING HANDS, LEVEL 1 INT, LEVEL 2 CHA
CT 1 **R** 5 ft. **D** instant
SV none **SR** yes **COMP** V, S

A thin sheet of flame shoots from the caster's outspread fingertips, striking any creature in the spell's semicircular area of effect (5 feet. long and 10 feet. wide). Creatures in the area of the flames take damage at 1d2+1 HP per level of the caster. Flammable materials such as cloth, paper, parchment and thin wood ignite and burn if the flames touch them.

C

CALL LIGHTNING, LEVEL 3 WIS
CT 10 min. plus 1 rd per bolt **R** 450 ft. **D** 10 min./lvl.
SV dexterity half **SR** yes **COMP** V, S

If the caster is in a stormy area, this spell allows him to call bolts of lightning from the sky. The caster can call down one bolt every 10 minutes, for the duration of the spell. The character need not call a bolt of lightning immediately. Other actions, even spell casting, can be performed during the spell's duration. Calling a bolt, however, takes the caster's action for that round. A bolt causes 1d10 hit points of damage per caster level. It strikes in a vertical stroke at whatever target point the character chooses, within the spell's range. The bolt takes the shortest possible unobstructed path between a nearby cloud and the target. Any creature within a 10 foot radius of the path or the point where the lightning strikes is affected. This spell can only be used outdoors.

CHAIN LIGHTNING, LEVEL 6 INT
CT 1 **R** 450 ft. **D** instant
SV dexterity save half **SR** yes **COMP** V, S

Bolts of lightning spring from the caster's fingertips, striking a target and then arcing to other targets within 50 feet of the Prime target. The bolt deals 1d6 points of damage per caster level on the primary target. After the bolt strikes, the lightning can arc to as many secondary targets as the caster has levels. The secondary bolts each strike one target and deal half as many dice of damage as the primary (rounded down). All subjects can attempt dexterity saving throws for half damage. The character chooses the secondary targets, but they must all be within 50 feet of the primary target, and no target can be struck more than once. The character can choose to affect fewer secondary targets than the maximum.

CHANGE SELF, LEVEL 1 INT, LEVEL 1 CHA
CT 1 **R** touch **D** 10 tn./lvl.
SV Intelligence negates **SR** no **COMP** V, S

The spell changes the caster's appearance, including clothing, weapons and equipment. The caster can seem one foot shorter or taller, thin, fat or in between. The spell cannot change the character's species. Otherwise, the extent of the apparent change is up to the caster. The spell does not provide the abilities or mannerisms of the chosen form. It does not alter the perceived tactile (touch) or audible (sound) properties of the character or any equipment. Creatures get an intelligence save to recognize the glamer as an illusion if they interact with it.

CHARM MONSTER, LEVEL 3 CHA, LEVEL 4 INT
CT 1 **R** 50 ft. **D** 1 day/lvl.
SV charisma negates **SR** yes **COMP** V,S

This charm makes a monster regard the caster as a trusted friend and ally. If the monster is being threatened or attacked by the caster or the caster's allies, however, the monster receives a +5 bonus to its saving throw. The spell does not enable the caster to control the charmed creature as if it were an automaton, but it perceives the caster's words and actions in the most favorable way. The caster can try to give the subject orders, but the caster must succeed at a Charisma check to convince it to do anything it wouldn't ordinarily do. Any act by the caster or the caster's apparent allies that threatens the charmed creature breaks the spell. Note also that the caster must speak the creature's language to communicate commands.

CHARM PERSON, LEVEL 1 INT
CT 1 **R** 50 ft. **D** 1 hr./lvl.
SV charisma negates **SR** yes **COMP** V,S

This charm makes a medium-size or smaller humanoid regard the caster as a trusted friend and ally. If the target is being threatened or attacked by the caster or the caster's allies, however, it receives a +5 bonus to its saving throw. The spell does not enable the character to control the charmed creature as if it were an automaton, but the subject does perceive the caster's words and actions in the most favorable way. The caster can try to give the subject orders, but the caster must succeed at a Charisma check to convince it to do anything it wouldn't ordinarily do. Any act by the caster or the caster's apparent allies that threatens the charmed creature breaks the spell. Note also that the caster must speak the creature's language to communicate commands.

CHARM PERSON OR ANIMAL, LEVEL 1 CHA, LEVEL 2 WIS
CT 1 **R** 50 ft. **D** 1 hr./lvl.
SV charisma negates **SR** yes **COMP** V,S.

This spell is exactly like charm person, but it can also affect animals, beasts and magical beasts.

CLAIRAUDIENCE/ CLAIRVOYANCE, LEVEL 3 INT, LEVEL 3 CHA
CT 1 **R** see below **D** 1 tn./lvl.
SV none **SR** no **COMP** V, S, F/ DF

Clairaudience or clairvoyance enables the character to concentrate upon some locale and hear or see (the character's choice) almost as if the character were there. Distance is not a factor, but the locale must be a place familiar to the character. The spell does not allow magically enhanced senses to work through it. If the chosen locale is magically dark, the character

sees nothing. If it is naturally pitch black, the character can see in a 10 foot radius around the center of the spell's effect. Lead sheeting or magical protection blocks the spell, and the caster senses that the spell is so blocked. The spell can be dispelled, and it functions only on the plane of existence the character is occupying.

CLONE, Level 8 Int, 9 Cha
CT 1 hour **R** touch **D** permanent
SV n/a **SR** n/a **Comp** V, S, M

This spell creates a duplicate of a creature. To create the duplicate, the caster must spend $500 for research and creation and must have a piece of flesh taken from the original's living body, with a volume of at least one cubic inch. The piece of flesh need not be fresh, but it must be kept from rotting. Once the spell is cast, the duplicate must be grown in a laboratory for 2d4 months.

The clone has the personality, memories, levels, attributes, and abilities that the original had at the time the piece of flesh was taken. The spell duplicates only the original's body and mind, not its equipment.

CLOUDKILL, Level 5 Int
CT 1 **R** 150 ft. **D** 1 tn./lvl.
SV see text **SR** yes **Comp** V, S

A bank of yellowish-green poisonous fog billows out from the point the caster designates and affects a 20 foot high x 30 foot wide x 20 foot thick area. The fog obscures all sight, including extraordinary vision, beyond 5 feet. A creature within 5 feet has one-half concealment. Creatures farther away have total concealment. The fog's vapors kill any living creature with 3 or fewer HD (no save) and causes creatures with 4 to 6 HD to make constitution saving throws or die. Living creatures above 6 HD, and creatures of 4 to 6 HD who make their saving throws, take 1d10 points of poison damage each round while in the cloud. Holding one's breath doesn't help unfortunately.

The cloudkill moves away from the caster at 10 feet per round, rolling along the surface of the ground. Because the vapors are heavier than air, they sink to the lowest level of the land, even pouring down openings. A moderate wind (11+ mph) disperses the fog in four rounds; a strong wind (21+ mph) disperses the fog in one round.

COLOR SPRAY, Level 1 Cha
CT 1 **R** 25 ft. **D** instant
SV wisdom negates **SR** yes **Comp** V, S, M

A rainbow cone springs forth from the caster's hand, causing nearby creatures to fall asleep. The spell can affect a number of creatures equal to 1d4 + level. The cone is 5 feet wide and 25 feet long, and the closest creatures in the cone are affected first. The material component are small colored objects.

The result of the spell depends upon the HD of the targeted creatures. Creatures of 2 HD or less are struck unconscious for 2d4 rounds; creatures of 3 to 4 HD are blinded for 1d4 rounds; and creatures of 5 HD or greater are stunned for one round. Creatures of the same level or HD as the caster, and all creatures with 5 HD or greater may make a wisdom saving throw to shake off the color spray. Sightless creatures are not affected by color spray.

COMMAND, Level 1 Wis, Level 1 Cha
CT 1 **R** 25 ft. **D** 1 rd
SV charisma negates **SR** yes **Comp** V

The caster utters a one-word directive, which the subject or subjects, up to one creature for every 2 levels, obeys to the best of their ability unless they make a charisma saving throw. The command must be clear and understood by the targeted creature. A command of "die" causes the subject to fall unconscious for the duration of the spell, whereas a command of "suicide" would fail because it is generally used as a noun, not as a command. A command of "awake" will counter magically induced unconsciousness caused by sleep and color spray.

COMMAND PLANTS, Level 8 Wis
CT 1 **R** 150 ft. **D** see text
SV see text **SR** yes (see text) **Comp** V, DF

The caster causes plants, fungi and plant creatures to do the character's bidding with a 50 foot diameter cirle. There are three versions of the spell described below.

ANIMATE: The spell imbues trees or other large, inanimate vegetable life with mobility. The animated plants then attack whomever or whatever the character first designates. Animated plants gain humanlike senses. The plants' armor class, attacks and special abilities vary with their size and form, as described for animated objects. The character can animate two trees, four shrubs or eight vines. All plants to be affected must be within 50 feet of each other. The character can animate different types of plants if desired. The effect lasts one hour per caster level.

CHARM: Against plant and fungus creatures, command plants functions in the same manner as a mass charm spell. The character can command a number of plant creatures whose combined level or HD do not exceed three times the character's level. No two affected creatures can be more than 25 feet from each other, and each is allowed a charisma saving throw. The effect lasts 1 day per caster level.

ENHANCED ENTANGLE: This version acts as an enhanced entangle spell, allowing all plants within the area of effect to entwine about any creatures within, or moving through the area, holding them fast. A successful dexterity save means that the creature manages to avoided becoming entangled for that particular round. An entangled creature suffers a -2

penalty to attack, a -4 penalty to effective dexterity, and also cannot move, making the casting of a spells with a somatic component impossible. Breaking free requires a successful strength check. Each round, the plants once again attempt to entangle all creatures who have avoided or escaped entanglement. Spell resistance does not keep creatures from being entangled. Plants can also free creatures trapped by an entangle spell the enhanced entangle version of command plant. The effect lasts one hour per caster level.

COMMUNE, Level 5 Wis

CT 10 min **R** see text **D** special
SV n/a **SR** n/a **Comp** V, S, M , DF

The caster can attempt to contact the character's deity or agents and ask questions that can be answered by a simple yes or no answer. A arcanist with no particular deity contacts a philosophically allied deity. This spell should be used sparingly, as disfavor could be gained with frequent use. The caster needs incense, holy symbol or other religious items.

The caster is allowed one question per caster level. The answers given are correct within the limits of the deity's knowledge. Any question that cannot be answered with an answer of yes or no will result in no answer and will count against the caster's maximum number of questions. If a caster doesn't focus on the conversation, such as discussing answers with others, the deity becomes angry or irritated, and ends the spell.

COMPREHEND LANGUAGES, Level 1 Int

CT 1 **R** n/a **D** 10 min./lvl.
SV n/a **SR** n/a **Comp** V, S

The character can understand the spoken words of creatures and read otherwise incomprehensible written messages. Note that the ability to read does not necessarily impart insight into the material, merely its literal meaning. Note also that the spell enables the character to understand or read an unknown language, not speak or write it. Written material can be read at the rate of one page (250 words) per minute. Magical writing cannot be read, other than to know it is magical. The spell does not decipher codes or reveal messages concealed in otherwise normal text.

CONE OF COLD, Level 5 Int

CT 1 **R** see below **D** 1 rd.
SV dexterity half **SR** yes **Comp** V, S, M

A cone of extreme cold shoots from the caster's hand affecting an area 5 feet wide x 50 feet long, or from a focus, causing 1d6 points of damage per caster level. Water is needed to cast the spell.

CONFUSION, Level 4 Int, Level 4 Cha

CT 1 **R** 150 ft. **D** 1 rd./lvl.
SV wisdom negates **SR** yes **Comp** V, S

This spell causes creatures in an area 50 feet x 50 feet to behave randomly, as indicated on the following table:

1D10	BEHAVIOR
1	Wander away for 1 turn (unless prevented)
2-3	Attempt mundane task, like cooking, for 1 round
4-6	Do nothing for 1 round
7-8	Try to locate lost items for 1 round
9	Attack nearest creature for 1 round
10	Act normally for 1 round

Except on a result of one, roll each round to see what the subject does. Wandering creatures leave the scene as if disinterested. Any confused creature who is attacked automatically attacks its attackers on its next turn.

CONSECRATE*, Level 2 Wis

CT 3 **R** 50 ft. **D** 2 hrs./lvl.
SV n/a **SR** n/a **Comp** V, S, M, DF

This spell blesses an area 50 feet x 50 feet with positive energy. All attempts to turn undead made within the area gain a +3 bonus. Undead entering this area suffer minor disruption, giving them a -1 penalty on attack, damage and saving throws. Undead cannot be created or summoned into a consecrated area. If the consecrated area contains a permanent fixture dedicated to the character's deity, pantheon or aligned higher power, the modifiers listed above are doubled. Consecrate counters and dispels desecrate, but not within a permanent fixture of the opposing spell caster's deity. The cast needs religious materials worth $12 to cast the spell.

Desecrate is the reverse of this spell. It imbues an area with negative energy, and all attempts to turn undead within it suffer a -3 penalty. Undead entering this area gain +1 to attack, damage and saving throws. Undead created within or summoned into a desecrated area gain +1 hit points per HD. If the desecrated area contains an altar, shrine or other permanent fixture dedicated to the caster's deity, pantheon or aligned higher power, the effects are doubled.

Desecrate counters and dispels consecrate, but not within a permanent fixture of the opposing spell-caster's deity.

CONTACT OTHER PLANE, Level 5 Int

CT 10 min. **R** see below **D** 1 rd./2 lvls.
SV n/a **SR** n/a **Comp** V

The caster projects his mind to another plane of existence in hopes of receiving advice and information from powers that reside there. The powers reply in a language the character understands, or by telepathy, but they often resent such contact and as a result give brief answers. The Game Master will answers questions with yes, no, maybe, never, unclear, irrelevant or some other one-word answer.

The character must concentrate to maintain the spell, and may ask one question per round. The question is answered during the same round. A caster may ask one question for

every two caster levels. Upon first making contact, the caster must make an intelligence saving throw. Failure results in the spell ending immediately, and the caster suffering an attribute loss and possible insanity as indicated on the table below. Except for contact with an elemental plane, a saving throw roll of natural one always results in insanity.

The caster can contact an elemental plane or some plane further removed. Contact with a mind far removed from the caster's home plane increases the likelihood of a successful answer, but likewise increases the probability that the caster will suffer adverse effects. On rare occasions, this form of divination may be blocked by an act of certain deities or forces. The following table shows the possible consequences and results of the attempt.

Failed Saving Throw: If the caster fails an intelligence save against the indicated CL, the caster's intelligence and charisma scores are decreased as indicated on the table, for one week's duration. Lowering of intelligence can result in the loss of bonus spells, and if reduced to 8 or less, the loss of daily spells entirety. Additionally, the caster may go insane when contacting a plane other than an elemental plane. A saving throw failed by 5 or more results in insanity in the caster. A saving throw roll of natural 1 always results in insanity. Insanity lasts as follows:

Astral: 1 week

Demigod: 1d4 weeks

Lesser Deity: 1d8 weeks

Greater Deity: 1d12 weeks

Results of a Successful Contact: The Game Master rolls % to generate the result shown on the table:

CONTINUAL FLAME, Level 2 Int, 2 Cha, 3 Wis

CT 1 **R** 5 ft. **D** permanent
SV none **SR** yes **Comp** V, S

A flame, equivalent in brightness to a torch, springs forth from an object that the character touches. The flame looks like a regular flame, but it creates no heat and doesn't use oxygen. The flame can be covered and hidden, but not smothered or quenched.

CONTROL PLANTS, Level 4 Wis

CT 1 **R** 50 ft. **D** 1 tn./lvl.
SV charisma negates (see text) **SR** yes **Comp** V, S

This spell allows the caster to control and to converse, in very rudimentary terms, with all sorts of plants and plantlike creatures (including fungi, molds and plantlike monsters) in a 25 foot x 25 foot area. The caster automatically exercises limited control over normal plants, but plantlike creatures can negate the control effect with a charisma save. The spell does not enable plants to uproot themselves and move about, but it does allow them to move their branches, stems and leaves. The plants can duplicate the effect of an entangle spell, or free creatures trapped by that spell.

CONTROL WATER, Level 4 Wis

CT 1 **R** 450 ft. **D** 10 min./lvl.
SV n/a **SR** n/a **Comp** V, S, M/DF

The spell allows the caster to either raise or lower water.

LOWER WATER: This use of the spell causes water (or any similar liquid) to sink away to a minimum depth of 1 inch. The depth can be lowered by up to 2 feet per caster level. The water is lowered within a squarish depression whose sides are up to 10 feet long per caster level. In extremely

CONTACT OTHER PLANE

Plane Contacted	Saving Throw Challenge Level	Loss of Int	Loss of Cha	True Answer	Don't Know	Lie	Random Answer
Elemental Plane	3	1	01-35	36-65	66-85	86-100	
Astral Plane	5	2	1	01-40	41-65	66-85	86-100
Outer Plane,demigod	7	4	2	01-55	56-75	76-90	91-100
Outer Plane,lesser deity	9	6	3	01-70	71-85	86-95	96-100
Outer Plane,greater deity	12	8	4	01-90	91-92	93-100	

True Answer: The character gets a true, one-word answer. Questions not capable of being answered in this way are answered as unclear.

Don't Know: The entity tells the character that it doesn't know.

Lie: The entity intentionally lies to the character.

Random Answer: The entity tries to lie but doesn't know the answer, so it makes one up.

large and deep bodies of water, a powerful caster can create a whirlpool that sweeps ships downward, putting them at risk of damage and rendering them unable to leave by normal movement for the duration of the spell. When cast on water elementals and other water-based creatures, this spell acts as a slow spell. The spell has no effect on other creatures.

RAISE WATER: This use of the spell causes water (or any similar liquid) to rise in height. Boats raised in this way slide down the sides of the hump that the spell creates. If the area affected by the spell is adjacent to land, the water can spill over onto dry land.

CONTROL WEATHER, Level 6 Int, 7 Wis

CT 10 min. (see text) **R** 2 miles **D** 4d12 hrs.
SV n/a **SR** n/a **Comp** V, S, M/DF

The caster changes the weather in the local area, 2 miles x 2 miles centered on caster. It takes 10 minutes to cast the spell and an additional 10 minutes for the effects to manifest. The caster can only call forth weather appropriate to the climate and season of the area, but can almost always change the direction of the wind and control its intensity from calm to strong. The character cannot control the specific applications of the weather. When the character selects a certain weather condition to occur, the weather assumes that condition 10 minutes later (changing gradually). The weather continues as the caster left it for the duration, or until the character designates a new kind of weather, which fully manifests 10 minutes later. Contradictory conditions are not possible simultaneously. Control weather can do away with atmospheric phenomena (naturally occurring or otherwise) as well as create them.

SEASON	POSSIBLE WEATHER
Spring	Tornado, thunderstorm or sleet
Summer	Torrential rain, heat wave, or hailstorm
Autumn	Hot or cold weather, fog, or sleet
Winter	Frigid cold, blizzard, or thaw

CONTROL WINDS, Level 5 Wis

CT 1 **R** 50 ft. **D** 10 min./lvl.
SV none **SR** none **Comp** V, S

The caster alters wind force in a 100 foot diameter sphere/ level, centered on the caster. The caster can make the wind blow in a certain direction or manner, and increase or decrease its strength. The new wind direction and strength persist until the spell ends or the caster chooses to alter the spell, which requires concentration. The caster may create an "eye" of calm air up to 50 feet in diameter at the center of the area if the character so desires, and the character may choose to limit the effect to any area less than the spell's full area of effect.

WIND DIRECTION: The caster may choose one of four basic wind patterns to function over the spell's area: a downdraft blows from the center outward in equal strength in all directions; an updraft blows from the outer edges in toward the center in equal strength from all directions, veering upward before impinging on the eye in the center; a rotation causes the winds to circle the center in clockwise or counterclockwise fashion; a blast simply causes the winds to blow in one direction across the entire area from one side to the other.

WIND FORCE: For every three caster levels, the character can increase or decrease wind force by one level of strength. Strong winds (21+ mph) make sailing difficult. A severe wind (31+ mph) causes minor ship and building damage. A windstorm (51+ mph) drives most flying creatures from the skies, uproots small trees, knocks down light wooden structures, tears off roofs and endangers ships. Hurricane force winds (75+ mph) destroy wooden buildings, sometimes uproot even large trees and cause most ships to founder. A tornado (175+ mph) destroys all nonfortified buildings and often uproots large trees.

CREATE FOOD AND WATER*, Level 3 Wis

CT 10 min **R** 50 ft. **D** permanent
SV n/a **SR** n/a **Comp** V, S, DF

This spell creates simple food of the caster's choice and a volume of drinking water. The food decays as normal food, but the water does not go bad. The caster can create enough food and water to sustain three humans or one horse for 1 day per caster level. The reverse of this spell, spoil food and water, makes the same amount of food or water inedible.

CREATE GREATER UNDEAD, Level 7 Cha, 8 Wis

CT 1 hour **R** 50 ft. (one) **D** permanent
SV n/a **SR** n/a **Comp** V, S, M

This evil spell allows the caster to create powerful kinds of undead if the arcanist is of the appropriate level: mummy (13), spectre (15), vampire (17) or ghost (19). The caster may create less powerful undead than the caster's maximum capability if desired. Created undead are not automatically under the control of their animator. The caster may gain command of the undead as it forms by making a successful Wisdom check with a CL equal to the hit dice of the monster. This spell must be cast at night and the caster must spend $100 per corpse.

CREATE UNDEAD, Level 5 Cha, 6 Wis

CT 1 hour **R** 50 ft. (one) **D** permanent
SV n/a **SR** n/a **Comp** V, S, M

This evil spell allows the caster to create powerful kinds of undead if the arcanist is of the appropriate level: ghouls (9), shadow (10), ghasts (12), wights (14) or wraiths (18). The caster may create less powerful undead than the caster's maximum

capability if desired. Created undead are not automatically under the control of their animator. The caster may gain command of the undead as it forms by making a successful turning check. This spell must be cast at night.

CREATE WATER, Level 0 Wis
CT 1 **R** 50 ft. **D** permanent
SV n/a **SR** n/a **Comp** V, S

This spell generates wholesome, drinkable water. Water can be created in an area as small as will actually contain the liquid, or in an area three times as large (possibly creating a downpour or filling many small receptacles). The caster can create 2 gallons of water per caster level (enough to fill 4 waterskins). Water weighs about 8 pounds per gallon, and one cubic foot of water contains roughly 8 gallons and weighs about 65 pounds.

CREEPING DOOM, Level 6 Cha, 7 Wis
CT 1 **R** 150 ft. **D** 1 tn./lvl.
SV none **SR** no **Comp** V, S

The caster calls forth a mass of 1,000 venomous, biting and stinging spiders, scorpions, beetles and centipedes. The carpetlike mass swarms in a square 25 feet on a side. Upon the caster's command, the swarm creeps forth at 10 feet per round toward any prey within 150 feet. Each vermin in the creeping doom effect automatically bites a creature for 1 point of damage and then dies. Each creature overrun by the swarm takes enough hit points of damage to kill it, destroying that number of vermin in the process. If there aren't enough vermin to kill all the creatures in the spell's effect, damage is distributed among the survivors equally. If the creeping doom travels more than 100 feet away from the character, it loses 50 of its number for each additional 10 feet it travels. Anything that would deter or destroy normal insects is effective against these insects.

CURE CRITICAL WOUNDS*, Level 5 Wis
CT 1 **R** touch **D** permanent
SV see text **SR** yes (h) **Comp** V, S, DF

When the caster lays hands upon a living creature, the target is cured of 5d8 hit points of damage. The curative version of this spell automatically deals the same damage against undead, while the reverse of the spell deals damage to living creatures. In those situations, a successful wisdom save indicates half damage.

CURE LIGHT WOUNDS*, Level 1 Wis
CT 1 **R** touch **D** permanent
SV see text **SR** yes (h) **Comp** V, S, DF

When the caster lays hands upon a living creature, the target is healed for 1d8 hit points of damage. The curative version of this spell causes the same amount of damage to undead creatures, while the reverse of this spell deals damage to living creatures. In those situations, a successful wisdom save indicates half damage.

CURE SERIOUS WOUNDS*, Level 3 Wis
CT 1 **R** touch **D** permanent
SV see text **SR** yes (h) **Comp** V, S, DF

When the caster lays hands upon a living creature, the target is cured for 3d8 hit points of damage. The curative version of this spell causes the same amount of damage to undead creatures, while the reverse causes the same damage to living creatures. In those situations, a successful wisdom save indicates half damage.

D

DANCING LIGHTS , Level 0 Int, 0 Cha
CT 1 **R** 150 ft. **D** 1 tn.
SV see text **SR** no **Comp** V, S

Depending on the version selected during casting, the caster creates up to four lights that resemble lanterns or torches (and provide the same amount of light), or up to four glowing spheres of light (which look like will-o'-wisps), or one faintly glowing, vaguely humanoid shape. The dancing lights must stay within 20 feet of each other, but otherwise move as the caster desires (no concentration required): forward or back, up or down, straight or turning corners, etc. The lights can move up to 100 feet per round. A light winks out if its distance from the caster exceeds the spell's range. A creature that interacts with a dancing light gets a wisdom saving throw to recognize it is an illusion.

DARKNESS*, Level 1 Cha, 2 Int, 2 Wis
CT 1 **R** 50 ft. **D** 10 min./lvl.
SV none **SR** none **Comp** V, M/DF

This spell causes an object or surface to radiate darkness out to a 20-foot radius. Not even creatures that can normally see in the dark can see in an area shrouded in magical darkness. Normal lights do not work, nor do light spells of a lower spell level.

The reverse of this spell is called daylight. Daylight causes an object or surface to shed light as bright as full daylight in a 60 foot radius. Creatures that suffer penalties in bright light suffer them while exposed to this magical light. Darkness and daylight cancel each other out, leaving whatever light conditions normally prevail in the overlapping areas of the spells. Higher-level light spells are not affected by darkness, and the reverse is true for daylight. If either spell is cast on a small object that is then placed inside or under a lightproof covering, the spell's effects are blocked until the covering is removed.

DAZE, Level 1 Cha

CT 1 **R** 25 feet **D** 1 rd.
SV intelligence neg **SR** yes **Comp** V, S, M

This enchantment clouds the mind of a humanoid creature with 4 or fewer hit dice so that it takes no actions. Humanoids of 5 or more hit dice are not affected. A dazed subject is not stunned, so attackers get no special advantage against it. A pinch of wool is needed to cast this spell.

DEATH WARD, Level 5 Cha, 5 Wis
CT 1 **R** touch **D** 10 min./lvl.
SV none **SR** yes (h) **Comp** V, S, DF

The caster imbues one subject with immunity to all death spells and magical death effects. The spell does not protect against other sorts of attacks, such as hit point loss, poison, petrification or other effects even if they might be lethal.

DELAY POISON, Level 2 Wis
CT 1 **R** touch **D** 1 hr./lvl.
SV constitution negates (h) **SR** yes (h) **Comp** V, S, DF

The caster imbues one subject with immunity to poison. Any poison in the subject's system, or any poison the subject is exposed to during the spell's duration, does not affect the subject until the spell has expired. Delay poison does not cure any damage that poison may have already done.

DELAYED BLAST FIREBALL, Level 6 Wis
CT 1 **R** 450 ft. **D** up to 5 rnds
SV dexterity half **SR** yes **Comp** V, S, M

This spell is an enhanced version of fireball, except the caster can choose to delay the detonation for up to 5 rounds. With a gesture, the caster sends a small ball of fire hurtling through the air to detonate with a low roar at the height and distance the caster desires as long as it is within the spell's maximum range. The explosion fills the area of effect, a 40 foot diameter sphere, with intense fire and heat, causing 1d6 +1 per level fire damage to all creatures and objects within the area. It ignites combustibles and damages objects, and melts anything with a low melting point such as bronze, copper, silver, lead or gold. The explosion creates almost no pressure. A small lump of coal is required to cast the spell.

The fireball can detonate immediately in the same round that the spell is cast, or the caster can choose to delay the explosion for up to 5 rounds. The caster chooses the amount of delay upon completing the spell, and the delay cannot be changed once it has been set.

Unlike the fireball spell, impact against a solid barrier does not cause early detonation. If the caster chooses a delayed blast, the glowing bead sits at its destination until it detonates. A creature can pick up and hurl the fireball like a rock. If the caster attempts to send the ball through a narrow passage, such as an arrow slit, the character must hit with a ranged attack roll, or else the bead strikes the barrier and falls to a resting point until detonation.

DETECT CHAOS, EVIL, GOOD, OR LAW, Level 0 Wis
CT 1 **R** 150 ft. x 10 ft. **D** 10 min./lvl.
SV none **SR** none **Comp** V, S, DF

By means of this spell, the caster can sense the presence of a specific alignment aspect (chaos, evil, good or law) in the direction the caster is facing, along a path 150 feet long and 10 feet wide. The caster must spend one round concentrating along the path to detect the alignment aspect, although the caster may both cast the spell and begin detecting in the same round as the spell is cast. Chaos radiates a wave-like aura, whereas law's aura is constant. Good's aura creates pleasurable emotion, whereas evil's aura creates brief irritation and anger in the caster. The strength of each aspect's aura will be revealed as faint, strong, or overwhelming if it is supernatural. The spell can penetrate barriers, but 1 foot of stone, 1 inch of common metal, a thin sheet of lead or 3 feet of wood or dirt blocks it.

DETECT ILLUSION, Level 0 Cha
CT 1 **R** touch **D** 1 tn./lvl.
SV none **SR** none **Comp** V, S

By means of this spell, the caster can detect the presence of illusions in the direction the caster is facing, along a path 50 feet long and 10 feet wide. Unlike detect magic, this spell may be cast on another creature by touch.

The caster must spend one round concentrating along the path to detect any illusion, although the caster may both cast the spell and begin detecting in the same round that the spell is cast. The strength of the illusion detected will be revealed as lingering, faint, moderate, strong or overwhelming. The spell can penetrate barriers, but 1 foot of stone, 1 inch of common metal, a thin sheet of lead or 3 feet of wood or dirt blocks it. Illusory areas, multiple types of illusion or strong illusory emanations may confuse or conceal weaker auras, although the Game Master may allow the caster to spend additional rounds concentrating to decipher the confusion or reveal auras. The Game Master may require an intelligence check to do so.

DETECT MAGIC, Level 0 Cha, 0 Int, 0 Wis
CT 1 **R** 50 ft. x 10 ft. **D** 1 tn./lvl.
SV none **SR** none **Comp** V, S

By means of this spell, the caster can detect the presence of magical auras in the direction the caster is facing, along a path 50 feet long and 10 feet wide. The caster must spend one round concentrating along the path to detect magic, although the caster may both cast the spell and begin detecting in the same round that the spell is cast. The strength of the magic detected will be revealed as lingering, faint, moderate, strong or overwhelming. The spell can penetrate barriers, but 1 foot

of stone, 1 inch of common metal, a thin sheet of lead or 3 feet of wood or dirt blocks it. Outsiders and elementals are not inherently magical, but if they have been conjured, the conjuration spell will be detected.

Magical areas, multiple types of magic or strong local magical emanations may confuse or conceal weaker auras, although the Game Master may allow the caster to spend additional rounds concentrating to decipher the confusion or reveal weaker auras. The Game Master may require a intelligence check to do so.

DETECT NEUTRALITY, Level 0 Wis

CT 1 **R** 150 ft. x 10 ft. **D** 10 min./lvl.
SV none **SR** none **Comp** V, S, Df

By means of this spell, the caster can sense the presence of neutrality in the direction the caster is facing along a path 150 feet long and 10 feet wide. The caster must spend one round concentrating along the path, although the caster may cast the spell and detect in the round the spell is cast. If an additional round is spent concentrating, the spell reveals the type of neutrality, either lawful neutral, neutral good, neutral, neutral evil, or chaotic neutral. The spell can penetrate barriers, but 1 foot of stone, 1 inch of common metal, a thin sheet of lead or 3 feet of wood or dirt blocks it.

DETECT POISON, Level 0 Int, 0 Wis

CT 1 **R** 50 ft. **D** 10 min./lvl.
SV n/a **SR** n/a **Comp** V, S

The caster can determine whether one creature, one object or a 25 foot x 25 foot area has been poisoned or is poisonous. The character can determine the type of poison with a successful wisdom check. The spell can penetrate barriers, but 1 foot of stone, 1 inch of common metal, a thin sheet of lead or 3 feet of wood or dirt blocks it.

DETECT TRAPS, Level 2 Wis

CT 1 **R** 50 ft. x 10 ft. **D** 10 min./lvl.
SV none **SR** none **Comp** V, S

The caster can detect traps, mundane or magical, in the direction the caster is facing, along a path 50 feet long and 10 feet wide. The caster must spend one round concentrating along the path, although the caster may both cast the spell and begin detecting in the same round as the spell is cast. The spell does not detect natural hazards. The spell can penetrate barriers, but 1 foot of stone, 1 inch of common metal, a thin sheet of lead or 3 feet of wood or dirt blocks it.

DETECT SCRYING, Level 4 Int

CT 1 **R** unlimited **D** 1 day
SV none **SR** none **Comp** V, S

When using this spell, the caster immediately becomes aware of any attempt to observe the character by means of clairaudience, clairvoyance, or any other means of scrying, including crystal balls or other magic scrying devices. If the means of scrying is within the area of effect, 150 feet of the caster, the caster immediately gains knowledge of its location.

DETECT SECRET DOORS, Level 1 Wis

CT 1 **R** 60 ft. **D** 1 min./lvl.
SV none **SR** none **Comp** V,S

The caster can use this spell to find secret doors, hidden compartments and other such hidden areas specifically constructed to escape detection. After 1 round of concentration, the presence or absence of secret doors is revealed. After 2 rounds, the number of secret doors and their location are revealed. If the location is out of sight, the spell reveals what direction the secret item is in, but not its location. In subsequent rounds, up to the limit of the spell's duration, mechanisms or triggers for specific secret doors or compartments are revealed. This spell can penetrate barriers, but 1 foot of stone, 1 inch of metal, a thin sheet of lead or 3 feet of wood or dirt blocks the spell.

DETECT SNARES AND PITS, Level 1 Wis

CT 1 **R** 50 ft. x 10 ft. **D** 10 min./lvl.
SV none **SR** none **Comp** V, S

The caster can detect simple pits, deadfalls, snares of wilderness creatures, and primitive traps constructed of natural materials in the direction the caster is facing along a path 50 feet long and 10 feet wide. The caster must spend one round concentrating along the path, although the caster may cast the spell and detect in the round the spell is cast. The spell does not detect complex traps. The spell detects certain natural hazards such as quicksand (registers as a snare), a sinkhole (pit), or unsafe walls of natural rock (deadfall). It does not, however, reveal other potentially dangerous conditions. The spell does not detect magic traps (except those that operate by pit, deadfall or snaring), nor mechanically complex ones, nor those that have been rendered safe or inactive. The spell can penetrate barriers, but 1 foot of stone, 1 inch of common metal, a thin sheet of lead or 3 feet of wood or dirt blocks it.

DETECT THOUGHTS*, Level 2 Cha, 2 Int

CT 1 **R** 50 ft. x 10 ft. **D** 10 min./lvl.
SV none **SR** yes **Comp** V, S, F, DF

The character can detect surface thoughts, and get a general impression of the level of intelligence involved. The caster detects the presence or absence of thoughts (from conscious creatures with intelligence scores of 1 or higher) in the direction the caster is facing, along a path 50 feet long and 10 feet wide. The caster must spend one round concentrating along the path, although the caster may both cast the spell and begin detecting in the same round as the spell is cast. Once thoughts are detected, if the caster concentrates an additional round, the general level of intelligence will be revealed as one of the following: animal, very low, low, average, high, very high, genius, supra-genius, or deific. The spell can

penetrate barriers, but 2 feet of stone or metal, 2 inches of common metal, a thick sheet of lead or 5 feet of wood or dirt blocks it. The reverse of this spell, hide thoughts, obscures a subject's thoughts and counters detect thoughts. The spell's component is a copper piece.

DETECT UNDEAD, Level 0 Cha, 1 Wis

CT 1 **R** 50 ft. x 10 ft. **D** 1 min./lvl.
SV none **SR** none **Comp** V, S, DF

By means of this spell, the caster can detect undead in the direction the caster is facing, along a path 150 feet long and 10 feet wide. The caster must spend one round concentrating along the path, although the caster may cast the spell and detect in the round the spell is cast. The strength of the undead will be revealed as faint (1 HD or less), moderate (2-4 HD), strong (5-10 HD), or overwhelming (11+ HD). The spell can penetrate barriers, but 1 foot of stone, 1 inch of common metal, a thin sheet of lead or 3 feet of wood or dirt blocks it.

DIMENSION DOOR, Level 4 Int

CT 1 **R** 450 ft. **D** instant
SV n/a **SR** n/a **Comp** V

The caster instantly transports from the caster's current location to any other spot within range. The character always arrives at exactly the spot desired whether by simply visualizing the area or by stating direction. After using this spell, the character can't take any other actions until the next round. If the character arrives in a place that is already occupied by a solid body, the character becomes trapped in the astral plane. All that the caster wears and carries is teleported, up to 500 pounds.

DISCERN LIES*, Level 4 Cha, 4 Wis

CT 1 **R** 50 ft. **D** 1 rd./lvl.
SV charisma negates **SR** yes **Comp** V, S, DF

Each round, the caster may concentrate on one subject in range and will instantly know if the subject deliberately speaks a lie. The spell does not reveal the truth, uncover unintentional inaccuracies, or reveal evasions. Each round, the character may concentrate on a different subject. The reverse of this spell, hide lies, obscures the truthfulness of a person.

DISCERN LOCATION*, Level 8 Wis

CT 10 min. **R** unlimited **D** instant
SV none **SR** none **Comp** V, S, DF

With this spell, the caster learns the exact location of a person or object. Discern location circumvents normal means of protection from scrying or location. The spell reveals the exact name and location (community, county, country, continent and plane) where the subject is to be found. To find a creature with the spell, the character must have seen the creature or have some item that once belonged to it. To find an object, the character must have seen or touched the object at least once. The reverse of this spell, hide location, obscures the location of a person or object from detection by spell, crystal ball, or other means of scrying.

DISINTEGRATE, Level 6 Int

CT 1 **R** 150 ft. **D** instant
SV charisma partial **SR** yes **Comp** V, S, M.

A thin green ray springs from the caster's pointing finger, causing the creature or object it strikes to glow and vanish, leaving behind only a trace of fine dust. The ray affects one creature or up to a 10-foot cube of nonliving matter (thus, the spell disintegrates only part of any very large object or structure). The ray affects even magical matter, or energy of a magical nature, but not a globe of invulnerability or an antimagic field. A creature or object that makes a successful charisma save is only partially affected, taking 5d6 points of damage instead of disintegrating. Only one creature or object can be affected, and the ray is not blocked by normal barriers.

DISJUNCTION, Level 9 Cha, 9 Int

CT 1 **R** 50 ft. **D** see below
SV charisma negates (objects) **SR** none **Comp** V

This powerful spell rips asunder all magical effects within the spell's 25 foot x foot area of effect. That is, spells and spell-like effects are separated into their individual components (ending the effect as a dispel magic spell does), and permanent magic items must make successful constitution saves or be turned into normal items. Even artifacts are subject to disjunction, though there is only a 1% chance per caster level of actually affecting such powerful items. If an artifact is destroyed by the spell, the caster must succeed at a charisma save or permanently lose all spell-casting abilities. The abilities cannot be recovered by mortal magic, nor even by a wish. Destroying artifacts is a dangerous business, and it is 95% likely to attract the attention of some powerful being who has an interest in, or connection with, the device. When casting the spell at an antimagic field, the caster has a 1% chance per caster level of destroying it. If the antimagic field survives the disjunction, no items within it are disjoined.

DISMISSAL, Level 4 Cha, 4 Wis

CT 1 **R** 50 ft. **D** instant
SV charisma negates **SR** yes **Comp** V, S, F, DF

This spell forces an extraplanar creature back to its proper plane if the creature fails a charisma saving throw. If the spell is successful, the creature is instantly whisked away. The material component is any item distasteful to the subject.

DISPEL CHAOS, EVIL, GOOD OR LAW, Level 5 Wis

CT 1 **R** touch **D** 1 rd./lvl.
SV none **SR** none **Comp** V, S, DF

Colored energy surrounds the caster, shielding them against creatures of a chosen alignment aspect chaos (blue), evil (white), good (black), or law (red). The caster gains a +4 bonus to armor class against attacks by creatures of the selected aspect, and

with a touch the caster can automatically dispel any one spell cast by them (except those spells that cannot be dispelled by dispel magic). Additionally, the caster may force a summoned, enchanted or extraplanar creature back to its proper plane with a successful touch attack. The creature gets no saving throw, but use of this effect immediately ends the spell.

DISPEL ILLUSION, Level 3 Cha
CT 1 **R** 150 ft. **D** see below
SV none **SR** yes **Comp** V, S

This spell ends ongoing illusions within an area 30 feet x 30 feet x 30 feet, or counters another spell caster's illusion. The caster must make a successful intelligence check against each illusion in the area of effect to succeed. Some illusions, as detailed in their descriptions, can't be defeated by dispel illusion. All illusions in the area of effect are affected. The caster automatically succeeds at the dispel check against any arcanist spell that the character cast, as long as the character is of the same or higher level as when the spell was cast.

DISPEL MAGIC, Level 3 Wis, level 3 sorcerer, 4 Cha
CT 1 **R** 150 ft. **D** see below
SV none **SR** yes **Comp** V, S

This spell ends ongoing spells and spell-like effects that have been cast on a creature or object, temporarily suppresses the magical abilities of a magic item or counters another spell caster's spell within an area 30 feet x 30 feet x 30 feet. The caster must make a successful intelligence check against each spell, effect, object or creature in the area of effect to succeed. Some spells, as detailed in their descriptions, can't be defeated by dispel magic. The effects of spells with instantaneous duration can't be dispelled, because the magic effect is already over before dispel magic can take effect.

All magic within the area of effect is affected. The functioning of magic items is suppressed for 1d4 rounds, but artifacts are unaffected. Interdimensional portals close for a number of rounds equal to the caster's level. A creature or object whose presence is maintained by an ongoing spell, such as a summoned monster, is sent back to whence it came, because the spell that conjured it ends. If an ongoing spell's area overlaps that of the dispel, the effect is ended only within the area of the dispel magic. The caster automatically succeeds at the dispel check against their own spells as long as the character is of the same or higher level as when the spell was cast.

DISTORT REALITY, Level 8 Cha
CT 1 **R** n/a **D** see below
SV see text **SR** see text **Comp** V

This spell is similar to limited wish, but reality is altered through illusion. As with limited wish, the caster must be careful in creating the illusion. The spell may duplicate the effects of any Int-based arcanist spell of 7th level or lower, or any Wis-based spell of 5th level or lower. It may also grant other effects in line with the power of such spells, although any effects must be approved by the Game Master. Duplicated spells allow saving throws and spell resistance as normal, except that all saves will always be against intelligence, not the designated attribute in the spell duplicated.

DIVINATION, Level 4 Wis
CT 10 min. **R** n/a **D** see below
SV n/a **SR** n/a **Comp** V, S, M

This spell provides the caster with a useful piece of advice in reply to a question concerning a specific goal, event or activity that is to occur within 1 week. The advice can be as simple as a short phrase, or it might take the form of a cryptic riddle or omen. The Game Master controls what information the character receives. It should be noted that if the caster's party doesn't act on the information, the conditions may change so that the information is no longer useful. The base chance for a correct divination is 70% + 1% per caster level. The Game Master adjusts the chance if unusual circumstances require it (if, for example, unusual precautions against divination spells have been taken). If the die roll fails, the character knows the spell failed, unless specific magic yielding false information is at work. Multiple divinations about the same topic by the same caster use the same die result as the first divination and yield the same answer each time.

DREAM, Level 5 Cha
CT 1 min. **R** unlimited **D** see text
SV none **SR** yes (h) **Comp** V, S

The caster, or a messenger touched by the caster, sends a phantasmal message to others in the form of a dream. At the beginning of the spell, the caster must name the recipients or identify them by title and in no way leaves any doubt as to their identities. The messenger then enters a trance, appears in the intended recipient's next dream, and delivers the message. The message can be of any length, and the recipient remembers it perfectly upon waking. The communication is one-way: the recipient cannot ask questions or offer information, nor can the messenger gain any information by observing the recipient's dreams. Once the message is delivered, the messenger's mind returns instantly to his or her body. The duration of the spell is the time required for the messenger to enter the recipient's dream and deliver the message.

If the recipient is awake when the spell begins, the messenger can choose to remain in the trance or to awaken (ending the spell). The messenger can remain in the trance until the recipient goes to sleep, then enter the recipient's dream and deliver the message as normal. Creatures who don't sleep or dream cannot be contacted by this spell.

If the messenger is disturbed during the trance, the messenger awakens, and the spell ends. The messenger is unaware of

his or her own surroundings or the activities around him or her while in the trance. The messenger is defenseless, both physically and mentally (always fails any saving throw, for example) while in the trance.

E

EARTHQUAKE, Level 8 Int

CT 10 min. **R** 450 ft. **D** 1 rd.
SV see text **SR** no **Comp** V, S, M, DF

Drawing upon elemental forces, this spell creates an intense but highly localized tremor, within a 50 foot diameter circle, that ripples the ground, knocking creatures down, collapsing structures, and opening gaping fissures. The earthquake affects standing creatures in its area in a variety of ways.

All creatures standing in the area must make a dexterity save or fall down. Even if they remain standing, they suffer a -10 penalty to any actions attempted during the spell's duration, and find it impossible to move at more than half their normal speed, if at all. All spell casters standing in the area find it impossible to cast spells while the earthquake is in effect, and lose any spells they were in the process of casting.

Fissures rip open in the ground without warning, with a 25% chance of opening beneath each creature in the area. Such creatures must make dexterity saves to avoid falling into the fissure, taking 1d6 damage if they fail. The worse threat, however, is that all such fissures grind shut with impossible force at the end of the round, crushing any trapped creatures to death.

The earthquake also has additional effects based on the terrain it effects:

Cave or Tunnel: The roof collapses, dealing 8d6 damage to any creature caught under the cave-in (dexterity save, half).

Cliffs: The cliff crumbles, causing a landslide that travels as far horizontally as it fell vertically. An earthquake cast at the top of a 100 foot cliff would sweep 100 foot outward from the base of the cliff. Any creature in the path of the landslide suffers 8d6 damage (dexterity save, half).

River, Lake, or Marsh: Fissures open underneath the water, draining it away from the area to form a quagmire. Soggy marsh or swampland becomes quicksand for the duration of the spell, sucking down creatures and structures. All creatures in the area must make dexterity saves or sink down in the mud and quicksand. At the end of the spell, the rest of the body of water rushes in to replace the drained water, possibly drowning those caught in the mud.

Structure: Most structures standing on open ground collapse, dealing 8d6 damage to those caught in or beneath the rubble (dexterity save, half).

EMOTION, Level 4 Cha

CT 1 **R** 150 ft. **D** concentration
SV charisma negates **SR** yes **Comp** V, S

This spell induces a powerful emotion in the hearts and minds of the creatures it effects, eclipsing their natural feelings. It effects a 25 foot x 25 foot area.

The caster may choose which emotion to inflict:

Despair: A lack of all hope crushes the targeted creatures' morale. They suffer a -2 penalty to all saves, attacks, attribute checks, ability checks and damage rolls. Despair dispels Hate.

Fear: Fear of the caster grips the hearts of the targeted creatures. They flee as if subject to a fear spell. Fear dispels Rage.

Hate: Fiery hate and bile rise in the targeted creatures. They react poorly to others and may become antagonistic or hostile. They gain a +2 bonus to saves, attacks, attribute checks, ability checks and damage rolls. Hate dispels Despair.

Rage: Sheer blind fury and wrath engulfs the targeted creatures, and they are compelled to fight, heedless of danger. They gain a +2 bonus to strength and constitution scores, and a +1 bonus to saves against fear, but suffer a -1 penalty to armor class. Rage dispels Fear.

ENDURE ELEMENTS, Level 0 Int, 0 Wis

CT 1 **R** person **D** 24 hrs.
SV none **SR** yes **Comp** V, S, DF

Protective magical energies merge with the caster's body, providing protection against natural elements. The subject can withstand extreme temperatures, such as sub-zero or extremely hot temperatures, or other natural effects harmful to a normal person. For example, this spell allows the subject to travel through a snowstorm wearing normal clothing.

ENERGY DRAIN, Level 9 Wis

CT 1 **R** 50 ft. **D** see below
SV constitution negates **SR** yes **Comp** V, S, DF

One of the most hated of all spells, this spell wracks the unfortunate target, draining 2d4 levels of experience. If cast on an undead creature, it gains 2d4 x5 temporary HP for 1 hour.

ENHANCE ATTRIBUTE*, Level 2 Int

CT 1 **R** touch **D** 1 hr./lvl.
SV constitution negates (h) **SR** yes (h) **Comp** V, S, M

This spell temporarily raises one attribute score of the creature touched. The caster selects the attribute to be raised at the time of casting. It can only affect one creature. The spell's effect differs depending upon whether the attribute to be raised is a Prime attribute or non-Prime attribute. The spell raises Prime attributes by 1d4+1 points, but only raises non-Prime attributes by 1d2+1 points. The material component is

a hair or piece from an animal considered strong, dextrous, tough, intelligent, wise, or appealing.

Diminish Attribute is the reverse of this spell. A creature failing a constitution save suffers a loss of 1d4+1 points in a Prime attribute or 1d2+1 points in a non-Prime attribute.

ENTANGLE, Level 2 Wis

CT 1 **R** 450 ft. **D** 1 tn./lvl.
SV dexterity (see text) **SR** no **Comp** V, S, DF

This spell animates all plants in the affected area, causing them to attempt to entertwine about and entangle any creature within, or moving through, their location, holding them fast. A successful dexterity save means that the creature manages to avoid becoming entangled for that particular round. An entangled creature suffers a -2 penalty to attack, a -4 penalty to effective dexterity, and cannot move, making the casting of spells with a somatic component impossible. Breaking free requires a successful strength check. Each round, the plants once again attempt to entangle all creatures who have avoided or escaped entanglement.

ERASE, Level 1 Int, 1 illusion

CT 1 **R** 50 ft. or touch **D** see below
SV n/a **SR** none **Comp** V, S

This spell removes writings of mundane or magical nature. The spell clears as much writing as might be found on a scroll, or up to two pages of parchment. It even removes explosive runes, glyphs of warding and arcane marks, but does not remove symbols or illusory script. Removal of dangerous magical writing such as explosive runes, requires the caster to touch them and make an intelligence check. Failure indicates that the effect of the dangerous writing is triggered as it is erased. Nonmagical writings are automatically erased.

ETHEREAL JAUNT, Level 5 Wis

CT 1 **R** see below **D** 1 rd./lvl.
SV n/a **SR** n/a **Comp** V, S

The energies of this spell allow the caster to enter the ethereal plane, a place which overlaps the material world. The caster may pass through all material objects in the material world without impediment, and may not be seen or interacted with by any mundane means. To the caster, the world appears as a hazy, insubstantial place. If the caster ends the spell, becoming material while inside a material object such as a solid wall, they are shunted off to the nearest open space, taking 1d6 damage per 5 ft. they were shunted. Ethereal travelers should be aware that some predators and other beings make the ethereal plane their home.

EXPLOSIVE RUNES, Level 3 Int

CT 1 tn. **R** touch **D** see text
SV dexterity half (see text) **SR** yes **Comp** V, S

This spell allows the caster to inscribe innocuous-looking runes which detonate when they are read. The spell is used to protect and prevent access to a book, map, scroll, or similar object containing written information. When read, the runes explode causing 6d6 points of damage to the reader. The reader receives no saving throw. Creatures and objects within 10 feet of the blast must make a dexterity saving throw and suffer only half damage if successful. The book or other object upon which the runes are written also takes damage, and may be utterly ruined in the absence of some protection from magical fire.

The caster, along with anyone else the caster chooses to specify, may read the runes without triggering them. The caster can also remove the runes at any time. Otherwise, the runes are permanent until triggered or removed by dispel magic or other counterspell.

F

FAERIE FIRE, Level 1 Cha, 1 Wis

CT 1 **R** 150 ft. **D** 1 tn./lvl.
SV no **SR** yes **Comp** V

This spell outlines creatures or objects with a harmless, pale-colored firein a 10 foot x 10 foot area. The fire is about as bright as a candle, making the things outlined highly visible in darkness. It also outlines invisible subjects and those under such spells as blur. Attackers gain a +1 to hit outlined creatures and objects. All creatures and objects within the area of effect are outlined by the fire.

FAITHFUL HOUND, Level 5 Int, 5 Cha

CT 2 rd. **R** 50 ft. **D** 1 hr./lvl. (see text)
SV n/a **SR** n/a **Comp** V, S, M

Arcane energy forms into a phantom hound dedicated to guarding an area or the caster. The caster may order the hound to do either at any time during the spell's duration. The hound will consider party members as allies unless ordered otherwise. Should a larger creature approach within 50 feet, the hound immediately lets out a frightful and eerie howl. Those hearing the howl must save versus fear or suffer a -2 to attacks and morale. This also effects allies of the caster. If an intruder approaches to within 10 feet of the hound or caster, the guard dog ceases barking and attacks with a vicious bite. The hound's bite is considered a magical weapon, and it attacks once per round. The hound gains a bonus to hit equal to the caster's level, and it deals 2d6+3 damage upon a successful bite. It continues to attack until the intruder retreats at least 25 feet away.

The most effective way to combat the hound is by dispelling it, but it can be hurt by magic and weapons. The hound has an armor class of 18 and as many hit points as the caster did when the spell was cast. If the caster is ever more than 150 feet from the hound, the spell ends. The spell lasts for 1 hour per caster level, but once the hound begins barking, it lasts only 1 round per level.

FALSE TRAP, Level 2 Cha

CT 1 **R** 50 ft. **D** 1 tn./lvl.
SV see below **SR** see below **Comp** V, S, M

To cast false trap the arcanist needs the shattered fragments of a deliberately distorted mirror ($5) placed in a small bowl of water, and a pinch of powdered moonstone ($5) cast into the air. The caster cloaks one object with a shroud of magic, making it appear trapped to any creature seeking to detect traps by mundane means. If the creature attempting to find a trap is of an equal or higher level than the caster of the false trap, the creature gets to make an intelligence check to detect the illusion. Any manipulation or attempt to disarm the trap breaks the spell and dispels the illusion. Magical detection will indicate that there is no trap, possibly causing confusion if visual inspection follows. It effects a 25 foot x 25 foot area.

FALSE VISION, Level 5 Cha

CT 1 **R** 50 ft. **D** 1 tn./ lvl.
SV see below **SR** see below **Comp** V, S, M

To cast false vision the arcanist needs the shattered fragments of a deliberately distorted mirror ($5) placed in a small bowl of water, and a pinch of powdered moonstone ($5) cast into the air. The caster cloaks the area of effect with a shroud of magic, making everything within undetectable to any scrying. Also, if the caster is aware of an attempt to scry, they may concentrate on creating an illusory image with sound effects, which is what the person scrying will see and hear. It affects a 25 foot x 25 foot area.

FEAR, Level 4 Int, 4 Cha

CT 1 **R** 50 ft. **D** 1 rd./lvl.
SV charisma negates **SR** yes **Comp** V, S

Panic and terror race through the hearts of the creatures affected by this spell, causing them to flee from the caster as fast as possible. The creatures cower in abject horror if cornered, and if forced to confront the caster, any effected creature suffers a -2 penalty to all rolls. It effects a 25 foot x 25 foot area.

FEATHER FALL, Level 1 Int

CT 1 **R** 150 ft. **D** 1 rd./lvl.
SV no **SR** yes (h) **Comp** V

Creatures and objects affected by this spell fall gently, drifting downwards through the air much like a feather. Subjects affected by the spell take no damage from a fall of any height. The spell may be cast with the utterance of a single word, making it fast enough to save the caster in case of an unexpected fall of any notable height. A total weight of up to 1500 pounds can be affected. The creatures and objects affected by the spell fall at a rate of 50 feet per round. Should the spell end while they are still falling, they fall normally from that point and take damage only for the distance fallen. The spell works only upon free-falling objects. It does not affect a sword blow or a charging or flying creature. It might have effect upon a ranged weapon or projectile, at the Game Master's discretion. It effects a 20 foot diameter sphere.

FEEBLEMIND, Level 5 Int, 5 Cha

CT 1 **R** 150 ft. **D** see text
SV charisma negates **SR** yes **Comp** V, S

This spell drains the target's higher intellect, reasoning and even base cunning, reducing the target to an intelligence below that of even some animals. Still, even at such low intelligence, the spell's target instinctively recognizes friends, and can follow them and protect them in a very primitive manner. The unfortunate victim remains in this state until a heal, restoration, wish, or equivalent are used to dispel it.

FIND THE PATH*, Level 6 Wis, 8 Cha

CT 3 **R** touch **D** 10 min./lvl.
SV none **SR** yes (h) **Comp** V, S, F

With unerring instinct, the subject of this spell can locate the shortest, most direct physical route to a specified location on the same plane of existence, though this destination must be a location, not an object or creature. The character can even sense the correct direction that will eventually lead to the destination, indicating at the appropriate times the exact path to follow or physical actions to take, enabling the spell's target to escape labyrinths, underground tunnel networks and mazes, magical or mundane. This spell also instantly counters and dispels the maze spell. The material component of the spell is a Y-shaped stick.

The reverse of this spell makes the subject lost, no matter the place being sought. The subject wanders aimlessly, always straying off the path. The subject can be led by someone else, or could even use a map if able to normally do so.

FINGER OF DEATH, Level 7 Int, 8 Wis

CT 1 **R** 50 ft. **D** permanent
SV charisma partial **SR** yes **Comp** V, S

The caster points at one living creature and utters a death curse, instantly killing the creature unless it successfully makes a charisma saving throw. If the creature makes its save, it sustains 3d6 damage +1 point per caster level.

FIREBALL, Level 3 Wis

CT 1 **R** 450 ft. **D** instant
SV dexterity half **SR** yes **Comp** V, S, M

With a gesture, the caster sends a small ball of fire hurtling through the air to detonate with a low roar at the height and distance the caster desires, as long as it is within the spell's maximum range. The explosion fills the area of effect with intense fire and heat, causing 1d6 damage per caster level to all creatures and objects within the area. It ignites combustibles, damages objects and melts anything with a low melting point such as bronze, copper, silver, lead or gold. The explosion creates almost no pressure. It effects a 40 foot diameter sphere. The material component is a small lump of coal.

The fireball follows a straight path, and if it impacts a solid barrier prior to attaining the prescribed range, the impact causes early detonation. If the caster attempts to send the ball through a narrow passage, such as an arrow slit, the character must hit with a ranged attack roll, or else the bead strikes the barrier and detonates prematurely.

FIRE SEEDS, Level 6 Wis

CT 1 per seed **R** see below **D** 1 tn./lvl. or burst
SV dexterity half **SR** yes **Comp** V, S, M, DF

The caster binds elemental fire into acorns or holly berries, making them into weapons that burst into flame upon impact.

Acorns: Up to four acorns may be altered with this spell. Each can be thrown with reasonable accuracy up to 50 feet. A successful roll to hit must be made. Each acorn bursts upon hitting a firm surface, blossoming into flame that deals 4d8 damage and igniting any combustibles.

Holly Berries: Up to eight holly berries may be altered with this spell. They are normally placed by hand, but they can be thrown up to 25 feet. The berries burst into flame if the caster speaks a word of command from within 200 feet. They ignite instantly, and each deals 2d8 damage to any creatures within a 5 foot radius. The explosion will also ignite combustible materials.

FIRE SHIELD, Level 4 Int, 5 Wis

CT 1 **R** see below **D** 1 rd./lvl.
SV none **SR** see text **Comp** V, S, M

Wispy, colorful flame wreathes the caster, surrounding the character like a cloak of fire. The fire may be freezing cold or burning hot, whichever the caster desires. Any creature striking the caster with its body or handheld weapons deals normal damage, but at the same time the attacker takes 1d6 points of damage +1 per caster level due to the intense flames. Spell resistance applies to this damage. Weapons with exceptional reach do not endanger the attacker.

The flame-clad character gives off light like a dim torch, the color of which is selected by the caster (blue or green for a chill shield, violet or reddish-orange for a hot shield). Characters surrounded by a hot shield take only half damage from cold-based attacks, and no damage if the attack allows a save for half damage and the caster succeeds. Chill shields operate exactly the same way, but protect against heat/fire-based attacks.

FIRE STORM, Level 7 Wis

CT 1 R150 ft. **D** instant
SV dexterity half **SR** yes **Comp** V, S

Raging elemental flame fills the area of effect (10 ft. cubes/level), causing 1d6 damage per caster level. The flames do not harm natural vegetation, ground cover, and plant creatures in the area, unless the caster so desires.

FIRE TRAP, Level 2 Wis, 4 Int

CT 10 min. **R** touch **D** until discharged
SV dexterity half **SR** yes **Comp** V, S, M

Set upon any closeable item, a fire trap erupts into flame when anyone other than the caster, or any other caster-selected characters, opens the item that the spell is warding. When triggered, a fiery explosion fills the area within 5 feet of the item (10 foot diameter sphere). The explosion deals 1d4 damage +1 point per caster level. The item remains unharmed by the spell. A knock spell does not prevent the effects of a fire trap in any way. An unsuccessful dispel magic spell will not detonate the spell. To cast the spell the caster

needs fragments of flint and a stick of charcoal, the latter used to draw around the closure, the former scattered over it, this process leaves no visible runes.

FIRST AID, Level 0 Wis
CT 1 **R** touch **D** permanent
SV n/a **SR** yes (h) **Comp** V, S

When the caster lays hands upon a living creature, this minor healing spell magically bandages any wound on the creature's body, preventing further loss of hit points from bleeding. It prevents infection, but cures no damage.

FLAME STRIKE, Level 5 Wis
CT 1 **R** 150 ft. **D** instant
SV dexterity half **SR** yes **Comp** V, S, DF

The caster calls down a roaring, vertical column of divine fire, in an area 10 feet in diameter and 40 feet high, inflicting 1d6 damage per caster level, to anyone caught within it. Half the damage is fire damage; the other half results from divine power and is therefore not subject to being reduced by magic or powers that confer protection from fire.

FLOATING DISK, Level 1 Int
CT 1 **R** 10 ft. **D** 1 hr./lvl.
SV n/a **SR** n/a **Comp** V, S, M

This spell creates a slightly concave, circular plane of shimmering force that follows the caster about and carries equipment, treasure or any other burdon. The disk is 3 feet in diameter, and can bear up to 1000 pounds of weight, or hold up to 2 gallons of fluid. The disk floats 3 feet above the ground at all times, and always remains level, though it may not travel faster than the caster normally walks. When the spell ends or the caster moves more than 50 feet away from the disk, it vanishes, dropping its contents. To cast the spell the caster needs a small glass or metal disk.

FLY, Level 3 Int
CT 1 **R** touch **D** 10 min./lvl.
SV none **SR** yes (h) **Comp** V, S, M

This spell empowers the caster to fly at up to 90 feet per round. The character can ascend at 45 feet per round, or dive at 180 feet per round. This flight feels as natural as walking, enabling the character to fight or cast spells quite normally, though the character cannot bear aloft more weight than a normal maximum load. The material component of the spell is a single feather.

FOG CLOUD, Level 2 Int, 2 Cha
CT 1 **R** 150 ft. **D** 10 min./lvl.
SV none **SR** no **Comp** V, S.

A dense bank of bilious fog billows out from the point the caster designates, obscuring all sight (including special vision abilities) beyond 5 feet, partially concealing creatures within 5 feet, and totally concealing those further away. It covers an area 50 feet x 20 feet x 20 feet. The fog drifts very slowly across the ground, blown by the wind (if any) though it cannot be blown back towards the caster. A strong wind disperses the fog in 4 rounds, and a greater wind will disperse it in 1 round. The heavy vapors produced by this spell always sink to the lowest level of the land, even pouring down openings such as sinkholes.

FREEDOM OF MOVEMENT, Level 4 Wis, 4 Cha
CT 1 **R** touch **D** 10 min./lvl.
SV n/a **SR** yes (h) **Comp** V, S, DF

Whether underwater or moving through some other liquid, or impeded by spells such as hold person or web, the creature affected by this spell can move and attack normally for the spell's duration. No benefits other than free movement are conferred; a character freely moving underwater still needs to find some other means of breathing.

G

GASEOUS FORM , Level 3 Int
CT 1 **R** touch **D** 1 tn./lvl.
SV n/a **SR** yes (h) **Comp** S.

The creature touched and all of the creature's gear becomes insubstantial, appearing as a misty, fog-like form. While in this state, the character cannot be effectively touched or physically interacted with, becoming immune to any attacks that are not magical in nature (such as the strikes of spells and clearly supernatural abilities). The character cannot walk, but can fly at 10 feet per round. The character may also filter through small holes or narrow openings, even mere cracks, with all they were wearing or holding, as long as the spell persists. On the downside, the character gains no AC bonus due to material armor, cannot physically attack or affect others, cannot cast spells, cannot move more rapidly, may be blown about by stiff winds and may not enter water or other liquids. It effects one willing creature.

GATE, Level 9 Int, 9 Wis
CT 2 **R** 50 ft. **D** special
SV none **SR** no **Comp** V, S

A shimmering, mystical gate appears, hovering just above the ground. The gate is an interdimensional portal between the plane the caster is on and another plane of existence. The caster chooses which plane to connect to upon casting the spell, but must have some knowledge of the other plane. The gate can be used in two ways.

First, the gate may be used as a means of travel. Anything or anyone moving through the gate instantly transports to the other plane. The gate is 5 feet in diameter, but the caster can increase the diameter by 1 foot per level. The caster may hold the gate open for no more than 1 round per level, and must concentrate to do so.

Second, the gate may be used to summon an individual creature or type of creature from the plane to which the gate is connected. The caster names the creature individually or a specific creature type upon casting, and the gate opens near the individual or creature. This spell does not give the caster any control over creatures summoned through the gate. The actions of a summoned creature vary depending upon the situation, the caster's motive, alignment and perhaps, additional spells that may be active. Deities and other unique entities are under no compulsion to come through the gate unless they choose to. An uncontrolled being acts as it pleases, often to the detriment of the caster, and may return to its home plane at any time. When used in this manner, the gate remains open only until the summoned creature(s) passes through the gate. Neither the caster nor anyone or anything on the caster's plane may enter the gate.

Typically, the caster will ask a summoned creature to perform a service. It is easier to gain service from creatures weaker than the caster. Deities and beings with a strong will are often ill-disposed toward the caster for interfering with their life's activities.

Even if a service is given, the creature may return to its home plane at any time, at will, whether the service is completed or not, unless the caster has used some other spell to bind the creature and force servitude. Contractual service is entirely more involved, but more likely beneficial for the caster, because the summoned creature is less likely to be ill disposed towards its summoner when some form of recompense is offered. The negotiation of a contract must be roleplayed, bearing in mind the nature of the creature, its desires, and its intellect; few such creatures have any need for gold or coin, and their desires may seem alien at best, or utterly vile. Some creatures may attempt to subvert their contract, especially if they feel they have been tricked or treated poorly, interpreting a contract in ways that will hopefully cause the caster distress or peril.

Failure to fulfill a contract on the caster's part can have terrible consequences. A creature, its liege, or master may all attempt to enact some measure of revenge at some time. Or, if the caster violates his alignment or code, or fails to uphold a sworn oath, the caster's deity may impose some penalty or dishonor.

GEAS, Level 6 Int, 6 Wis, 6 Cha
CT 1 **R** 10 ft. **D** see text
SV Cha negates **SR** yes **Comp** V, DF

"Do as I desire or suffer the consequences" is the essence of this spell. The caster places a magical command on the spell's target to carry out some quest or service, or to refrain from some activity or course of action. If the geased individual fails to do as instructed, they sicken and most likely die. A geas must be carefully worded by the caster, or it may lead to a quest with a goal not intended, or the spell may simply fail altogether. The caster of the geas may release the effected creature from it at any time.

Although a geas can command almost any course of activity, it cannot compel a creature to commit suicide or perform acts that would result in certain death. The creature affected

must be able to understand the caster's command, or the spell fails. A geased creature is bound with the spell until the task is completed, no matter how long it takes, but if the instructions involve an open-ended task that the character cannot complete through its own actions, the spell ends after one day.

If a creature ignores the geas, or is prevented from obeying it, they suffer consequences. A creature will lose 1 point of strength and suffer a 1 penalty to all saving throws for every day during which the quest is not undertaken. If they again take up the quest, the penalties cease. If a creature ignores a quest for 5 days in a row, they must make a constitution save or sicken. A sickened character moves at half normal speed, suffers -4 penalty on constitution and dexterity, heals no damage naturally, and cannot benefit from magical healing. A sickened character must also again make a constitution save after a number of days have passed equal to the creature's normal constitution score. Failure means the creature is disabled, unable to move or act beyond a crawl. All of these effects end 1 day after the character deliberately attempts to resume the quest.

A geas and its effects can be removed magically by remove curse (but only if the caster of the remove curse is at least two levels higher than the level of the character who cast the geas , and the caster of the remove curse makes a successful charisma check), or a wish. Dispel magic does not affect a geas.

GHOST SOUND, Level 0 Int, 0 Cha

CT 1 **R** 150 ft. **D** 1 rd./lvl.
SV intelligence negates **SR** yes **Comp** V, S, M

Eerie rattles and wails, wolfish howls, warm laughter, quiet conversation, the rumble of thunder and clash of swords, the soft patter of bare feet; all these are sounds that can be created with this spell, sounds that can seem to rise, recede, approach or remain constant as the caster desires. Virtually any type of sound can be produced, emanating from anywhere within range, though the volume cannot exceed as much noise as four normal humans could produce. Small pieces of earwax are needed to cast this spell.

GLOBE OF INVULNERABILITY, Level 6 Int

CT 1 **R** personal **D** 1 rd./lvl.
SV none **SR** no **Comp** V, S, M

When this spell is cast, a faintly shimmering 10 foot diameter sphere of arcane energy surrounds the caster. The globe acts as an impenetrable field against any 1st, 2nd, 3rd, or 4th level spell, spell-like ability or spell-like effect, even if the globe is located within the areas eaffected by such spells. Spells and effects targeting or encompassing the globe are not dispelled, but wash harmlessly against and over it. Anyone in the globe, however, may cast spells in, through or outside of the globe. Spells of 5th level and higher are not affected by the globe, and the globe can be brought down by dispel magic. The globe moves with the caster. The caster needs a small, clear bead or sphere and a tiny glass sphere (2sp) to cast the spell.

GLYPH OF WARDING, Level 3 Int

CT 10 min. **R** touch **D** until discharge
SV see text **SR** yes (to effect) **Comp** V, S, M

To cast a glyph of warding, the caster inscribes an area or object with an invisible inscription that harms those who enter, pass, open the warded area or object, or otherwise break the conditions of the ward set by the caster. It can encompass an area up to 25 feet x 25 feet. An ounce of oil ($1) mixed with incense ($5) and a powdered gemstone of color appropriate to the caster's deity ($20) is needed to activate the spell. Glyphs can be set to permit or ward against a specific individual or individuals, or even entire species or groups of species. They can be set only to admit characters of certain faiths or alignments, or carrying certain items, wearing certain garments, colors, or signs or uttering certain passwords. Any creature violating the warded area is subject to its magic.

Glyphs respond to invisible creatures normally, but can be fooled by polymorph and nondetection spells, and they are not triggered by those who travel past them ethereally. Multiple glyphs cannot be cast on the same area or object, although more than one glyphed object may be placed in close proximity. A glyph can be made to conform to any shape, up to the limitations of the spell's area.

Read magic permits a character to see a glyph, and a successful intelligence check allows the same character to identify the glyph. Identifying the glyph does not discharge it and allows the character to know the basic nature of the glyph. Glyphs are affected by dispel magic. Depending on the version selected, a glyph either blasts the intruder or activates a spell:

Blast Glyph: This glyph causes 1d4 damage per caster level to the intruder and all within 5 feet of the intruder. A successful Wis save reduces damage by one-half. Damage may be either from acid, cold, electricity, fire, or sonic, as determined by caster. Because the damage is entirely divine, however, the type of damaging agent has no secondary effect.

Spell Glyph: Stores any single spell of up to 3rd level that the caster knows. The spell must be cast as part of the process of inscribing the glyph. When it is violated, the spell operates as if the caster cast it at that time, allowing normal saves as per the spell.

GREATER RESTORATION, Level 7 Wis

CT 1 hour **R** touch **D** permanent
SV see text **SR** yes (h) **Comp** V, S, DF

This spell cures the draining touch of the undead as well as many other deleterious effects. Greater restoration dispels all effects reducing or penalizing a character's abilities, cures all temporary and permanently drained attribute scores, and

also removes all forms of insanity, confusion, feeblemind or similar mental effects. Even more potently, it restores all levels previously drained (and all class benefits such as hit points and abilities) by undead. Drained levels can only be restored if this spell is cast no more than 1 week per caster level after the drain. It does not restore levels or constitution points lost as a result of death.

GREATER SCRYING, Level 7 Int, 7 Wis

CT 1tn **R** see below **D** 1 tn/lvl.
SV none **SR** no **Comp** V, S, M, F

Focusing on a mental image of the person they wish to observe, the caster sends their mind's eye to gaze over the character, watching and listening regardless of distance. Astute characters (intelligence 13+) may, upon a successful intelligence check, get the feeling they are being watched. Successfully focusing the mind's eye in this manner is difficult, and requires an intelligence check adjusted by the following cumulative modifiers:

Caster knows the character well:	+5
Caster has only met the character:	-5
Caster has only heard of the character:	-10
Caster has no knowledge of character:	-15
Caster has likeness of character:	+5
Caster has possession of the character:	+5
Caster has body part (like a lock of hair):	+5
Character is on another plane:	-15

If the scrying is successful, the caster may cast the following spells through the scrying: comprehend languages, detect chaos, detect evil, detect good, detect law, detect magic, message, read magic, tongues. The material component is a $100 gem.

GREATER SHADOW CONJURATION, Level 5 Cha

CT 1 **R** 150 ft. **D** 1 rd/lvl
SV intelligence (see text) **SR** no **Comp** V, S

The caster shapes quasi-real illusions, resembling monsters, that can attack the caster's foes. The shadow conjurations remain semi-solid, even to those who disbelieve them. The caster can create one or more illusions whose total HD are equal to the caster's level. The caster chooses what form the illusions take, be they lion, tiger, bear, Nazi or flying pugilistey, but size is restricted to medium or small. The shadow creatures have only 40% of the normal or maximum hit points of a creature of the chosen type.

Characters interacting with these illusions believe them to be real creatures, unless they make a successful intelligence save. If the saving throw fails, the creatures deal normal damage and have all the normal abilities and weaknesses of a creature of that type. If the saving throw succeeds, the creatures' special abilities, armor class, damage and all other aspects will be only 40% as strong as the real thing. Those who succeed at their saves see the conjurations as transparent images superimposed on vague, shadowy forms.

GREATER SHADOW EVOCATION, Level 6 Cha

CT 1 **R** special **D** special
SV Int (see text) **SR** yes **Comp** V, S

The caster creates a quasi-real illusion, one possessed of some substance and reality, that mimics one of the following spells: cloudkill, cone of cold, fireball, ice storm, lightning bolt, Arcane Bolt, stinking cloud, wall of fire, wall of force, wall of ice, wall of iron, wall of stone, or web. The mimicked spell has its full normal effect, range, duration, saving throw allowances, SR, and so on, unless the targeted creature(s) makes an Int saving throw. A successful saving throw reduces the mimicked spell to 40% of its normal damage, effect and strength.

GUARDS AND WARDS, Level 6 Int, 5 Cha

CT 30 min. **R** special **D** 1 hr./lvl.
SV see text **SR** see text **Comp** V, S, M

This mighty spell is a useful tool in the defense of towers, strongholds, and other dwellings. The caster must be somewhere within the area being warded to cast the spell. A strand of giant spider's silk ($2), an ounce of fine wine $1, a small decorated silver key $2 and a page of fine parchment to be lit (10 cents) a re the material components needed to cast the spell. The spell radiates out and away from the caster in a 20 foot/level diameter sphere, creating the effects detailed below within the building. The whole warded area radiates magic with incredible intensity. A dispel magic cast on a specific effect, if successful, removes only that effect. A successful disjunction destroys the entire guards and wards spell.

Any creature facing a choice in direction, such as a corridor intersection or side passage, becomes subject to a minor confusion-type effect, making it 50% likely that they will believe they are going in the exact opposite direction from the one they actually chose. SR: Yes.

All corridors within the area of the spell fill with an eerie fog, obscuring all sight, including darkvision, beyond 5 feet A creature within 5 feet has one-half concealment; creatures farther away have full concealment. SR: No.

All doors are subjected to the lock spell (see knock). SR: No.

One door per caster level is covered by an illusion to appear as if it were a plain wall, and may only be detected through with a intelligence (disbelief) save. SR: No.

Webs fill all stairs from top to bottom, the strands identical to those of the web spell, except that they regrow in 10 minutes if they are burned or torn away while the guards and wards spell is in effect. SR: Yes.

The caster may also select one of the following:

A gust of wind in one corridor or room. SR: No.

A magic mouth in two places. SR: No.

A stinking cloud in two places. The vapors appear and linger in the places the caster designates; they return within 10 minutes if dispersed by wind while the guards and wards spell lasts. SR: Yes.

A suggestion in one place. The caster selects a 10 x 10 ft area (or less), and any creature who enters or passes through the area receives the suggestion mentally. SR: Yes.

Dancing lights in four corridors. The character can designate a simple routine that the lights will repeat for as long as the guards and wards spell lasts. SR: No.

GUST OF WIND, Level 3 Int

CT 1 **R** 150 ft. **D** 1 rd.
SV strength negates **SR** no **Comp** V, S.

A powerful, howling blast of air originates from the caster in the direction they are facing, and extending out to 10 feet high and 10 feet wide. This gust automatically extinguishes candles, torches, and similar small unprotected flames; it fans larger flames such as bonfires; it scatters any small, light items such as a wind ordinarily would; and it causes protected flames, such as those of lanterns, to dance wildly, with a 50% chance that they too will be extinguished. Small-sized flying creatures must make a strength save to avoid being blown wildly out of control by the spell, while small and medium-sized landborne creatures, as well as medium-sized flying creatures, must make a strength save to successfully continue moving normally.

H

HALLOW*, Level 4 Wis

CT one day **R** touch **D** one year
SV none **SR** see text **Comp** V, S, M, DF

This spell sanctifies a large 150 foot radius area of a holy site. The caster must have religious trappings worth $100 to cast the spell. The spell has four effects.

First, the entire area operates as a magic circle against evil (or good, chaos or law, as chosen by the caster). All warded creatures in the area receive a +2 bonus to armor class and saves against attacks by creatures of the selected alignment. Likewise, the spell blocks any attempt to possess or mentally control a warded creature, and prevents bodily contact by summoned or conjured creatures. The protection against contact by summoned or conjured creatures ends if a warded individual makes an attack against such a creature. Spell resistance can allow a summoned creature to overcome this protection and touch the warded creature. These effects are not cumulative with protection from evil.

Second, all attempts to turn undead gain a +3 bonus. Attempts to command undead suffer a -3 penalty.

Third, any dead body interred in a hallowed site cannot be turned into an undead creature.

Fourth, the character may choose to affix a single spell effect to the hallowed site. The character must cast the spell when casting hallow. The spell effect lasts for one year and functions throughout the entire consecrated site, regardless of its normal duration and area of effect. The caster may designate whether the effects apply to all creatures, or only to creatures who share the character's faith or alignment. At the end of the year, the chosen effect lapses, but it can be renewed or replaced simply by casting hallow again. Spell effects that may be tied to a hallowed site include aid, bless, cause fear, detect evil (good, chaos, law), detect magic, dispel magic, endure elements, freedom of movement, protection from elements, remove fear, resist elements, silence and tongues.

The reverse of this spell, unhallow, provides the above effects, but against good creatures. Any dead body buried in an unhallowed area, however, will rise as a zombie in 24 hours.

HALLUCINATORY TERRAIN, Level 3 Int, 3 Cha

CT 10 min. **R** 150 ft. **D** see text
SV intelligence **SR** no **Comp** V, S, M

The caster makes natural terrain look, sound and smell like some other sort of natural terrain. Structures, equipment and creatures within the area are not hidden or changed in appearance. The illusion persists until dispelled or disbelieved by an intelligent creature. It effects a 10 foot x 10 foot area per level of the caster.

HASTE*, Level 3 Int

CT 1 **R** 50 ft. **D** 1 rd./lvl.
SV constitution (h) see text **SR** yes (h) **Comp** V, S, M

Haste is a powerful but dangerous magic that is usually cast in times of great desperation. Haste affects one creature. Haste doubles the affected creature's movement rate and number of attacks per round. Neither spell casting nor other actions are accelerated. A creature affected by haste ages one year, and assumes the risk of permanent bodily damage from the strain of the spell. At the end of the spell's duration, an affected creature must make a successful constitution saving throw or lose 1 hit point permanently.

Slow is the reverse of *haste*. It reduces by 1/2 a creature's movement and number of attacks per round. A creature affected by slow suffers no aging or other bodily strain. Haste dispels and counters slow, and vice-versa.

HEAL*, LEVEL 6 WIS
CT 1 **R** touch **D** permanent
SV none **SR** yes (h) **COMP** V, S, DF.

This powerful curative enables the caster to wipe away disease and injury. It completely cures all hit point damage, all diseases, blindness, deafness and all temporary ability damage. It neutralizes poisons in the subject's system, so that no additional damage or effects are suffered. It nullifies a feeblemind spell. It cures mental disorders caused by nature, spell, or injury to the brain. Heal does not remove negative levels, restore permanently drained levels, or restore permanently drained ability scores. If used against an undead creature, heal acts as its reverse, harm.

Harm drains the target of all but 4 hit points and causes disease in the subject (see remove disease). If used against an undead creature, harm acts like heal.

HEALING CIRCLE, LEVEL 4 WIS
CT 1 **R** see below **D** permanent
SV see text **SR** yes (h) **COMP** V, S

This spell releases waves of energy in all directions from the caster, up to a 20 foot radius sphere, curing 2d8 points of damage to all living creatures in the area of effect, including allies and enemies. The curative version of this spell deals the same damage to undead, while the reverse, harming circle, deals damage to living creatures. In those situations, a successful wisdom save indicates half damage. Harming circle heals undead creatures.

HEAT METAL*, LEVEL 2 WIS
CT 1 **R** 50 ft. **D** 7 rd.
SV none **SR** no **COMP** V, S

This spell raises the temperature of metal items, such as weapons and armor, while its reverse, chill metal, lowers the temperature. Magical metal items are not affected. The spell affects the equipment of one creature per every two caster levels and the creatures can be no more than 25 feet apart, or it affects 25 pounds of metal per level (not held or worn by a creature).

This spell lasts for 7 rounds. On the first and seventh round of the spell, the metal becomes warm or chilly, and uncomfortable to touch but deals no damage. During the second and sixth rounds, burning heat or icy coldness causes pain and 1d4 damage. In the third, fourth and fifth rounds, the metal is searing hot or freezing cold, causing disabling pain and 2d4 damage per round. The disabling pain results in the hands and/or body becoming totally disabled for a number of days equal to the creature's constitution divided by 4.

Any heat or cold intense enough to damage the creature negates heat or cold damage from this spell (and vice versa) on a point-for-point basis. Underwater, heat metal deals half damage and boils the surrounding water, and chill metal deals no damage, but ice immediately forms around the affected metal, making it more buoyant.

HOLD MONSTER, LEVEL 5 INT
CT 1 **R** 50 ft. **D** 1 rd./lvl.
SV wisdom negates **SR** yes **COMP** V, S, M

This spell holds a single, non-human, creature rigidly in place. It is aware and breathes normally but cannot take any physical action. It can, however, execute purely mental actions. This spell can affect any monster or animal, be it living, undead, constructed or magical in nature.

HOLD PERSON, LEVEL 3 INT
CT 1 **R** 50 ft. **D** 1 rd./lvl
SV wisdom negates **SR** yes **COMP** V, S, M

This spell holds a single medium-sized or less humanoid target rigidly in place. It is aware and breathes normally but cannot take any physical action. It can, however, execute purely mental actions.

HOLD PERSON OR ANIMAL, LEVEL 2 WIS
CT 1 **R** 50 ft. **D** 1 rd./lvl
SV wisdom negates **SR** yes **COMP** V, S, M

This spell holds a single medium-sized or less human or animal target rigidly in place. It is aware and breathes normally but cannot take any physical action. It can, however, execute purely mental actions.

HOLD PORTAL, LEVEL 1 INT
CT 1 **R** 50 ft. **D** see below
SV n/a **SR** n/a **COMP** V, S

This spell magically bars a door, gate, window, shutter of wood, metal or stone. The magic holds the portal fast, just as if it were securely closed and normally locked. A knock spell or a successful dispel magic can negate the hold portal. Portals held shut by this spell can still be battered down.

HOLY AURA, LEVEL 8 WIS
CT 1 **R** see below **D** 1 rnd/lvl.
SV see text **SR** yes (h) **COMP** V, S, DF

A divine radiance surrounds all good-aligned subjects in the radius (one creature/level in a 25 foot radius), protecting them from attacks, granting them resistance to spells cast by creatures, and blinding evil creatures when they strike the subjects. The warded creatures gain a +4 bonus to armor class and saves, and a SR of 16 against evil spells and spells cast by evil creatures. The spell also blocks possession and mental influence just as protection from evil does. Finally, if an evil creature succeeds at a melee attack against a warded creature, the offending attacker is blinded unless they make an intelligence save (see remove blindness).

HOLY WORD*, Level 7 Wis
CT 1 **R** see below **D** permanent
SV none **SR** yes **Comp** V

A powerful arcanist uttering a holy word (good) or unholy word (evil) speaks with the voice of their deity. The spell instantly banishes extraplanar creatures within a 25 foot radius area to their home planes. Creatures so banished cannot return for at least 1 day. This effect takes place regardless of whether the creatures hear the holy word. Additionally, creatures in the area of effect who hear the holy word and are not good suffer the following effects:

Level or HD	Effect
12 or more	Deafened
Less than 12	Blinded, deafened
Less than 8	Paralyzed, blinded, deafened
Less than 4	Killed, paralyzed, blinded, deafened

Deafness lasts 1d4 rounds. Blindness lasts 2d4 rounds. Paralyzation lasts 1d10 minutes with the subject unable to move or act in any way. Killed means that living creatures instantly die (undead are destroyed).

HYPNOTIC PATTERN, Level 2 Cha
CT 1 **R** 50 ft. **D** concentration
SV intelligence negates **SR** yes **Comp** S

The caster creates a pattern of shifting and weaving colors, fascinating creatures who see it. The spell effects a 25 foot x 25 foot area. Effected creatures gaze at the lights, doing nothing and heedless of all else. Each creature in the area gets an intelligence save to avoid the spell's effect, but the caster can affect no more than 2d4 +1 HD per caster level of creatures. Creatures with fewer HD are affected first. The caster need not utter a sound to cast this spell, but must gesture and concentrate to maintain the weaving pattern of lights. Sightless creatures are not affected.

HYPNOTISM, Level 1 Cha
CT 1 **R** 25 ft. **D** 1d2 rnd+1 rnd/lvl.
SV intelligence negates **SR** yes **Comp** V, S

The caster gestures and utters a droning incantation which causes nearby creatures to stop and stare blankly at the character. The caster can use this rapt attention to make suggestions and requests seem quite plausible. The spell affects 2d4 HD of creatures in a 25 foot x 25 foot area. Creatures with fewer HD are affected first. Only creatures that can see or hear the character are affected. Hypnosis can succeed regardless of whether or not the target creatures can comprehend the caster's speech.

Hypnotized creatures cannot move or act, though they can be "snapped out of it" if attacked or disturbed in any way. Hypnotized creatures will not remember being entranced. Hypnosis will not succeed in the thick of combat or other dangerous situations.

While the subject is hypnotized, the caster can make a suggestion or request. The suggestion must be brief and reasonable. Each suggestion takes one round to communicate. If the suggestion is reasonable, it can influence the subject's actions, according to the discretion of the Game Master. The Game Master may allow additional intelligence saves for the subject if the suggestion is less than reasonable. Even once the spell ends, an affected creature retains its new attitude toward the caster, but only with respect to a particular suggestion.

I

ICE STORM, Level 4 Int, 5 Wis
CT 1 **R** 150 ft. **D** see below
SV none **SR** yes **Comp** V, S, M

This spell causes snow and hailstones to pound the area of effect, a 50 foot diameter cylinder that is 50 feet tall. The storm inflicts 5d6 points of damage to anything in the area. It also reduces subsequent movement in the area by half, for 1 round per caster level. The spell caster needs a small drop of water to cast the spell.

IDENTIFY, Level 1 Int, 1 Cha
CT 10 min. **R** 5 ft. **D** 1 rd./lvl.
SV none **SR** no **Comp** V, S, M

This spell reveals a single function of one magic item for each round it is in effect. The most basic functions are revealed first, including how to activate that function or the item, and how many charges remain. For a weapon, this will be the plus to attack and damage. If a magic item has multiple different functions that are equally basic, the Game Master determines which is first identified. Multiple castings of this spell may be cast at the same time, taking 10 minutes per spell. After casting this spell, the caster becomes exhausted, and loses 1d4 points of constitution. After resting for 1 hour per each separate spell cast, constitution is returned to normal. The caster needs materials valued at $100 to cast the spell. In a pulp setting, the Legend Lore class ability often can make this spell unnecessary.

ILLUSORY SCRIPT, Level 3 Cha
CT 1 min. **R** touch **D** permanent
SV see text **SR** no **Comp** V, S, M

This spell writes instructions or other information on any suitable writing material. The script appears to be some form of foreign or magic writing. Only the person (or people) designated by the character at the time of the casting are able to read the writing. The script is completely unintelligible to any other character, although an arcanist will recognize it as illusory script.

Any unauthorized creature attempting to read the script triggers a potent illusory effect and must make an intelligence saving throw, or become subject to a suggestion implanted in the script by the caster. The suggestion lasts only 30 minutes.

If successfully dispelled by dispel magic, the illusory script and its secret message disappear. The hidden message can be read by a combination of the true seeing spell with the read magic or comprehend languages spell. The casting time depends on the length of the message written, but it is always at least 1 turn (1 minute). To cast the spell the caster needs special ink valued at $5.

ILLUSORY WALL, Level 4 Cha

CT 1 tn. **R** 50 ft. **D** permanent
SV intelligence (if disbelieve) **SR** no **Comp** V, S.

This spell creates the illusion of a wall, floor, ceiling or similar surface. It appears absolutely real when viewed, but physical objects can pass through it without difficulty. When the spell is used to hide pits, traps or normal doors, any detection abilities that do not require sight work normally. Touching or probing the surface reveals its illusory nature, though that does not cause the illusion to disappear. It effects an area 10 feet x 10 feet x 1 foot.

IMPRISONMENT, Level 9 Int, 9 Cha

CT 1 **R** touch **D** permanent
SV none **SR** yes **Comp** V, S

This spell requires a successful touch attack to affect the target who is then entombed, in a state of suspended animation in a small sphere, far beneath the surface of the earth. For the victim, time ceases to flow. The creature does not grow older, its body functions virtually cease and no force or effect can harm it. Most divinations will not reveal the creature but discern location does. The subject remains entombed unless the reverse of this spell, freedom, is cast where the imprisonment took place. A wish spell will not free a creature but will reveal where it is entombed. The imprisonment spell functions only if the target's name and some facts about its life are known.

IMPROVED INVISIBILITY, Level 4 Cha

CT 1 **R** touch **D** 1 tn + 1 rd./lvl.
SV none **SR** yes **Comp** V, S.

The recipient (and his or her gear) vanishes from sight for the duration of the spell. Unlike other forms of invisibility, improve invisibility allows the recipient to attack, cast spells or use magic items offensively without causing the spell to end. The invisibility is effective against all forms of natural vision. Items dropped or put down by an invisible creature become visible; items picked up disappear if tucked into the clothing or pouches worn by the creature. Light, however, never becomes invisible, although a source of light can become so (thus, the effect is that of a light with no visible source). Any part of an item that the subject carries but that extends more than 10 feet from it becomes visible. The subject is not silenced and noise can render the recipient detectable, as can other common-sense factors (e.g. stepping in a puddle).

INCENDIARY CLOUD, Level 8 Wis

CT 1 **R** 150 ft. **D** 1 rd./2 lvl.
SV dexterity halves **SR** yes **Comp** V, S

This spell creates a cloud of roiling smoke shot through with white-hot embers. The smoke obscures all sight, including special visions, beyond 5 feet. A creature within 5 feet has one-half concealment; creatures farther away have total concealment. The spell effects an area 20 feet high by 30 feet and 30 feet thick.

In addition, the white-hot embers within the cloud deal 3d6 points of fire damage each round (half damage on a successful dexterity save). A moderate wind (11+ mph) disperses the smoke in 4 rounds; a strong wind (21+ mph) disperses the smoke in 1 round. The spell does not function underwater.

INFLUENCE, Level 0 Cha

CT 1 **R** 25 ft. **D** 3 rd.
SV charisma negates **SR** yes **Comp** V,S

This minor charm makes one medium-size or smaller humanoid regard the caster as a trusted friend and ally. It lasts for three rounds (during which time another spell is often cast to gain better advantage of the charm's effect). If the target is being threatened or attacked by the caster or the caster's allies at the time of casting, the target receives a +5 bonus to its saving throw. The spell does not enable the caster to control the charmed creature as if it were an automaton, but the subject perceives the caster's words and actions in the most favorable way. The caster can try to give the subject orders, but must succeed at a charisma check to convince it to do anything it wouldn't ordinarily do. Any act by the caster or the caster's apparent allies that threatens the influenced creature breaks the spell. Note also that the caster must speak the creature's language to communicate commands.

INSANITY, Level 7 Cha

CT 1 **R** 50 ft. **D** permanent
SV intelligence negates **SR** yes **Comp** V, S

This spell causes a creature to permanently lose its mind, becoming unstable and unpredictable. Creatures affected by this spell will behave randomly. Possible behavior includes, but is not limited to, wandering away, staring blankly into the distance, babbling incoherently, suffering paranoia, or even acting normally, although any of these behaviors may last anywhere from 1 round to several days or years. Attackers are not at any special advantage when attacking stricken creatures. Any creature who is attacked automatically returns the attack on its next turn. Remove curse does not remove insanity. Heal, limited wish, distort reality, and wish can restore the creature.

INSECT PLAGUE, Level 5 Wis

CT 1 **R** 450 ft. **D** 1 tn./lvl.
SV see text **SR** no **Comp** V, S, DF

A horde of insects swarm forth from the spell's point of origin, in a 180 foot diameter thick cloud. The insects limit vision

to 10 feet, and spell casting within the cloud is impossible. Creatures inside the insect plague, regardless of AC, sustain 1 point of damage at the end of each round they remain within it. All creatures with 2 or fewer HD are driven from the cloud at their fastest possible speed in a random direction, and flee until they are at least 100 feet away from the insects. Creatures with 3 to 5 HD flee as well, unless they succeed at a charisma saving throw.

The horde of insects does not move from the targeted area of effect. Heavy smoke or fire drives the insects away, but single torch is ineffective against the horde. Lightning, cold, and ice are ineffective, but a strong wind (21+ mph), that covers the entire plague area, disperses the insects and ends the spell.

INSTANT SUMMONS, Level 7 Int

CT 1 tn. **R** n/a **D** n/a
SV none **SR** yes **Comp** V, S, M

This spell allows the caster to summon a pre-prepared item from virtually any location directly to the caster's hand. The item must be a single item weighing no more than 10 pounds, and it cannot be over 6 feet in length, width, or depth unless it is the caster's personal staff. The caster places a personal mark on the item, and casts the spell on a gem worth at least $250, which magically and invisibly inscribes the name of the item on the gem. Thereafter, the character can summon the item by speaking a special word set by the character when the spell is cast, and crushing the gem. The item appears instantly in the caster's hand. Only the original caster can use the gem in this way. If the item is in the possession of another creature, the spell does not work, but the caster immediately knows who the possessor is, and roughly where he, she, or it is located when the summons is cast. The item can be summoned from another plane, but only if no other creature has claimed ownership of it.

INVISIBILITY, Level 2 Int, 2 Cha

CT 1 **R** touch **D** permanent
SV none **SR** yes **Comp** V, S, M

The recipient of this spell (and all of his or her gear) vanishes from all forms of natural sight, including special visions. Items dropped or put down by an invisible creature become visible; items picked up disappear if tucked into the clothing or pouches worn by the creature. Light, however, never becomes invisible, although a source of light can become so (thus, the effect is that of a light with no visible source). Any part of an item that the subject carries but that extends more than 10 feet from it becomes visible, such as a trailing rope.

The spell ends if the subject attacks any creature. For purposes of this spell, attacks include any spell that can inflict damage upon or otherwise negatively impact a creature, or any similarly targeted action undertaken with a magical item, such as a wand, ring, or scroll. Note that spells specifically affecting allies but not foes are not attacked for this purpose, even when they include foes in their area.

An eye wrapped in tar. clay or the like is the only component used for this spell.

INVISIBILITY SPHERE, Level 3 Int, 3 Cha

CT 1 **R** see below **D** 1 tn./lvl.
SV none **SR** yes **Comp** V, S, M

All creatures (including carried gear) within 10 feet of the recipient vanish from all forms of natural sight, including special visions. Items dropped or put down by an invisible creature become visible; items picked up disappear if tucked into the clothing or pouches worn by the creature. Light, however, never becomes invisible, although a source of light can become so (thus, the effect is that of a light with no visible source). Any part of an item that the subject carries but that extends more than 10 feet from it becomes visible, such as a trailing rope.

For each subject, the invisibility ends if the subject attacks any creature. For purposes of this spell, attacks include any spell that can inflict damage upon or otherwise negatively impact a creature, or any similarly targeted action undertaken with a magical item, such as a wand, ring or scroll. Note that spells specifically affecting allies but not foes are not attacks for this purpose, even when they include foes in they area.

Those affected by this spell cannot see each other or themselves. Any affected creature moving out of the area becomes visible, but creatures moving into the area after the spell is cast do not become invisible.

An eye wrapped in tar. clay or the like is the only component used for this spell.

INVISIBILITY TO UNDEAD, Level 1 Wis

CT 1 **R** touch **D** 10 min./lvl.
SV none (See text) **SR** yes **Comp** S, DF

This spell completely shields the recipient from all perception by undead creatures. Nonintelligent undead are automatically affected and act as though the warded creature is not present. Intelligent undead are entitled to an intelligence saving throw. Failure indicates that they cannot perceive the warded creature, but if intelligent undead creatures have reason to believe unseen opponents are present, it can attempt to find or strike it despite failure of the save. If a warded character attempts to turn or command undead, touches an undead, or attacks any creature (even with a spell), the spell ends.

IRONWOOD, Level 6 Wis

CT 10 min. + 1 min./lb. **R** touch **D** permanent
SV none **SR** no **Comp** V, S, M

By using this spell, the caster makes normal wood into magical wood that is as strong, heavy and resistant to fire as steel. Spells that affect metal or iron do not function on ironwood. Spells that affect wood do affect ironwood, although ironwood does not burn. Using this spell, the character can fashion wooden items that function as steel items, such as weapons and armors.

However, the wood to be transformed into ironwood must be shaped prior to the transformation. The spell can be used to alter 5 pounds of material per level of the caster.

J

JUMP, Level 1 Int

CT 1 **R** touch **D** 1 tn./lvl.
SV none **SR** yes **Comp** V, S, M

One recipient may make astounding leaps and bounds, launching up to 25 feet forward, or 10 feet backward or upwards, although safe landing at the end of such a magnificent jump requires a successful dexterity check. The hind leg of a cricket or other leaping animal or insect is used in the casting of this spell.

K

KNOCK*, Level 2 Int

CT 1 **R** 50 ft. **D** permanent
SV none **SR** no **Comp** V

This spell opens stuck or locked doors, even magically held ones. It slides bolts and lifts latches. It opens secret doors, as well as locked or trick-opening boxes or chests, and also loosens shackles or chains that have been employed to hold closures shut. Knocked doors do not relock themselves once opened. Knock can not raise portcullises or similar impediments, nor can it undo or untangle knots. Each spell can undo up to two means of preventing egress through a portal. If used to open a magically locked closure, knock does not remove the spell but simply inhibits its functioning for 10 minutes.

Lock is the reverse of knock. It magically locks a single portal, chest or box, preventing it from being opened by any mundane means short of breaking or bypassing the portal itself; any magical means of opening, such as dispel magic or knock work normally. The caster can freely pass the character's own lock without affecting it.

KNOW DIRECTION, Level 0 Wis

CT 1 **R** n/a **D** see below
SV n/a **SR** n/a **Comp** V

The caster instantly and unerringly knows which direction is north. The caster will retain this knowledge for one day, or longer if the character can locate some external reference point to help keep track of direction.

L

LEGEND LORE, Level 6 Int, 7 Wis

CT see text **R** see text **D** see text
SV n/a **SR** n/a **Comp** V, S, M

Great deeds, events and powers are writ large in legend, and with this spell the caster can draw upon these great tales,

bringing to light knowledge about a legendary person, place or thing. If the person or thing is close at hand, or if the caster is in the place in question, the casting time is only 1d4 x 10 minutes. If the caster only possesses detailed information on the person, place or thing, casting time is 1d10 days, and the resulting knowledge gleaned is less complete and specific. If the caster knows little beyond rumor, casting time is 2d6 weeks, and the resulting lore is vague and incomplete, though it may enable the caster to locate more detailed information. While casting this spell, the caster cannot engage in anything other than routine activities such as sleeping and eating. Casting the spell requires $25 of powdered gems, a magic item, incense, blank parchment, ink, quills or silver pens.

When completed, the spell brings the legends, if any exist, about the individual, location or thing to the caster's mind,. The tales reveal themselves as long-forgotten and sometimes cryptic memories, riddles or rhymes, regardless of whether the legends are current, long forgotten or obscure. Subjects lacking legendary importance provide no information whatsoever. As a rule of thumb, characters of 10th level and higher are legendary, as are the sorts of creatures they strive against, the major magical items they wield, and the places where they performed their great or nefarious deeds.

LESSER RESTORATION, Level 2 Wis

CT 10 min. **R** touch **D** permanent
SV n/a **SR** yes (h) **Comp** V, S, DF

The strength-sapping touch of the ray of enfeeblement, the fiendish attacks of certain foul creatures and the insidious effects of some poisons may sap a character's attributes, reducing strength, inhibiting constitution and so on. Lesser restoration completely dispels any magical effects that have reduced the character's attribute scores, but cannot reverse permanent attribute drain.

LEVITATE, Level 2 Int

CT 1 **R** personal/50 ft. **D** 10 min./lvl.
SV intelligence negates **SR** yes (h) **Comp** V, S, F

Levitate allows the caster to float up or down through the air at a luxurious pace, moving no more than 20 feet up or down per round. Alternatively, the caster may levitate another creature or object weighing no more than 100 lbs. per level, although an unwilling creature is entitled to a saving throw. Levitation does not enable horizontal movement, although a levitating character could clamber along the face of a cliff or push against a ceiling to move laterally (generally at half base speed). The caster needs a slender gold wire worth 5pg to cast the spell.

LIGHT, Level 0 Int, 0 Wis, 0 Cha

CT 1 **R** 150 ft. **D** 10 min./lvl.
SV none **SR** no **Comp** V, F

This spell causes an object to shed light, clearly illuminating the area around it as much as a torch, albeit with clear, white light. Although the effect is immobile, it can be cast on a movable object. Light taken into an area of magical darkness does not function. The caster needs a piece of clear quartz crystal, natural, cut or polished worth $1.

LIGHTNING BOLT, Level 3 Int

CT 1 **R** see below **D** instant
SV dexterity half **SR** yes **Comp** V, S, M

The caster unleashes a blinding, sizzling arc of forking electricity that deals 1d6 points of damage per caster level. The caster channels the electricity through a small iron rod (1sp) that has been left out in a thunderstorm. The bolt is 10 feet wide x 50 feet long or 5 feet wide x 100 feet long. The bolt erupts from the caster's fingertips, staff, rod or wand. It strikes creatures and objects along its sinuous path and even a couple of feet to either side, igniting combustibles, sundering wooden doors and melting metals with a low melting point, such as lead, gold, copper, silver or bronze.

If the damage caused to an interposing barrier shatters or breaks through it, the bolt continues beyond the barrier to the extent of its range. If the bolt does not break through or is deflected, it rebounds toward the caster up the full length of the bolt or until it strikes another barrier and rebounds again.

LIMITED WISH, Level 7 Int

CT 1 **R** n/a **D** see below
SV see text **SR** see text **Comp** V.

Though the scope of the wish granted by this potent spell may be limited, much can be accomplished by the imaginative caster within its strict bounds. This spell may duplicate the effects of any Wis-based spell of 6th level or lower, or any Cha-based arcanist spell of 5th level or lower. It may also grant other effects in line with the power of such spells, although any effects must be approved by the Game Master. The caster must be cautious in phrasing the spell though, for the desires of the greedy often end in disaster, and the spell is very literal in its fulfillment of the caster's wish. Duplicated spells allow saving throws and spell resistance as normal.

LOCATE CREATURE, Level 4 Int

CT 1 **R** 450 ft. **D** 10 min./lvl
SV n/a **SR** n/a **Comp** V, S, F

Using this spell, the caster may locate the nearest creature of a known type that they have encountered before (such as a human or unicorn), or a specific individual creature whom the caster has met, provided it is within range. The caster must possess part of the creature type sought (such as a Nazi's tooth), or part or all of an item, garment, or part of an individual creature sought (such as a lock of hair, a strip of cloth from an individual's cloak, etc. in order to use the spell. The caster slowly turns on the spot after casting the spell, attempting to sense the direction of the creature. The spell locates the nearest creature of a given type if more than one such creature is within range. Running water blocks the spell, and it can be fooled by mislead, nondetection, and polymorph spells. It cannot detect objects.

LOCATE OBJECT*, Level 2 Int

CT 1 **R** 450 ft. **D** 10 min./lvl.
SV n/a **SR** n/a **Comp** V, S, F, DF

With this spell, the caster need never fear misplacing his tower key again, for it enables the caster to sense the direction of a well-known or clearly visualized object, including apparel, jewelry, furniture, tools, weapons or even such mundane implements as a ladder. All the caster needs is a small glass lens or opaque crystal. The spell may be used to search for general items such as a stairway, a sword or a jewel, in which case the spell locates the nearest such object within its range, or the spell may be used to find a specific item, such as a particular piece of jewelry. A unique object (such as *Gideon Thorne's gold-plated quill*) may not be located unless the caster has observed that particular item firsthand. The spell is blocked by lead, fooled by polymorphing, and cannot detect creatures.

Obscure object, the reverse of this spell, may be cast on an object, thereby preventing it from being located by spells of this type, or by divinatory means such as scrying, for the duration of the spell.

M

MAGE HAND, Level 0 Int

CT 1 **R** 25 ft. **D** concentration
SV none **SR** yes **Comp** V, S

The caster points a finger at an object of 5 pounds or less, and can then lift and move it at will from a distance. The caster can move the object up to 15 feet in any direction in a round, though the spell ends if the distance between the caster and the object ever exceeds the spell's range.

MAGIC AURA, Level 0 Cha

CT 1 **R** touch **D** n/a
SV none **SR** yes (object) **Comp** V, S, F

The caster makes an item's aura appear magical, and thus register to detection spells (and similar spells). Identify or a similar detection reveals the aura as false. The spell can effect 5 pounds per level of the caster.

MAGIC CIRCLE (against chaos, evil, good or law), Level 3 Int, 3 Wis

CT 1 **R** creature touched **D** 3 rd./lvl.
SV none **SR** no (see text) **Comp** V, S, M/DF

This spell creates a magical barrier around the subject, to a distance of 10 feet, that offers protection against one axis of alignment (evil, good, chaos, or law) which is decided at the time of casting. Only one such protective spell can be in effect in one place at the same time, even if each protects against a different alignment.

The barrier moves with the subject and grants a +2 bonus to armor class and saving throws against creatures of the chosen alignment. The spell prevents bodily contact by summoned or conjured creatures of any alignment: the melee attacks of such creatures fail and the creatures recoil from the protective magic. The protection against contact by summoned or conjured creatures ends if the warded creature makes an attack against, or tries to force the barrier against, the blocked creature. Spell resistance can allow a summoned or conjured creature to overcome this protection and touch the warded creature.

The magical circle also blocks any attempt to possess or exercise mental control over the warded creature by foes of any alignment. The protection does not prevent a spell that gains mental control, but it prevents the caster of such a spell from mentally commanding the protected creature. If the protection ends before the mental control does, the enemy caster would then be able to exercise such mental control of the creature. Likewise, the barrier keeps out a possessing life force but does not expel one if it is in place before the spell is cast.

This spell has a special function that the character may choose when casting the spell. A magic circle can be focused inward rather than outward. In this case, it serves as an immobile, temporary magical prison for a summoned creature. The creature cannot cross the circle's boundaries. The caster must beat a creature's SR in order to keep it at bay, but the bonuses and the protection from mental control apply regardless of an enemy's SR. If a creature is too large to fit into the spell's area, the spell succeeds but for that creature only.

MAGIC JAR, Level 5 Int, 5 Cha

CT 1 **R** 150 ft. **D** 1 tn./lvl.
SV charisma save negates **SR** yes **Comp** V, S, M

By casting magic jar, the caster places their own soul into a gem (which must be of at least $100 in value) or large crystal

(known as the magic jar), leaving the caster's own body lifeless. The caster may then attempt to take control of a nearby body, forcing the target's soul into the magic jar.Then the caster can attempt to take control of a nearby body, forcing its soul into the magic jar. While in the magic jar, the caster can sense and attack any life force within 10 feet per caster level (on the same plane). The caster, however, cannot determine the exact creature types or positions of these creatures. In a group of life forces, the caster can sense a difference of four or more HD and can determine whether a life force is positive or negative energy. Attempting to possess a body is an attack, and it is blocked by protection from evil or a similar ward. The caster possesses the body and forces the creature's soul into the magic jar unless the subject succeeds at a charisma save. Failure to take over the host leaves the caster's life force in the magic jar, and the target automatically succeeds at further saving throws if the caster attempts to possess its body again.

If successful, the caster's life force occupies the host body, and the host's life force is imprisoned in the magic jar. The caster keeps his or her intelligence, wisdom, charisma, level, class, base attack bonus, Prime attributes, alignment, and mental abilities while the host body retains its strength, dexterity, constitution, hit points, natural abilities and extraordinary abilities such as water breathing or regeneration. A body with extra limbs does not allow the caster to make more attacks (or more advantageous two-weapon attacks) than normal.

The caster can't choose to activate the body's extraordinary or supernatural abilities. The creature's spells and spell-like abilities do not stay with the body.

The caster may move back to the jar, returning the trapped soul to its body, at any time; and may thereafter attempt to possess another body. The spell ends when the caster chooses to return to the caster's own body (leaving the receptacle empty).

To cast the spell, the magic jar must be within spell range. When the caster's soul transfers to the jar, the caster's original body is, as near as anyone can tell, dead.

If the host body is slain, the caster returns to the magic jar, if within range, and the life force of the host departs (that is, it is dead). If the host body is slain beyond the range of the spell, both the caster and the host die. Any life force with nowhere to go is treated as slain.

If the spell ends while the caster is in the magic jar, the caster returns to the caster's body (or dies if the caster's body is out of range or destroyed). If the spell ends while the caster is in a host, the caster returns to the caster's body (or dies, if it is out of range of the caster's current position), and the soul in the magic jar returns to its body (or dies if it is out of range). Destroying the receptacle ends the spell. A magic jar may also be dispelled by casting a dispel magic (or greater) spell on either the receptacle or the host.

MAGIC MOUTH, Level 2 Int, 2 Cha

CT 1 **R** touch **D** permanent
SV n/a **SR** yes (object) **Comp** V, S

This spell imbues an object with an enchanted mouth that appears and speaks its message when a specified event occurs. The message, which must be twenty-five or fewer words long, can be in any language known by the caster. The mouth cannot cast spells.

The spell activates when specific conditions set by the caster are fulfilled. Commands can be as general or as detailed as desired, although only visual and audible triggers can be used. The spell reacts to what appears to be real: disguises and illusions can fool it. Normal darkness does not defeat a visual trigger, but magical darkness or invisibility does. Silent movement or magical silence defeats audible triggers. Audible triggers can be keyed to general types of noises or to a specific noise or spoken word. Note that actions can serve as triggers if they are visible or audible. A magic mouth cannot distinguish invisible creatures, alignments, level, HD or class (except by external garb). The range limit of a trigger is 5 feet per caster level.

MAGIC STONES, level 1 Wis

CT 1 **R** touch **D** n/a
SV n/a **SR** n/a **Comp** M

The caster enchants three pebbles or rocks, no larger than sling bullets, to strike with great force when thrown or slung. The creature using the stones makes a normal ranged attack at +1 to hit. Each magic stone that hits deals 1d6+1 points of damage. Against undead creatures, this damage is doubled (2d6+2 points).

MAJOR CREATION, Level 5 Cha

CT 10 min. **R** 10 ft. **D** see text
SV n/a **SR** n/a **Comp** V, S, M

This spell creates a nonmagical item of vegetable, stone, crystal, metal or gem matter. The volume of the item created cannot exceed 1 cubic foot per caster level. The caster must succeed at an intelligence check to make a complex item. The duration of the created item varies with its relative hardness and rarity: vegetable matter lasts 2 hours/level; stone, crystal and base metals last 1 hour/level; precious metals last 20 minutes/level; gems last 10 minutes/level; mithral lasts 2 rounds/level; adamantite lasts 1 round/level.

MAJOR IMAGE, Level 3 Cha

CT 1 **R** 450 ft. **D** concentration+3rd.
SV intelligence (if disbelieves) **SR** no **Comp** V, S

This spell creates the illusion of an object, creature, or force, as visualized by the caster. Sound, smell, and thermal illusions are all within the spells powers to create. Creatures who view the illusion believe it, and can suffer damage from illusions. Hit point damage is suffered from damage to the mind/psyche. While concentrating, the caster can move the image within the range. The image persists for 3 rounds after the caster ceases concentrating. The image disappears if an opponent makes the saving throw. The spell affects a 40 foot cube area + 10 feet cube per level.

MASS CHARM, Level 8 Int, 8 Cha

CT 1 **R** 50 ft. **D** 1 day/lvl.
SV charisma negates **SR** yes **Comp** V,S

This charm affects a number of creatures whose combined HD do not exceed twice the caster's level (a minimum of one creature regardless of HD) and are located within a 50 x 50 foot area. If there are more potential targets than the caster can affect, the caster chooses them one at a time until reaching a creature whose HD bring the total above the spell's maximum.

The targets regard the caster as a trusted friend and ally. If the creatures are currently being threatened or attacked by the caster or the caster's allies, they receive a +5 bonus on their saving throw. The spell does not enable the caster to control the charmed creatures like automatons, but the subjects perceive the caster's words and actions in the most favorable way. The caster can try to give a subject orders, but must succeed at a charisma check to convince the subject to do anything it wouldn't ordinarily do. Any act by the caster or the caster's apparent allies that threatens the charmed creature breaks the spell. Note also that the caster must speak the creature's language to communicate commands.

MASS HEAL*, LEVEL 8 WIS
CT 1 **R** 25 ft. **D** n/a
SV none **SR** yes (h) **COMP** V, S, DF

This powerful curative enables the caster to wipe away disease and injury in several creatures within a 25 square foot area. It completely cures all hit point damage, all diseases, blindness, deafness and all temporary ability damage. It neutralizes poisons in a subject's system, so that no additional damage or effects are suffered. It nullifies a feeblemind spell. It cures mental disorders caused by nature, spell or injury to the brain. Mass heal does not restore permanently drained levels, or restore permanently drained ability scores. If used against an undead creature, mass heal acts like its reverse, mass harm.

Mass harm drains the targets of all but 4 hit points and causes disease (see remove disease). If used against an undead creature, mass harm acts like mass heal.

MASS INVISIBILITY, LEVEL 7 INT, 7 CHA
CT 1 **R** 50 ft. **D** n/a
SV Int negates (h) **SR** yes (h) **COMP** V, S, M

The group of creatures targeted vanish from sight, even from special forms of vision. If the recipients are carrying gear, the gear vanishes too. Individuals in the group cannot see each other, unless they can normally see invisible things or employ magic to do so. Items dropped or put down by an invisible creature become visible; items picked up disappear if tucked into the clothing or pouches worn by the creature. Light, however, never becomes invisible, although a source of light can become so (thus, the effect is that of a light with no visible source). Any part of an item that the subject carries but that extends more than 10 feet from it becomes visible, such as a trailing rope.

The subjects are not magically silenced, and certain other conditions can render the recipients detectable (such as stepping in a puddle). The spell ends if anyone in the group attacks any creature, including casting a spell targeting a foe or whose area or effect includes a foe. Actions directed at unintended objects do not break the spell. Causing harm indirectly is not an attack. If the subject attacks directly it becomes visible immediately along with all its gear. Note that spells specifically affecting allies but not foes are not attacks for this purpose, even when they include foes in their area.

The spell is broken for any individual who moves more than 180 feet from the nearest member of the group. (If only two individuals are affected, the one moving away from the other one loses its invisibility. If both are moving away from each other, they both become visible when the distance between them exceeds 80 feet.)

MASS SUGGESTION, LEVEL 6 INT, 5 CHA
CT 1 **R** 50 ft. **D** 1 hr./lvl.
SV charisma negates **SR** yes **COMP** V, M

The spell is the same as suggestion except that this spell can affect more creatures. The caster influences the actions of the creatures by suggesting a course of activity (limited to a sentence or two). The number of creatures affected is equal to one per level of the caster and all must be within a 25 foot area. The suggestion must be worded in such a manner as to make the activity sound reasonable. The victim must understand the language of the caster making the suggestion. Any attempt to suggest an act that would be harmful to the victim or something severely at odds with their behavior will allow the affected creature to automatically break the enchantment. The Game Master is free to factor in penalties to the victim's saving throw for quite reasonable suggestions as well as give the target bonuses to their saves for unreasonable or harmful suggestions.

The suggested course of activity can continue for the entire duration. If the suggested activity can be completed in a shorter time, the spell ends when the subject finishes what he was asked to do. The caster can instead specify conditions that will trigger a special activity during the duration. If the condition is not met before the spell expires, the activity is not performed. A small piece of wool is needed to cast the spell.

MAZE, LEVEL 8 INT, 7 CHA
CT 1 **R** 25 ft. **D** see text
SV none **SR** yes **COMP** V, S

The caster conjures up an extradimensional labyrinth, and the subject vanishes into it. The subject's intelligence score determines the time it takes to find a way out of the maze: under 3 takes 2d4 days; 3-5 takes 1d4 days; 6-8 takes 5d4 hours; 9-12 takes 4d4 turns; 13-15 takes 3d4 rounds; 16-17 takes 2d4 rounds; 18 takes 1d4 rounds.

If the subject doesn't attempt to escape, the maze disappears in 10 minutes, forcing the subject to leave. On leaving the maze, the subject reappears in the spot it had been in when the maze spell was cast. If this spot is filled with a solid object, the subject appears nearby. Spells and abilities that move a creature within a plane do not help a creature escape a maze spell, although the character can escape by using spells to a different plane. Minotaurs and the like are not affected by this spell.

MENDING, LEVEL 0 INT
CT 1 **R** 25 ft. **D** n/a
SV n/a SP n/a **COMP** V, S

This spell repairs small breaks or tears in objects of no more than 5 pounds in weight. In metallic objects, it will weld a broken ring, a chain link, a medallion or a slender dagger, providing but one break exists. Ceramic or wooden objects with multiple breaks can be invisibly rejoined to be as strong as new. A hole in a leather sack or wineskin is completely fixed over by mending. The spell cannot repair a magic item.

MESSAGE, LEVEL 0 INT, 0 CHA
CT 1 **R** 450 ft. **D** 1 rd./lvl.
SV n/a **SR** n/a **COMP** V, S

The caster can whisper messages and receive a reply with little chance of being overheard. The caster points a finger at one

creature to be included in the spell effect and must mouth the words and whisper, possibly allowing the opportunity to read lips. Magical silence blocks the spell, but otherwise, as long as the caster can see the targeted creature, the message is heard. The creature who receives the message can whisper a reply that the caster hears. The spell doesn't transcend language barriers.

METEOR SWARM, Level 9 Wis
CT 1 **R** 450 ft. **D** instant
SV see text **SR** yes **Comp** V, S.

Meteor like fireballs, spewing sparks and leaving a fiery trail, streak in a straight line from the caster toward a chosen spot. The caster may choose either four large spheres (2 foot diameter) or eight small spheres (1 foot diameter). Any creature in the straight line path of these spheres takes 9d6 points of fire damage with no save allowed. The large spheres follow a path 10 feet wide, and the small spheres follow a path 5 feet wide.

If the spheres reach their destination, each bursts in a spread. Each spread indicated below creates overlapping areas of effect, and creatures in an overlap area must save against each sphere separately or suffer damage. A successful dexerity save reduces damage by half for the burst damage indicated below.

The four large spheres explode with their points of origin forming a diamond or box pattern around the spell's target designated upon casting. Each large sphere has a 30-foot-diameter spread, and each blast is 20 feet apart along the sides of the pattern, creating overlapping areas of the spell's effect and exposing the center to all four blasts. Each sphere deals 1d4 x 10 fire damage.

The smaller spheres have a 15 foot diameter spread, and each deals 1d4 x 5 fire damage. They explode with their target forming a pattern around the spell's central point of origin (which the sorcerer designated upon casting) of a box within a diamond or vice versa, with each of the outer sides measuring 20 feet long. The center has four areas of overlapping effect, and numerous peripheral areas have two or three overlapping areas of the spell's effect.

MIND BLANK, Level 8 Int, 9 Wis, 9 Cha
CT 1 **R** 25 ft. **D** 1 day
SV charisma negates (h) **SR** yes (h) **Comp** V, S.

The subject is protected from all devices and spells that detect, influence, or read emotions or thoughts, and is immune against all mind-affecting spells and effects as well as information gathering by divination spells or effects. Mind blank even foils limited wish and wish, when they are used in such a way as to affect a subject's mind or to gain information about him. In the case of scrying that scans an area the spells' subject is in, the spell works but the spell's subject simply isn't detected. Scrying attempts targeted specifically at the subject do not work at all.

MINOR CREATION, Level 4 Cha
CT 1 tn. **R** 10 ft. **D** 1 hr./lvl.
SV n/a **SR** n/a **Comp** V, S, M

This spell creates a magical item of nonliving vegetable matter. The volume of the item created cannot exceed 1 cubic foot per caster level. The caster must succeed at an intelligence check to make a complex item. The material component is a tiny piece of matter to create.

MINOR GLOBE OF INVULNERABILITY, Level 4 Int
CT 1 **R** personal **D** 1 rd./lvl.
SV none **SR** no **Comp** V, S, M

When this spell is cast, a faintly shimmering 10 foot diameter sphere of arcane energy surrounds and is centered on the caster. The globe acts as an impenetrable field against any 1st, 2nd, or 3rd level spell, spell-like ability or spell-like effect, even if the globe is located within the areas affected by such spells. Spells and effects targeting or encompassing the globe are not dispelled, but wash harmlessly against and over it. Anyone in the globe, however, may cast spells in, through or outside of the globe. Spells of 4th level and higher are not affected by the globe itself, but can be brought down by dispel magic. The globe moves with the caster. The material component is a small clear bead or sphere.

MINOR IMAGE, Level 2 Cha
CT 1 **R** 450 ft. **D** see below
SV intelligence **SR** no **Comp** V, S

This spell creates the illusion of an object, creature or force as visualized by the caster. Its area of effect is a 40 foot cube + 10 cubic feet per level. The spell includes some minor sounds,

but not understandable speech. The illusion does not create smell, texture or temperature. The caster's can move the image within the limits of the spell's area of effect. The image persists for 2 rounds after the caster's concentration ceases.

Creatures who view the illusion believe it, and can suffer damage from it. The image disappears if the viewer makes a saving throw.

MIRAGE ARCANA, Level 4 Cha

CT 5 min. **R** 150 ft. **D** see text
SV intelligence **SR** no **Comp** V, S, M

This spell is like hallucinatory terrain, but it can effect or add man-made structures to the illusion. The area of effect is 10 feet x 10 feet per level. The caster makes natural terrain look, sound, feel and smell like some other sort of natural terrain. Structures in the area can be altered to look different, or illusory structures can be added. Items and creatures within the area are not hidden or changed in appearance, although they can hide within the illusion as if it were real. The illusion includes audible, visual, tactile and olfactory elements. The illusion persists until dispelled or disbelieved by an intelligent creature and requires an appropriate piece of terrain to mimic.

MIRROR IMAGE, Level 2 Int, 2 Cha

CT 1 **R** see below **D** 3 rd./lvl.
SV none **SR** no **Comp** V, S

Illusory duplicates of the caster pop into being and mimic the caster's actions, making it difficult for enemies to know which target to attack. The spell creates 1d4+1 images. The images stay near the caster and disappear when struck. The images remain in a cluster or form a line, each within 5 feet of at least one other figment or the caster. Observers can't use vision or hearing to tell which one is the caster and which the image. Enemies attempting to attack the caster or cast spells at the caster must select from among indistinguishable targets. Generally, roll randomly to see whether the selected target is real or a figment. Any successful attack roll against a figment destroys it. A figment's armor class is equal to the caster's. An attacker must be able to see the images to be fooled.

MISDIRECTION, Level 2 Cha

CT 1 **R** 50 ft. **D** 1 rd./lvl.
SV wisdom negates **SR** no **Comp** S

This spell misdirects other spells that reveal auras and information. On casting the spell, the caster chooses a subject and another object (within range) to serve as the decoy. For the duration of the spell, detection spells provide information based on the target rather than on the actual target of the detection attempt, unless the caster of the detection succeeds at a wisdom saving throw.

MISLEAD, Level 6 Cha

CT 1 **R** 25 ft. **D** 1 rd./lvl.
SV intelligence (disbelief) **SR** no **Comp** S

An illusory double of the caster appears, and at the same time, the caster is affected as if by an invisibility spell. The caster is free to go elsewhere while the caster's double moves away. The double appears within the spell's range, but thereafter moves according to the caster's intent at the time of casting. The caster can make the figment appear superimposed perfectly over the character's own body so that observers don't notice an image appearing and the caster turning invisible. The caster and the figment can then move in different directions. The double moves at the caster's speed, can talk and gesture as if it were real, and even smells and feels real. The double cannot attack or cast spells, but it can pretend to do so.

MNEMONIC ENHANCER, Level 4 Int

CT 10 min. **R** n/a **D** see below
SV n/a **SR** n/a **Comp** V, S, M, F

The caster prepares or retains additional spells. The additional spell or spells prepared or retained fade after 24 hours (if not cast). The caster requires a $5 item that has a flat surface, such as a mirror, and a special ink worth $5. There are two versions of the spell.

Prepare: The caster prepares up to three additional levels of spells. A 0 level spell counts as one-half level for these purposes. The character prepares and casts these spells normally.

Retain: The caster retains any spell up to 3rd level that the caster had cast up to 1 day before casting the mnemonic enhancer. This version restores the previously cast spell to the caster's mind.

MOVE EARTH, LEVEL 6 INT
CT see text **R** 450 ft. **D**
SV none **SR** no **COMP** V, S, M

This spell moves dirt, possibly collapsing embankments, moving hillocks, shifting dunes, etc. Rock formations cannot be collapsed or moved. The area to be affected determines the casting time. For every 10 foot x 10 foot area, casting takes 3 minutes. The maximum area, 800 feet by 800 feet, takes 4 hours to move. The earth moved cannot exceed10 feet. Casting the spell requires a handful of earth and a wand, rod or staff.

This spell does not violently break the surface of the ground. Instead, it creates wavelike crests and troughs, the earth reacting with glacierlike fluidity until the desired result is achieved. Trees, structures, rock formations and such are mostly unaffected except for changes in elevation and relative topography. The spell cannot be used for tunneling and is generally too slow to trap or bury creatures. Its primary use is for digging or filling moats or for adjusting terrain contours before a battle.

N

NEUTRALIZE POISON, LEVEL 3 WIS
CT 1 **R** touch **D** permanent
SV constitution negates (h) **SR** yes (h) **COMP** V, S, DF

The caster detoxifies any sort of venom in one creature or in one object touched. A poisoned creature suffers no additional damage or effects from the poison, and any temporary effects are ended. But the spell does not reverse effects the poison may have already inflicted, such as hit point damage, temporary ability damage, or effects that don't go away on their own.

This spell also neutralizes the poison in a poisonous creature or object. A poisonous creature replenishes its poison at its normal rate.

NIGHTMARE, LEVEL 5 CHA
CT 10 min. **R** unlimited **D** see below
SV charisma negates **SR** yes **COMP** V, S

The caster sends a hideous and unsettling phantasmal vision to a single specific creature whom the caster names or specifically designates. The nightmare prevents restful sleep and causes 1d10 points of damage. The nightmare leaves the subject tired and unrested, and unable to regain arcane spells for the next 24 hours. Dispel evil cast on the subject while the caster is casting the spell dispels the nightmare and stuns the caster for 10 minutes per caster level of the dispel evil. If the recipient is awake when the spell begins, the caster can choose to cease casting (ending the spell) or enter a trance until the recipient goes to sleep, whereupon the caster becomes alert again and completes the casting. If the caster is disturbed during the trance, the spell ends. If the caster chooses to enter a trance, the caster is not aware of the caster's surroundings or the activities around the caster while in the trance. The caster is defenseless, both physically and mentally, while in the trance. Creatures who don't sleep or dream are immune to this spell.

NONDETECTION, LEVEL 3 INT, 3 CHA
CT 1 **R** 25 ft. **D** 1 hr./lvl.
SV see text **SR** yes (h) **COMP** V, S, M

The warded creature or item becomes difficult to detect by a divination spell or device. If a divination is attempted against the warded creature or item, the caster of the divination must make a wisdom saving throw, with the challenge level being equal to the level of the spell caster who cast nondetection. If cast on a creature, nondetection wards the creature's gear as well as the creature itself. Nondetection can only be cast on one creature or item and requires a reflective device worth at least $5 to cast.

O

OBSCURING MIST, LEVEL 1 WIS AND LEVEL 1 CHA
CT 1 **R** n/a **D** 1 min./lvl.
SV none **SR** no **COMP** V, S

A stationary, misty vapor arises around the caster and obscures all sight, including special visions, beyond 5 feet but within an area of 25x 20 x 10 feet. A creature 5 feet away has one-half concealment, and creatures farther away have total concealment.

A moderate wind (11+ mph) disperses the fog in 4 rounds. A strong wind (21+ mph) disperses the fog in 1 round. A fire spell burns away any fog within the spell's area of effect. This spell does not function underwater. The caster can move out of the mist once it is created.

OPEN/ CLOSE. LEVEL 0 INT
CT 1 **R** 25 ft. **D** n/a
SV n/a **SR** n/a **COMP** V, S

The caster can open or close a normal latched door, chest, box, window, bag, pouch, bottle, or other container. If anything resists this activity the spell fails. The spell can only open and close things that are of standard weight.

P

PASSWALL, LEVEL 5 INT
CT 1 **R** 50 ft. **D** 1 hr./lvl.
SV n/a **SR** n/a **COMP** V, S, M

The caster creates a temporary passage through a wall that is 5 feet wide, 8 feet tall and 10 feet deep. Several passwall spells can form a continuing passage to breach very thick walls, when one spell is insufficient. When passwall ends, creatures within the passage are ejected to the nearest corridor or other exit. The material component for this spell is a ball of hardened candle wax which the caster pierces at the time of casting.

PASS WITHOUT TRACE, Level 1 Wis

CT 1 **R** touch **D** 10 min./lvl.
SV n/a **SR** n/a **Comp** V, S

Upon receiving this dweomer, the subject can move through any type of terrain and leave neither footprints nor scent. Tracking the subject is impossible by nonmagical means.

PERMANENCY, Level 5 Int

CT 2 + spell made permanent **R** n/a **D** permanent
SV none **SR** no **Comp** V, S

This powerful spell makes certain other spells permanent, assuming that the caster has attained a required level of experience and is otherwise able to cast the spell to be made permanent. Making spells permanent results in the temporary loss of 1 point of constitution for 1 month, with the caster needing to make a constitution saving throw to prevent the loss from remaining permanent.

The caster can make any of these spells permanent in regard to the character's person: comprehend languages, detect magic, detect poison, endure elements, protection from arrows, read magic, see invisibility, tongues, and water breathing. This application of permanency can be dispelled only by a caster of greater level than the caster was when he or she cast the spell.

In addition to personal use, permanency can be used to make the following spells permanent on the caster, another creature, an object, or an area (as appropriate): *alarm, confusion, dancing lights, enlarge, ghost sound, gust of wind, invisibility, magic mouth, phase door, prismatic sphere, scare, stinking cloud, symbol, teleportation circle, wall of fire, wall of force, and web*. Spells cast on other creatures, objects or locations (not on the caster) are vulnerable to dispel magic as normal.

The Game Master may allow other selected spells to be made permanent, based on an appropriate amount of time and money spent researching this application of a given spell. If the Game Master has already determined that the application is not possible, the research automatically fails.

PERMANENT IMAGE, Level 6 Cha

CT 1 **R** 150 ft. **D** permanent
SV intelligence **SR** no **Comp** V, S, M

This spell creates a permanent illusion of an object, creature or force, as visualized by the character. Sound, smell and thermal illusions are included in the spell effect. The illusion can cover a 20 foot cubic area plus 10 cubic feet per level of the spell caster. Creatures who view the illusion believe it, and can suffer damage from it. Hit point damage is suffered from damage to the mind/psyche. The illusion follows a script determined by the caster, without requiring the caster's concentration. The illusion can include intelligible speech if the caster wishes. The image disappears if an opponent disbelieves for some reason and makes the required saving throw. The material component of this spell is a $10 lens.

PERSISTENT IMAGE, Level 5 Cha

CT 1 **R** 150 ft. **D** 1 min./lvl.
SV intelligence **SR** no **Comp** V, S

This spell creates the illusion of an object, creature, or force, as visualized by the character. Sound, smell, and thermal illusions are included in the spell effect. Creatures who view the illusion believe it, and can suffer damage from it. Hit point damage is suffered from damage to the mind/psyche. The illusion follows a script determined by the caster, without requiring the caster's concentration. The illusion can include intelligible speech if the caster wishes. The image disappears if an opponent disbelieves for some reason and makes the required saving throw. The spell's area of effect is 20 foot cube plus 10 cubic feet per level of the caster.

PETRIFY*, Level 6 Cha, Level 7 Wis

CT 1 **R** 50 ft. **D** 2 hrs./lvl.
SV Special (See below) **SR** Yes **Comp** V, S, M

Using this rare and horrible spell, the sorcerer can turn a flesh target, along with its clothing and any equipment it currently carries, into living stone. When targeted, the victim must succeed at a Constitution-based saving throw. On a success, the spell has no effect. If the save fails by more than five, the victim is instantly and permanently turned to stone unless affected by the reverse of this spell, or by Greater Restoration. If the save fails by less than five, the target is restrained as if affected by the Hold Person spell, and begins a slow transformation. They can then, on the next turn, try once again to save and escape petrification; failing this second save results in being turned to stone.

Victims of this spell are stone in all ways–they cannot move, speak or take any actions. They are, however, still conscious of their surroundings and can hear and see (though as they cannot move their eyes they can only see straight ahead). The sole exception are flesh golems, who are turned into stone golems via this spell. Many normal people are trapped in this form for too long go quietly mad; those GMs using the Sanity rules may impose regular Sanity checks and loss at their discretion.

The reverse of this spell, *Restore Flesh*, can turn a living stone statue to life once again, though any sanity loss suffered will remain. If used on a normal statue, it will turn the statue into a mass of squamous flesh that has no life and will simply rot as normal. Such a creation will have no bones and will simply collapse to the ground. If used on a stone golem, *Restore Flesh* will effect a transformation to a flesh golem. Undead creatures targeted by petrify can later be restored to undeath using *Restore Flesh*; those undead creatures who are petrified and restored using Greater Restoration are destroyed.

PHANTASMAL KILLER, Level 4 Cha

CT 1 **R** 50 ft. **D** 1 rd./lvl.
SV see text **SR** yes **Comp** V, S

The caster causes a manifestation, in the target's mind, of the most horrific creature imaginable. This creature is the

formulation of all the subconscious fears of the target, brought into a very convincing and deadly illusion. Only the caster and the target can see the phantasmal killer. The killer makes an illusory attack upon the target, who must make a successful intelligence saving throw or instantly die from fear and psychic damage. A successful saving throw results in 4d6 damage.

The phantasmal killer cannot be damaged, and will pass through all physical barriers to reach the target. The killer cannot pass through magical protections such as a minor globe of invulnerability, or through any area of antimagic.

Likewise, if the arcanist casting the spell is killed before the effect reaches the target, the spell ends. In rare circumstances, such as when the target makes a successful saving throw and is wearing a helm of telepathy, the target can turn the killer back upon the caster just as if the target cast the spell in the first place.

PHASE DOOR, Level 7 Int
CT 1 **R** touch **D** one use/2 lvls.
SV n/a **SR** n/a **Comp** V

The spell creates an ethereal passage and space through a wall that only the caster can see and use. The caster disappears when entering the phase door and appears again upon exiting. The caster can enter the passage once for every two levels of experience, and it is permanent until the caster has done so. The caster may take additional creatures through the door, but each one counts as one use of the spell. The door does not allow light, sound or spell effects through it, nor can the caster see through it without exiting or entering it. Gems of true seeing and similar magic reveal the presence of a phase door but do not allow its use. A phase door is subject to dispel magic. Anyone inside a phase door when it is dispelled is killed instantly. The area of effect for this spell is a 5 x 8 x 10 feet.

PLANE SHIFT, Level 5 Wis
CT 1 **R** touch **D** n/a
SV see text **SR** yes (h) **Comp** V, S, DF

The caster and others (up to 8 creatures) are transported to another plane of existence or alternate dimension. If several willing persons link hands in a circle, up to eight creatures, including the caster, can be affected by the spell. The spell transports the creatures to the designated plane or dimension only. The subject of the spell must creatures need to find other means to travel back to the originating plane. Unwilling recipients of the plane shift can resist the effect with a successful wisdom save. The Game Master determines whether the caster reaches a specific destination and all other matter related to the travel and arrival on the other plane.

POLYMORPH ANY OBJECT, Level 8 Int, level 9 Cha
CT 1 **R** 50 ft. **D** see text
SV wisdom save negates **SR** yes (h) **Comp** V, S, M

While this spell can operate as a more powerful version of polymorph other, it is not restricted to transforming creatures. Objects and creatures targeted by this spell can be transformed into any other creature or object the caster desires. For example, this spell could be used to change a needle into a sword, a beetle into a dragon, a chair into a dog or a lizard into a horseshoe. The duration of the spell is determined by the degree of change enacted. This spell cannot be used to create magic items.

An unwilling living target is entitled to a wisdom saving throw to resist the effects of the spell. If the form assumed is inanimate, creatures are placed in a state of suspended animation until either the spell expires or until dispel magic is cast.

A living creature polymorphed into the form of another living creature risks assuming the consciousness of the new form as detailed in polymorph other, and the other details of that spell apply as well. Use of the spell in that manner has a permanent duration, unless the size changed into is more than double the creature's normal height. If more than double, the spell lasts 12 hours. Upon changing, the creature regains 1d4 hit points. If slain, the creature reverts to his or her original form, but remains dead.

The change is permanent for inanimate objects changed into other inaminate objects as long as the general size and volume remains the same or less. Changing an object into a larger size results in the spell lasting 12 hours.

Changing a creature into an object, or vice-versa, results in the spell lasting 1d4 hours if the size and volume remains the same or less. Changing creatures into larger sizes results in the spell lasting only 1d4 x 10 minutes.

This spell can also be used to duplicate the effects of polymorph other, transmute flesh and stone, transmute mud and rock, and transmute metal and wood. The material components of this spell are butterfly wings and a bit of clay.

POLYMORPH SELF/OTHER, Level 4 Int, level 8 Cha
CT 1 **R** n/a **D** 10min./lvl.
SV n/a **SR** n/a **Comp** V

The caster takes the form of another creature. The new form can range in size from as small as a hummingbird to a size up to twice the caster's normal height. A polymorphed character can be changed into a member of his or her own species. The caster can change his or her form as often as desired during the spell's duration. Each transformation takes one round.

The polymorphed caster acquires the physical and natural abilities of the new form while retaining his or her own mental abilities and limitations. Physical and natural abilities include the natural size, armor class, natural weapon attack types and damage and similar physical qualities such as mundane movement capabilities (like flying or swimming), and vision capabilities. Physical and natural abilities do not include magical flight and other magical forms of travel, spell-like abilities, supernatural abilities or other extraordinary abilities.

Moreover, a caster does not gain the ability to make more attacks than is normal for the character just because the creature type transformed and naturally has extra limbs, wings, or a tail. For example, a caster capable of one attack per round might polymorph into a lion. A lion can make three attacks per round – bite, and two claws. The caster polymorphed into a lion, however, may make only one attack although the caster may choose either a bite or a claw attack. If the attack succeeds, the damage inflicted is normal for a lion.

The caster can freely designate the new form's minor physical qualities such as hair color, hair texture and skin color within the normal ranges for a creature of that type. The new form's significant physical qualities such as height, weight and gender are also under the caster's control, but must fall within the norms for the new form's species.

Unlike physical abilities, the caster retains his own mental abilities, Prime attribute designations when applicable to the new form, level and class, hit points, alignment and class to hit bonus. If the new form possesses strength, dexterity and/or constitution attributes, the new scores are applied and thus may affect attack bonuses and attribute checks. The character retains his or her own type, extraordinary abilities, spells and spell-like abilities. A character that can cast spells needs a humanlike voice for verbal components and humanlike hands for somatic components.

When the polymorph occurs, the caster's equipment, if any, transforms to match the new form. If the new form is a creature that does not use equipment, the equipment melds into the new form and becomes nonfunctional. Components and foci melded in this way cannot be used to cast spells. If the new form uses equipment, the caster's equipment changes to match the new form and retains its properties. Incorporeal and gaseous forms cannot be assumed.

Upon changing back to his original form, the caster regains 1d4 hit points. If slain, the character reverts to his or her original form, but remains dead.

Common sense must be applied when a polymorph spell comes into play. The above description adequately will address most uses of the polymorph spell. In those other unique instances, the Game Master should utilize the above as a guideline for issuing rulings on the spell's effect to the players.

Alternately, the caster may cause another creature to assume the body, abilities and potentially the consciousness of another form or creature. An unwilling target gets a wisdom save to resist the spell. Additionally, a creature polymorphed into the form of another risks assuming the consciousness of the new form. For every 12 hours spent in the new form, the creature must succeed at a wisdom save or become a member of the species in question in both form and consciousness, forgetting everything associated with the prior form, including friends, family, experiences and training. If the magic is dispelled, the target regains its former memories and personality.

In all other regards, this spell acts like polymorph self. Size can be no larger than twice the creature's normal height. The caster retains control over minor physical qualities and significant physical qualities. Upon changing back to an original form, the polymorphed creature regains 1d4 hit points. If slain, the creature reverts to his or her original form, but remains dead. The material components of this spell are butterfly wings.

POWER WORD BLIND, Level 8 Int, 8 Cha
CT 1 **R** 50 ft. **D** see text
SV none **SR** yes **Comp** V

This one-word spell unleashes a torrent of power that blinds one or more creatures within the area of effect to a maximum of 100 HD. It affects creatures with the lowest hit point totals first, one at a time until the next target would put the spell over the limit of 100. Creatures with over 100 hit points are not affected. The duration of the spell depends on the total hit points of affected creatures. A creature with up to 50 hit points is blinded for 1d4 minutes, while a creature with 51 to 100 hit points is blinded for 1d4+1 rounds. The area of effect for this spell is 25 x 25 feet.

POWER WORD KILL, Level 9 Int, 9 Cha

CT 1 **R** 50 ft. **D** n/a
SV none **SR** yes **Comp** V

This one-word spell can blast the life out of either a single creature or a group of creatures within the area of effect. The caster must decide whether to target an individual creature or a group before the spell is cast. If targeted at a single creature, that creature dies if it has 70 or fewer hit points. If cast as an area spell effect, it kills all creatures in the area of effect that have 15 or fewer hit points, up to a total of 140 hit points of such creatures. The spell affects creatures with the lowest hit point totals first, until the next creature would put the total over the limit of 130. The area of effect for this spell is 25 x 25 feet.

POWER WORD STUN, Level 7 Int, 7 Cha

CT 1 **R** 50 ft. **D** see text
SV none **SR** yes **Comp** V

This one-word spell stuns one creature of the caster's choice, regardless of whether the creature can hear the word or not. A creature with 40 or fewer hit points remains stunned for 4d4 rounds; one with 41 to 80 hit points is stunned for 2d4 rounds; one with 81 to 120 hit points is stunned for 1d4 rounds; and a creature with 121 hit points or more is not affected. A stunned creature cannot act for the duration of the spell. The area of effect for this spell is 25 x 25 feet.

PRAYER, Level 3 Wis

CT 1 **R** see below Dur 1 rd./lvl.
SV none **SR** yes **Comp** V, S, DF

The caster and the caster's allies gain a +1 bonus on attack rolls, weapon damage rolls and saving throws while their foes suffer a -1 penalty on such rolls. The area of effect for this spell is 50 feet. Everyone in this area is effected.

PRESTIDIGITATION, Level 0 Int, 0 Wis, 0 Cha

CT 1 **R** 10 ft. **D** 1 tn./lvl.
SV n/a **SR** yes **Comp** V, S

The rudimentary prestidigitation spell is a building block for arcane study, and enables the caster to perform a variety of simple magical effects. This spell can clean, soil, or alter the color of items in a 1-foot cube. It can chill, warm or flavor 1 pound of nonliving material. It can move up to 1 pound of matter. It can create effects like a puff of smoke, very minor illusions, sound effects or temporary change in color. This spell can never inflict damage or disrupt the casting of other spell casters. Prestidigitation lacks the power to duplicate any other spell effects. Any actual change to an object (beyond just moving, cleaning or soiling it) persists for only 1 hour.

PRISMATIC SPHERE, Level 9 Int, 9 Cha

CT 1 **R** n/a **D** 10 min./lvl.
SV see text **SR** see text **Comp** V

This powerful spell conjures up an immobile, opaque globe of shimmering, multicolored light that surrounds and protects the caster from all forms of attack. The sphere flashes in seven colors, each of which has a distinct power and purpose. The caster can pass in and out of the sphere without harm. Typically, only the upper hemisphere of the globe is seen because the caster is at the center of the sphere, so the lower half is beneath ground level.

The sphere blocks any attempt to project something through it, including spells. Other creatures, who may attempt to attack the caster through the sphere or pass through it, suffer the effects of each color, one at a time.

Any creature with fewer than 8 HD within 20 feet of the sphere that gazes directly upon it is blinded for 2d4 minutes by the colors. The accompanying table shows the seven colors of the sphere, the order in which they appear, their effects on creatures trying to attack the caster or pass through the sphere and the magic needed to negate each color.

The sphere can be destroyed, color by color, in consecutive order, by various magical effects; however, the first must be brought down before the second can be affected, and so on. A rod of cancellation or a disjunction spell destroys a prismatic sphere, but dispel magic can only work against the violet globe. Spell resistance is effective against a prismatic sphere, but the check must be repeated for each color present. The area of effect for this spell is a 20 foot diamter sphere.

ORDER	COLOR	EFFECTS OF GLOBE	NEGATED BY
1st	Red	Stops nonmagical ranged weapons, causes 10 HP damage	Cone of Cold
2nd	Orange	Stops magical ranged weapons, causes 20 HP damage	Gust of Wind
3rd	Yellow	Stops poisons, gasses, and petrification, causes 40 HP damage	Disintegrate
4th	Green	Stops breath weapons, Con save vs. Poison or die	Passwall
5th	Blue	Stops divination and mental attacks, Wis save or turn to stone	Arcane Bolt
6th	Indigo	Stops all spells, Wis save or become insane	Continual Flame
7th	Violet	Energy field, Int save or banished to another plane	Dispel Magic

PRISMATIC SPRAY, Level 7 Cha

CT 1 **R** 50 ft. **D** 10 min./lvl. **SV** see text
SR see text **Comp** V, S AoE cone 15 ft wide x 50 ft long

This spell causes seven shimmering, intertwined beams of multicolored light to spray from the caster's hand. Each beam has a different power. Creatures in the area of the spell with 8 HD or less are automatically blinded for 2d4 rounds. All creatures in the area are randomly struck by one or more beams, as determined by rolling 1d8 for each beam.

1D8	COLOR OF BEAM	EFFECT
1	Red	10 points damage
2	Orange	20 points damage
3	Yellow	40 points damage
4	Green Poison	Con save vs. Poison or die
5	Blue	Wis save or turn to stone
6	Indigo	Wis save or become insane
7	Violet	Int save or banished to another plane
8	Struck by two rays	roll again twice, ignoring any result of 8.

PRISMATIC WALL, Level 8 Cha, level 9 Wis

CT 1 **R** 50 ft. **D** 10 min./lvl.
SV see text **SR** see text **Comp** V, S AoE 4x2/level wall

The spell is like prismatic sphere, except the spell takes the form of a wall. In all other respects but form, the spell acts as a prismatic sphere.

The wall's maximum proportions are 4 feet wide per caster level and 2 feet high per caster level. A prismatic wall materializing in a space occupied by a creature is disrupted, and the spell is wasted. The area of effect for this spell is a wall 4 x2 feet high per level of the caster.

PRODUCE FLAME, Level 2 Wis

CT 1 **R** n/a **D** 1 tn./lvl.
SV none **SR** yes **Comp** V, S

Upon casting this spell, a bright flame, about the size of a torch, appears in the caster's hand. The flames illuminate as torches do, and will not harm the caster. The flame is real, though, and will ignite combustible materials that are brought into contact with it.

The flames can be used to attack. The caster can hurl them or use them to touch enemies. Successful touch attacks deal 1d4+1 point per two caster levels. The flame can be thrown up to 50 feet, igniting any combustible materials at the point of impact and causing the same damage as a touch attack to any creature struck. The spell ends immediately after the attack.

PROGRAMMED IMAGE, Level 6 Cha

CT 1 **R** 150 ft. **D** 1 rd./lvl.
SV intelligence to disbelieve **SR** no **Comp** V, S, M

This spell creates the illusion of an object, creature or force, as visualized by the caster. Sound, smell and thermal illusions may be all included in the spell effect. Creatures who view the illusion believe it, and can suffer damage from illusions. Hit point damage is suffered from damage to the mind/psyche. The illusion activates when a specific condition occurs, chosen when the spell is cast. The trigger can be based upon any condition normally obvious to the senses. The illusion follows a script determined by the caster without requiring the caster's concentration, and can include intelligible speech if the caster wishes. The image disappears if an opponent makes the saving throw. The material component of this spell is a $10 lens.

PROJECT IMAGE, Level 5 Cha, 6 Int

CT 1 **R** 50 ft. **D** 1 rd./lvl.
SV n/a **SR** no **Comp** V, S, M

Upon casting this spell, the caster weaves a shadow duplicate of himself. The image is intangible, but looks, sounds and smells like the caster. The shadow mimics the caster's actions (including speech) unless the caster concentrates on making the duplicate act differently. The caster can use the duplicate's senses, and during the caster's turn in a round, the caster can switch from seeing through its eyes to seeing normally, or back again. Any spell the caster casts originates from the shadow instead of from the caster. The caster must maintain a line of sight to the shadow at all times. If the caster's line of sight is obstructed, the spell ends. The material component of this spell is a doll crudely resembling the caster.

PROTECTION FROM Chaos, Evil, Good, Law, Level 1 Int, 1 Wis

CT 1 **R** touch **D** 3 rd./lvl.
SV none **SR** no (see text) **Comp** V, S, M/DF

This spell creates a magical barrier around the subject at a distance of 1 foot offering protection against one axis of alignment; evil, good, chaos, or law. Only one protection spell can be in effect at a time, even if each would protect against a different alignment.

The barrier moves with the subject and grants a +2 bonus to AC and saving throws against creatures of the alignment chosen. The spell prevents bodily contact by all summoned or conjured creatures of any alignment: the melee attacks of such creatures fail and the creatures recoil from the protective magic. The protection against contact by summoned or conjured creatures ends if the warded creature makes an attack against, or tries to force the barrier against, the blocked creature. Spell resistance can allow a summoned or conjured creature to overcome this protection and touch the warded creature.

The spell can also block any attempt to possess the warded creature or to exercise mental control over the creature by creatures of any alignment. The protection does not prevent a spell that gains mental control, but it prevents the caster of such a spell from mentally commanding the protected creature. If the

protection ends before the mental control does, the caster would then be able to mentally command the controlled creature. Likewise, the barrier keeps out a possessing life force but does not expel one if it is in place before the spell is cast.

PROTECTION FROM ELEMENTS, Level 3 Wis

CT 1 **R** touch **D** 10 min./lvl.
SV none **SR** yes **Comp** V, S, DF

The target becomes suffused with protective magical energies which provide some measure of protection against one element: acid, cold/ice, heat/fire, electricity/lightning or sonic/air. The dweomer grants temporary invulnerability against the specified energy type. The spell absorbs 12 hit points per caster level of elemental damage, whether natural or magical. Once it has done so, the spell ends. The protection absorbs only damage; the recipient could still suffer unfortunate side effects, although the spell does protect the recipient's equipment.

PURIFY FOOD AND DRINK, Level 0 Wis

CT 1 **R** 10 ft. **D** permanent
SV none **SR** no **Comp** V, S

This spell makes spoiled, rotten, poisonous or otherwise contaminated food and water pure and suitable for eating and drinking. It does not prevent subsequent natural decay or spoilage. Unholy water and similar food and drink of significance is spoiled by purify food and drink, but the spell has no effect on creatures of any type, nor upon magic potions. The caster can purify 1 cubic foot per level. Note: one cubic foot of water contains roughly 8 gallons and weighs about 60 pounds.

PYROTECHNICS, Level 2 Int, 3 Wis

CT 1 **R** 150 ft. **D** see text
SV see below **SR** yes **Comp** V, S, M

Casting this spell transforms a fire into either a burst of blinding fireworks or a thick cloud of choking smoke, as chosen by the caster. The fireworks are a flashing, fiery, momentary burst of glowing and colored aerial lights. This effect blinds creatures within 100 feet of the fire source for 1d4 rounds (dexterity negates). Creatures must have line of sight to the fire in order to be affected. Spell resistance can prevent blindness. The smoke cloud is a writhing stream of choking smoke, billowing out from the source. The cloud spreads 20 feet in all directions and lasts for 1 round per caster level. All forms of natural sight (including special vision) are ineffective in or through the cloud. The spell consumes one fire source, which is immediately extinguished. Magical fires are not affected.

Q

QUENCH, Level 4 Wis

CT 1 **R** 150 ft. **D** see below
SV see text **SR** yes **Comp** V, S, DF

Quench extinguishes all nonmagical fires in a 50 foot x 50 foot area or one magic item. The spell also dispels fire-based spells in the area. In the latter case though, the caster must make an intelligence check with a challenge level equal to that of the level of the caster of the fire-based spell. Fire-based creatures within the spell's area take 1d4 points of damage per caster level.

Alternatively, the caster can target the spell on a single magic item that creates or controls flame. The item temporarily loses all its fire-based magical abilities unless it succeeds at an item saving throw. Artifacts are immune to this effect.

R

RAINBOW PATTERN, Level 4 Cha

CT 1 **R** 50 ft. **D** 1 rd./lvl.
SV intelligence negates **SR** yes **Comp** S, F

A glowing, rainbow-hued pattern of interweaving colors captivates those within a 25 foot diameter sphere. The pattern captivates a maximum of 24 HD of creatures. Creatures with the fewest HD are affected first. Among creatures with equal HD, those who are closest to the spell's point of origin are affected first. Creatures that fail their saves are captivated by the swirling pattern. Captivated creatures cannot move away from the pattern, nor can they take actions other than to defend themselves. An attack on a captivated creature frees it from the spell immediately. The spell does not affect sightless creatures.

With a simple gesture, the caster can make the rainbow pattern move up to 30 feet per round (moving its effective point of origin). All captivated creatures follow the moving rainbow of light, trying to get to, or remain within the effect. Captivated creatures that are restrained and removed from the pattern still try to follow it. If the pattern leads its subjects into a dangerous area, each captivated creature gets a second save.

RAISE DEAD*, Level 9 Wis

CT 1 tn. **R** touch **D** permanent
SV none **SR** no **Comp** V, S, DF

This spell restores life to a deceased human or humanoid. This includes all monstrous humanoid creatures, or creatures that are partially human, such as centaurs or sphinxes. The spell can raise creatures who have been dead longer than 1 day per caster level. The subject loses 1 point of constitution permanently when raised. If constitution is reduced to zero by this loss, the creature is permanently dead and cannot be brought back to life.

Creatures that are raised from the dead are considerably weakened by the process, and require 12 hours of complete rest for each day the creature was dead. During this time the creature is considered to have 1 HP and no mortal wounds. Normal poison and normal disease are cured in the process of raising the subject, but magical diseases and curses are not

undone. Missing appendages and parts are not regenerated upon return from the dead. Raise dead will not work on creatures that died from old age, or upon creatures that simply don't wish to return from the netherworld.

This spell carries with it a high price. The natural forces that govern the wheel of samsara were not meant to be toyed with, and any character attempting to restore the dead must make an immediate Con save with a CL of 15, or suffer 8d6 points of damage, plus one point of permanent Constitution loss.

The reverse of this spell, Slay Living, functions exactly as the Int and Cha spell, Power Word Kill.

RAY OF ENFEEBLEMENT, Level 2 Int

CT 1 **R** 50 ft. **D** 1 rd./lvl.
SV constitution negates **SR** yes **Comp** V, S

This hideously brown-colored, undulating ray strikes its intended target, who is entitled to a constitution save to resist the effects of the ray.

1. The spell temporarily changes all physical Prime attributes (strength, dexterity, constitution) into non-Prime attributes for the duration of the spell.

2. The victim suffers a -1 to hit and -1 to damage rolls for every four levels of the caster (-1 at 1st to 4th; -2 at 5th to 8th; -3 at 9th to 12th; etc.) for the duration of the spell.

READ MAGIC, Level 1 Int, 1 Cha

CT 1 **R** personal **D** 10 min./lvl.
SV n/a **SR** n/a **Comp** V, S, F

This spell allows the caster to read magical inscriptions. This deciphering does not normally invoke the magic contained in the writing, although it may do so in the case of a cursed scroll. Furthermore, once the caster has read the magical inscription, that writing can be read without recourse to the use of read magic. The focus for this spell is generally some sort of monocle, glasses, or magnifying glass.

REFUGE, Level 9 Int, 9 Wis

CT 1 **R** touch **D** until discharge
SV none **SR** none **Comp** V, S, M

This spell imbues an object, worth at least $100, with teleportation magic, giving it the power to instantaneously transport its possessor to the caster's abode. . This travel can occur across any distance, but must be within the same plane. Once the item is imbued with the spell's power, the caster must give it willingly to an individual and inform him or her of a command word to be spoken when the item is to be used. To make use of the item, the subject speaks the command word while rending or breaking the item. When this is done, the individual and all that he or she is wearing and carrying (up to a maximum of 50 lbs./level) are instantaneously transported to the caster's residence. No other creatures are affected (aside from a familiar, if it is touching the subject).

REGENERATE, Level 7 Wis, 9 Cha

CT 3 **R** touch **D**
SV none **SR** yes (h) **Comp** V, S, DF

This spell causes the subject's severed body parts, broken bones, and ruined organs to grow back. After the spell is cast, the physical regeneration will be completed in 1 round if the severed members are present and touching the creature, otherwise the process takes 2d10 rounds to complete. Regenerate also cures 1d8 points of damage +1 point per caster level. It can only be used on one creature.

REMOVE BLINDNESS OR DEAFNESS*, Level 3 Wis, 3 Cha

CT 1 **R** touch **D** permanent
SV constitution negates **SR** yes (h) **Comp** V, DF

This spell cures either blindness or deafness whether normal or magical in origin in one target. The spell does not restore ears or eyes that have been lost, but it repairs them if they are damaged.

The reverse of this spell causes the creature touched to become blinded or deafened, as chosen by the caster. In addition to the obvious effects, a blinded creature suffers -10 to attack rolls, loses any dexterity bonus to armor class, suffers a -2 to armor class, moves at half speed, and suffers a -4 penalty on strength and dexterity checks. A deafened character, in addition to the obvious effects, suffers a -4 penalty on initiative and has a 25% chance to miscast and lose any spell with a verbal (V) component that he tries to cast. Remove blindness or deafness counters and dispels the reverse of the spell.

REMOVE CURSE*, Level 3 Wis, 4 Int

CT 1 **R** touch **D** permanent
SV charisma (bestow only) **SR** yes (bestow only)**Comp** V, S

This spell allows the caster to remove the effects of a curse from an object or creature. Remove curse does not remove the curse from a cursed shield, weapon, or suit of armor, although the spell typically enables the person afflicted with any such cursed item to remove it and get rid of it. Certain special curses may not be countered by this spell, or may be countered only by a caster of a certain level or higher.

Bestow Curse: The reverse of this spell allows the caster to place a curse on a creature. The caster can choose one of the following effects: -6 to one ability score (which cannot reduce the score below 1), or a -4 penalty on attack rolls, saving throws and checks. Subject to the Game Master's approval, the caster may invent a new curse, but it must be no more powerful than the standard curses. The Game Master has final say on a curse's effect. A curse cannot be dispelled with dispel magic, but it can be nullified by limited wish, remove curse, or wish spell.

REMOVE DISEASE*, LEVEL 3 WIS
CT 1 **R** touch **D** permanent
SV constitution negates cause **SR** yes (h) **COMP** V, DF

This spell cures all diseases that the subject is suffering from, whether the source was normal or magical. It can only be applied to one creature. The reverse of this spell, cause disease, causes a random disease in the creature touched, although the severity of the disease is often tied to the level of the caster. The exact effect is determined by the Game Master. Remove disease counters and dispels the reverse of the spell, and vice-versa.

REMOVE FEAR*, LEVEL 1 WIS
CT 1 **R** touch **D** see text
SV none **SR** yes (h} **COMP** V, S, DF

The caster instills courage in one creature, granting the creature a +4 bonus against fear effects for 10 minutes. If the subject is suffering from a fear effect when the spell is cast, it gets a new save with a +1 bonus per caster level. Remove fear counters and dispels cause fear.

The reverse of the spell, cause fear, frightens the affected subject. It suffers a -2 penalty on attack rolls, weapon damage rolls, and saving throws. It flees from the character as well and as fast as it can. If unable to flee, the creature may fight. Creatures with 6 or more HD are immune the cause fear spell. Cause fear counters remove fear.

REMOVE PARALYSIS, LEVEL 2 WIS
CT 1 **R** touch **D** permanent
SV constitution negates **SR** yes **COMP** V, DF

This spell frees one creature from the effects of any temporary paralysis or related magic, including a ghoul's touch, a hold spell, or a slow spell.

REPEL VERMIN, LEVEL 4 WIS
CT 1 **R** see below **D** 10 min./lvl.
SV see text **SR** yes **COMP** V, S, DF.

This spell creates an invisible 20 foot diameter sphere barrier around the caster that repels all types of vermin, including insects, arachnids and rodents. Vermin with less than one-third the caster's level in HD cannot penetrate the barrier. Vermin with at least one-third the caster's level in HD can penetrate the barrier if they make a wisdom saving throw. Even so, vermin that cross the barrier suffer 1d6 points of damage.

REPULSION, LEVEL 6 CHA, 7 WIS
CT 1 **R** see below **D** 1 rd./lvl.
SV strength negates **SR** yes **COMP** V, S, DF.

This spell causes an invisible, mobile field to spring into being around the caster. The sphere is 10 feet in diameter per level of the caster. The field physically prevents creatures from approaching the caster. Creatures within or entering the field must attempt strength saves, or they become unable to move toward the caster for the duration of the spell. Repelled creatures' actions are not otherwise restricted. If the caster moves closer to an affected creature, the creature is not forced back and is free to make melee attacks against the caster if the caster comes within reach. If a repelled creature moves away from the caster and then tries to turn back, it cannot move any closer toward the caster if it is still within the spell's area.

RESILIENT SPHERE, LEVEL 4 INT
CT 1 **R** 50 ft. **D**
SV dexterity negates (h) **SR** yes (h) **COMP** V, S.

This spell causes a globe of force, to completely encase one creature, provided the creature is small enough to fit within the sphere. The spell's area of effect is a sphere with a diamater of 1 foot per caster level. The sphere is not subject to damage of any sort except from a rod of cancellation, a wand of negation, disintegrate, or dispel magic, all of which destroy the sphere without harm to the subject. Nothing can pass through the sphere, inside or out, though the subject can breathe normally. The subject may struggle, but that action will simply move the sphere slightly, and nothing more. The globe can be physically moved by people outside, or by the struggles of those within.

RESIST ELEMENTS, LEVEL 1 WIS
CT 1 **R** touch **D** 1 tn./lvl.
SV none **SR** yes **COMP** V, S, DF

The target becomes suffuse with protective magical energies providing some measure of protection against one element: acid, cold/ice, heat/fire, electricity/lightning or sonic/air. The dweomer grants a +2 saving throw bonus against the specified energy type, regardless of whether the source of damage is natural or magical. The spell protects the recipient's equipment as well.

Resist elements absorbs only damage: The caster could still suffer unfortunate side effects. Resist elements overlaps endure Eeements and protection from elements.

RESTORATION*, LEVEL 4 WIS
CT 1 hour **R** touch **D** permanent
SV see text **SR** yes (h) **COMP** V, S, DF

The caster repairs the life energy of a single creature. Restoration dispels any magical effects that reduce the subject's attribute scores temporarily. Restoration will not restore permanent attribute score loss. The spell also restores one experience level to a creature who has had a level drained. The drained level is restored only if the time since the creature lost the level is equal to or less than 1 day per caster level. It does not restore levels or Con points lost as a result of death.

The evil reverse of this spell, life drain, sucks one level from a creature. This version allows a Con saving throw to avoid the spell's effect.

ROPE TRICK, Level 2 Int, 3 Cha
CT 1 **R** touch **D** 1 hr./lvl.
SV none **SR** no **Comp** V, S, F

This spell attaches a section of rope at least 5 feet long to an extradimensional space large enough to hold up to eight medium-size or smaller creatures. The end of the rope rises into the air until the whole rope hangs perpendicular to the ground, as if affixed at the upper end. Creatures can climb the rope into the space and can pull the rope up behind them, making the rope disappear. If the rope is pulled up into the space, it counts as one of the eight creatures.

The extra-dimensional space is invisible from the outside, and those inside it cannot see outside. Those within cannot be targeted by spells or affected by area effects, but they cannot target spells or area effects outside of the space.

The rope is subject to its normal ability to support weight and withstand punishment. If the rope is not pulled in, a creature outside the extra-dimensional space can pull or break the rope free, ending the spell instantly. Anything inside the extra-dimensional space drops out when the spell ends, suffering damage from any fall. The rope can be used for normal climbing provided the climber does not climb all the way into the extradimensional space.

S

SANCTUARY, Level 1 Wis
CT 1 **R** touch **D** 1rd./lvl.
SV charisma negates **SR** no **Comp** V, DF

This spell prevents creatures from attacking the caster or the spell's recipient. Any creature attempting to attack a character with sanctuary must make a charisma saving throw in order to make the attack. A failed save means that the attacker ignores the person under the spell (it does not lose its attack, but must choose another target). If the warded character attacks or casts offensive spells then the sanctuary spell is negated. This spell does not prevent the warded creature from being affected by area of effect spells.

SCARE, Level 2 Int, 3 Cha
CT 1 **R** 50 ft. **D** 1 rd./lvl.
SV charisma negates **SR** yes **Comp** V, S, M

This spell causes creatures with fewer than 6 hit dice/levels to make a charisma saving throw or be overwhelmed by a wave of terror. Success allows the target to control its fear and react normally, while failure causes it to flee in panic. If cornered, the target fights but with a -1 penalty to attacks and damage. Monsters with more than 6 hit dice/levels are immune to this spell. Arcanists, elves, undead and planar creatures are unaffected. The spell requires the flesh or bone of an undead monster to cast.

SCREEN ILLUSION, Level 8 Cha
CT 10 min. **R** 50 ft. **D** 1 day
SV see text **SR** no **Comp** V, S

This spell hides a 25 foot cube/level area from scrying and normal vision. The caster creates an illusion of what will be observed in the spell's area. Once these images are set, they cannot be changed. Any attempts to scry the area automatically detect the illusory image with no save allowed; though direct observation may allow a save at the Game Master's discretion. Even entering the area does not cancel the illusion or necessarily allow a save, assuming that hidden beings take care to stay out of the way of those affected by the illusion.

SCRYING, Level 4 Int, 5 Wis
CT 10 min. **R** see below **D** 1 rd./lvl.
SV none **SR** no **Comp** V, S, M, F

Focusing on a mental image of a particular creature, the caster's mind's eye may gaze upon the target, watching and listening, regardless of distance. An astute character (intelligence 13+) may get the feeling they are being watched upon a successful Int check. Successfully focusing the mind's eye in this manner is difficult. It requires a gem worth at least $10 to channel the spell and an intelligence attribute check with the roll adjusted by the following cumulative modifiers:

Caster knows the target well:	+5
Caster has only met the target:	+5
Caster has only heard of the target:	+10
Caster has no knowledge of the target:	+15
Caster has likeness or picture of the target:	+5
Caster has garment or possession of the target:	+5
Caster has character body part,nail clippings,etc.:	+5
Target is on another plane:	+15

If the scrying is successful, the caster may cast the following spells through the scrying without a chance of failure: comprehend languages, read magic, tongues; the following spells have a 5% chance per caster level of operating correctly: detect chaos, detect evil, detect good, detect law, detect magic and message.

SECRET CHEST, Level 5 Int
CT 1 hr. **R** see below **D** 60 days
SV n/a **SR** n/a **Comp** V, S, F

This spell allows the caster to hide a chest in the ethereal plane and retrieve it as needed for up to 60 days. The chest can contain up to 1 cubic foot of material per caster level, regardless of the chest's actual size. To prepare the spell, the caster must have a chest created by master craftsmen from rare and expensive materials costing at least $500, as well as a perfect miniature

replica of said chest, costing $5. Once the chests are complete, the caster invokes the spell – with the result that the larger chest and any contents are sent to the ethereal plane.

The caster uses the smaller chest to retrieve the larger chest at will until the 60 days expiration. After 60 days, the chest begins to deteriorate rapidly. There is a 5% cumulative chance per day it will be forever lost. If the small chest is lost or destroyed, then the larger chest and its contents will be irretrievable, absent a wish. Any living creatures in the chest must eat, and will age normally. Only one set of chests can be owned at a single time.

SECRET PAGE, Level 3 Cha

CT 10 min. **R** touch **D** see text
SV none **SR** no **Comp** V, S, M

This spell masks any information on a page or scroll such that the page appears blank or covered with other information. The spell can also disguise explosive runes, allowing their effect without revealing their presence. The caster may invoke a command word to reveal the hidden information, and another command word to return the illusion. Uttering the reveal command word permanently dispels the dweomer. The caster needs a paste made of ground jellyfish or similar animal worth at least $5.

Comprehend languages cannot by itself reveal the true information unless cast with a true seeing spell. True seeing cast alone will reveal that there is hidden information, but will not reveal what it is. Detect magic reveals a dim magical aura, but not its nature. Dispel magic will dispel the spell, but may affect the hidden writing as well. Erase will remove both the illusion and any other information being hidden by the spell.

SEE INVISIBILITY, Level 1 Cha, 2 Int

CT 1 **R** as normal vision **D** 10 min./lvl.
SV none **SR** n/a **Comp** V, S, M

This spell allows the recipient to see any invisible, ethereal or astral beings as if they were normally visible. The dweomer does not allow the caster to recognize illusions nor detect things hidden by means other than invisibility. The spell requires a small pinch of dust, flour or powder.

SEEMING, Level 4 Cha

CT 1 **R** 50 ft. **D** 12 hrs.
SV none (int disbelieves) **SR** no **Comp** V, S

The caster causes the appearance, garb and equipment of the target(s), one creature for every two levels, to change to whatever the caster wishes, with the following limits. The recipients must maintain their basic forms (humanoid, horse, etc.), but can appear either 1 foot taller or shorter, as well as up to 50% lighter or heavier. The illusion provides the change in appearance, but not any change in demeanor, class abilities or other such manifestations. Furthermore, the dweomer is a visual illusion only; armor disguised as clothing will still creak and clink and will feel like armor to anyone touching it. Those disguised by the spell remain in the illusory form until the spell expires, the target is slain, or anyone scrutinizing them makes an intelligence saving throw.

SENDING, Level 4 Wis, 5 Cha

CT 10 min. **R** unlimited **D** see below
SV n/a **SR** n/a **Comp** V, S, M, DF

This dweomer allows the caster to contact a single creature with whom the caster is familiar. The message may be up to 25 words long and can even be sent to those with animal intelligence and the creature will understand the message. The message, however, does not create any compulsion to perform any act, and the creature's reaction will depend on its relation to the caster, its intelligence, alignment, etc. If the target and the caster are not on the same plane of existence, the caster must make a successful charisma saving throw, or the sending will not be transmitted.

SEQUESTER, Level 7 Int, 7 Wis, 7 Cha

CT 3 **R** touch **D** 1 day/lvl.
SV see text **SR** no **Comp** V, S, M

This spell provides complete protection from divinination spells for one creature or object for the duration of the illusion, and renders the affected creature or object invisible to any form of sight , divination or scrying. The spell does not prevent the subject from being discovered by touch or through the use of magic devices. Living creatures (and even undead creatures) affected by sequester become comatose, and are effectively in a state of suspended animation until the spell wears off or is dispelled. If the spell is cast upon an unwilling creature, the target may resist the spell on a successful charisma save. There is no save to see the sequestered creature or object, or to detect it with a divination spell. The spell requires a rare eye or eyestalk costing $50 or more.

SHADES, Level 6 Cha

CT 1 **R** 150 ft. **D** 1 rd./lvl.
SV intelligence disbelieves **SR** no **Comp** V, S

The caster shapes quasi-real illusions resembling monsters, that can attack the caster's foes. The shades remain semi-solid, even to those who believe them to be illusory. The caster can create one or more illusions of creatures whose total HD are equal to the caster's level. The caster chooses what form the illusions take, be it human, animal, or some other mythic beast, with size no larger than 1 foot per caster level in height or length. These shadow creatures, however, have only 60% the normal HP of a creature of the chosen type.

Characters interacting with these illusions believe them to be real creatures unless they make a successful intelligence save. If the saving throw fails, the creatures deal normal damage and have all the normal abilities and weaknesses of a creature

of that type. If the saving throw succeeds, the creatures' special abilities, armor class, damage and all other aspects are only 60% as strong as the real thing. Those who succeed at their saves see the conjurations as transparent images superimposed on vague, shadowy forms.

SHADOW CONJURATION, Level 4 Cha

CT 1 **R** 150 ft. **D** 1 rd./lvl.
SV see text **SR** no **Comp** V, S

The caster shapes quasi-real illusions resembling monsters, that can attack the caster's foes. The shadow conjurations remain semi-solid, even to those disbelieving them. The caster can create one or more illusions of creatures whose total normal HD are equal to the caster's level. The caster chooses what form the illusions take, human, animal, or mythic beast, but the size of the creatures must be small or medium. These shadow creatures have only 20% the normal HP of a creature of the chosen type.

Characters interacting with these illusions believe them to be real creatures unless they make a successful intelligence save. If the saving throw fails, the creatures deal normal damage and have all the normal abilities and weaknesses of a creature of that type. If the saving throw succeeds, the creatures' special abilities, armor class, damage and all other aspects are only 20% as strong as the real thing. Those who succeed at their saves see the conjurations as transparent images superimposed on vague, shadowy forms.

SHADOW EVOCATION, Level 5 Cha

CT 1 **R** special **D** see below
SV see below **SR** yes **Comp** V, S.

The caster creates a quasi-real illusion possessed of some actual substance and reality, that mimics one of the following spells: fireball, ice storm, lightning bolt, Arcane Bolt, stinking cloud, wall of fire, wall of ice, or web. The mimicked spell has its full normal effect, range, duration, saving throw allowances, SR and so on, unless the targeted creature(s) makes an intelligence saving throw. A successful saving throw reduces the mimicked spell to 20% of its normal damage, effect and strength.

SHADOW WALK, Level 7 Cha

CT 1 **R** touch **D** 1 hr./lvl.
SV intelligence negates (h) **SR** yes (h) **Comp** V, S.

This spell allows for rapid travel along a shadow pathway. To cast this spell, the caster must be in an area of heavy shadows. The caster and any creature touched, up to 1 per level, are then transported along a swirling pathway of shadowstuff to the edge of normal reality, where it borders a plane of shadow. The effect is largely illusory, but the path is quasi-real. Travelers on the the shadow path move at a rate of up to seven miles every 10 minutes. Movement appears normal on the shadow path, but is in reality rapid relative to the material plane. The caster is innately aware of location relative to the material plane and therefore will know exactly where the party will emerge. Any creature unwilling to continue traveling with the caster will either wander off into the plane of shadow, or return to a random spot on the material plane (50% chance of each).

The spell may also be used to travel to other planes that border the plane of shadow, but this requires the caster to actually traverse the plane of shadow and face its perils. Such a journey requires 1d4 hours to complete.

SHAPECHANGE, Level 8 Wis, 9 Int

CT 1 **R** see below **D** 10 min./lvl.
SV n/a **SR** n/a **Comp** V, S, M

The caster assumes the form of any creature known to the caster. The caster can change forms throughout the duration of the spell. Each change takes one round. The form is quite real, and grants the caster most of the abilities of the creature formed. The caster retains his own mind and intelligence, as well as wisdom scores and hit points. Other attributes might change as a result of the new form. The character retains his or her extraordinary abilities, spells and spell-like abilities. The character can cast spells for which he or she has components. The character needs a humanlike voice for verbal components and humanlike hands for somatic components. The caster does not gain the spell-like or supernatural abilities of the new form, but does gain the extraordinary abilities of the new form.

The size of the form being taken can range from a gnat to any creature not more than 200 feet in length. Even amorphous or gaseous states may be assumed by casting this spell. Upon changing, the caster regains 1d4 hit points. If slain, the caster reverts to his or her original form, but remains dead.

The spell requires a $250 wand created from a shapechanging creature's arm or leg bone, gilded with silver and mystic carvings. This wand is not consumed in the casting of the spell.

SHAPE STONE OR WOOD, Level 3 Wis

CT 1 **R** touch **D** see text
SV n/a **SR** n/a **Comp** V, S, M, DF

By use of this dweomer, the caster can shape a piece of stone or wood into any desired form. A stone or wooden weapon or piece of furniture or any other item is possible. Doors can be reshaped to allow entry/exit, walls parted with a passage, or anything else that the caster can imagine and that fits within the range of material that the spell effects is possible. It takes one round to shape each 1 cubic foot of material. Note that the creations will inevitably be crude, as fine workmanship and finishing are beyond the scope of this invocation. The spell's area of effect is 10 cubic feet +1 cubic foot per level. Casting the spell requires a splinter of wood or stone wrapped in clay.

SHATTER, Level 2 Int
CT 1 **R** 50 ft. **D** instant
SV see text **SR** yes (object) **Comp** V, S, M

This spell creates a sonic force that shatters any crystal or brittle substance within a 25 foot x 25 foot area into dozens of pieces. Such things as potion bottles, windows, mirrors, etc. are vulnerable to this spell so long as the weight is no greater than 1 pound per caster level. If the spell is concentrated upon one item, the item can be up to 10 pounds per caster level and be affected regardless of the composition the item has. All items get a constitution saving throw. Any beings of brittle fabrication as determined by the Game Master (such as crystal golems) take 1d6 damage per level of the caster with a successful constitution save meaning only half damage. Casting the spell requires something the caster can crush in their hand.

SHIELD, Level 1 Int
CT 1 **R** see below **D** 1 tn/lvl.
SV n/a **SR** no **Comp** V, S

Upon the incantation of this spell, a transparent, mobile wall of force appears in front of the caster, protecting him from frontal attacks and Arcane Bolts. Against melee and ranged attacks, the spell grants the caster a specified armor class as follows: melee attacks and high-yield projectiles (such as TNT or grenades), AC 16; device-propelled missiles such as arrows or bullets, AC 17; hand-hurled missiles such as spears, axes and darts, AC 18. The caster's dexterity bonus to armor class is added to the armor class score granted by the spell. Attacks from the side or rear are unaffected. The spell blocks and provides complete immunity against Arcane Bolts. The spell also grants a +1 bonus on all saving throws.

SHIELD OF FAITH, Level 1 Wis
CT 1 **R** touch **D** 1 tn./lvl.
SV none **SR** yes (h) **Comp** V, S, M, DF

This spell creates a protective shield of divine energy around its subject granting a +2 to armor class and to saving throws. The caster must have a drop of holy/unholy water to cast the spell.

SHILLELAGH, Level 2 Wis
CT 1 **R** touch **D** 1 tn./lvl.
SV none **SR** yes (object) **Comp** V, S, DF

This spell temporarily enchants a club or cudgel, granting it a +1 to hit allowing it to deal 1d6+1 damage. The spell also grants the ability to strike any monsters normally only struck by magic weapons or special substances (it will, for example, damage a werewolf as though it were silver).

SHOCKING GRASP, Level 1 Int
CT 1 **R** touch **D** until discharged
SV none **SR** yes **Comp** V, S

The caster generates a potent charge of electricity within the caster's hands. The caster who then touches a target will inflict 1d8 damage +1 damage per level (e.g. a 3rd level caster inflicts 1d8 +3 damage). A target actively defending against a touch attack requires the caster to make an attack roll. The spell ends after one successful hit on a target, though not when the target attacks the sorcerer. The charge can be transmitted by touching a conducting material that the target holds, such as a sword blade or length of metal wire.

SHOUT, Level 4 Int
CT 1 **R** see below **D** instant
SV see text **SR** yes **Comp** V

This spell enchants the caster's vocal cords with mighty power. The caster can then release a concentrated sonic blast in a cone up to 10 feet wide and 50 feet long; the sound deals 2d6 damage to any creature in the area of effect. Additionally, those that fail a Con save are deafened for a number of rounds equal to the damage they suffered. Any brittle substances in the path of this cone are treated as if subjected to a shatter spell. A shout spell will cancel a silence spell, but the cancellation also negates any damage or deafening effect.

SILENCE, Level 2 Wis, 2 Cha
CT 1 **R** 450 ft. **D** 1 tn./lvl.
SV see text **SR** no **Comp** V, S

The caster invokes silence in a 15 foot radius around the target. Within this silent area, no conversations can be made and no verbal spells cast. No one moving within the area can be heard. The dweomer can be cast at a target location or even at a point in the air. When cast on a creature, the area of silence moves with it. Anyone having the spell cast directly upon them may avoid it with a successful dexterity save, in which case the spell is cast upon a point immediately next to the target.

SILENT IMAGE, Level 1 Cha
CT 1 **R** 450 ft. **D** concentration
SV intelligence **SR** no **Comp** V, S

This spell creates a visual illusion of an object, creature or force, as visualized by the caster in a 40 foot cube, + 10 cubic feet per level. It cannot create sound, smell or tactile illusions. Creatures who view the illusion believe it, and can suffer damage from illusions. Hit point damage is suffered from damage to the mind/psyche. While concentrating, the caster can move the image within the range. The illusion disappears if an opponent makes the saving throw.

SIMULACRUM, Level 7 Cha
CT 12 hrs **R** n/a **D** n/a
SV n/a **SR** n/a **Comp** V, S, M

This spell creates a duplicate of any creature. A full magical laboratory is needed to create the duplicate. Further, some form of formative substance such as ice, snow, or clay, $100 of powdered gems and a piece of the creature to be duplicated are needed to complete this spell. While the duplicate will be a perfect physical match for the original in appearance,

there will be differences in knowledge and abilities. The simulacrum will only have 51% to 60% (50+1d10) of the hit points, knowledge (including level, skills and speech), and personality of the creature being duplicated. The simulacrum will radiate magic under a detect magic spell.

At all times the simulacrum remains under the caster's verbal command. The simulacrum has no ability to gain power through experience. It can be repaired by a complex process requiring at least 1 day, $10 per hit point, and a fully equipped magical laboratory. If destroyed, the simulacrum melts into nothingness.

SLEEP, Level 1 Int
CT 1 **R** 150 ft. **D** 1 tn./lvl.
SV none **SR** yes **Comp** V, S, M

All creatures within range and within a 30 foot diameter circle that are capable of sleep will fall into a comatose slumber, with weaker ones being felled prior to stronger ones. The spell will affect 2d4 HD of creatures. For creatures with equal HD, those who are closest to the spell's point of origin are affected first. No creature with 5 or more HD is affected, and HD that are not sufficient to affect a creature are wasted. The spell is centered on a location determined by the caster. Sleeping creatures are helpless. Slapping or wounding will awaken affected creatures, but normal noise does not. Sleep does not affect unconscious creatures, constructs or undead creatures. Sand or a pillow feather are the material components of this spell.

SLEET STORM, Level 4 Wis
CT 1 **R** 450 ft. **D** 1 rd./lvl.
SV see text **SR** no **Comp** V, S, DF

This spell creates a driving storm of sleet that obscures the vision of anyone within it. The storm also causes ground surfaces to become icy and slick, reducing movement rates by half. Any creature moving within the sleet must make a successful dexterity save each round or fall down. The spell effects an area 50 x 50 x 20 feet.

SNARE, Level 3 Wis
CT 3 **R** touch **D** triggered or broken
SV see text **SR** no **Comp** V, S, M

The caster creates a magical snare that is unlikely to be detected by anyone actively searching for it without magical means (hidden as if set by a 12th level hooligan). It can be created from a supple vine, rope, leather or any such similar material. Once enchanted, the snare blends into its environment and will wrap its loop around anything that steps within it. The snare can be up to 20 feet long.

If a supple tree is nearby, the snare will attach its other end to the tree and bend it down, snapping it up again when the snare is activated; this pulls the victim up into the air and causes 1d6 damage. If a tree is not available, the loop will whip around the victim, causing no damage but tightly binding it. An entangled creature suffers a -2 penalty to attack rolls and suffers a -4 penalty to dexterity. To break free requires a strength check against challenge level 5. The snare has 5 hit points and armor class 7.

SOLID FOG, Level 4 Cha
CT 1 **R** 150 ft. **D** 1 tn./lvl.
SV none **SR** no **Comp** V, S

This spell summons a barrier of swirling fog that acts like a fog cloud spell, but only a very strong wind may affect it and any creature attempting to move through it can only move at 1/10th the normal movement rate. Furthermore, all attacks within the fog suffer a -2 penalty to hit and damage. Any fire-based attack that does more than 12 hit points of damage will burn the fog barrier away in a single round. This spell effects a 25 foot diameter sphere.

SOUL BIND, Level 9 Wis
CT 1 **R** touch **D** permanent
SV none **SR** no **Comp** V, S, M, DF

This spell draws the soul from a dead body and places it into a gem (of at least $500 value). The victim must have been deceased for no longer than 1 round per caster level. Once the soul is contained in the gem, it cannot be returned to life via clone, raise dead, reincarnation, resurrection, true resurrection, or even a miracle or a wish. Only destroying the gem can free the soul.

SOUND BURST, Level 1 Wis
CT 1 **R** 50 ft. **D** n/a
SV see text **SR** yes **Comp** V, S, DF

The caster evokes a thunderclap of sound, eminating from any point up to 50 feet away and in a 20 foot diameter circle. Any creature within the area of effect takes 1d8 damage and must make a successful wisdom saving throw to avoid being stunned for 1 round.

SPEAK WITH ANIMALS, Level 2 Wis
CT 1 **R** n/a **D** 1 tn./lvl.
SV n/a **SR** n/a **Comp** V, S

This spell allows the caster to converse with animals with an intelligence score of 1 or more. This allows the caster to converse, question or have a discussion on friendly terms with the affected animal. This effect occurs regardless of the animal's alignment and allows the animal to reply. The replies are limited in complexity depending on the animals intelligence and ability to give meaning to the communication. The animal may even do a small favor for the caster.

SPEAK WITH DEAD, Level 2 Wis
CT 10 min. **R** touch **D** 1 tn./lvl.
SV n/a **SR** n/a **Comp** V, S, DF

This spell allows the caster to ask several questions of a corpse. The corpse can answer questions that the creature knew in life.

It will answer in its own language. Answers are usually brief, cryptic or repetitive. If the alignment of the caster is opposed to that of the corpse, it resists answering and the caster must make a check as if against spell resistance of 12. Only one speak with dead spell per week can be used on a corpse.

SPIDER CLIMB, Level 1 Int
CT 1 **R** n/a **D** 2 rd./lvl.
SV inttelligence negates (h) **SR** yes (h) **Comp** V, S, M

This spell grants the power of movement along walls and ceilings to the recipient just as if they were a spider. The recipient of the spell moves at one-half base movement on vertical and inverted surfaces. Hands and feet must be uncovered in order to make direct contact with the surface being climbed. A small spider is needed to enact this spell.

SPIKE STONES, Level 4 Wis
CT 1 **R** 150 ft. **D** 10 min./lvl.
SV see text **SR** no **Comp** V, S, DF

This spell causes stone formations around the caster (such as stone walls, floors or natural strata) to form into long and narrow points of sharpened stone. The spell caster can effect a 20 x 20 foot area per level. These points of stone remain unobtrusive until someone other than the caster happens upon them. In this case, they can deal damage and impede movement. The sharpened stones cause 1d8 damage to the unwary. Those carefully searching for the stones must make successful intelligence check at -1 per level of the arcanist who cast the spell to notice them. A creature moving through the area takes damage for each 5 feet of movement. Those aware of the stones but who move through the area anyway take 1d4 damage per 10 feet.

SPIRITUAL WEAPON, Level 3 Wis
CT 1 **R** 50 ft. **D** 1 rd./lvl.
SV none **SR** no **Comp** V, S, DF

By invoking a prayer, the caster creates a magical weapon out of divine energy which moves by telepathic command. It will move to attack foes in melee with or at a distance from the caster. The weapon will usually take the form of the favored weapon of the caster's patron deity or that of the caster's chosen weapon if the deity has no preferred weapon. The weapon is guided by the caster, and strikes as if the caster were wielding it in melee (at caster's level with strength bonuses). It does not have any special bonus to hit, and it deals 1d8 damage. The weapon can strike creatures only hit by magic weapons or special materials (it will, for example, damage a werewolf as though it were made of silver) as well as incorporeal creatures.

STINKING CLOUD, Level 3 Int, Cha
CT 1 **R** 30 ft. **D** 1 rd./lvl.
SV constitution negates **SR** no **Comp** V, S, M

This spell invokes a20 x 20 x 20 foot cloud of billowing, nauseous gas that is impenetrable to sight or special visions. Anyone caught within it must make a successful constitution save every round while within the cloud or become nauseated and helpless for 1d4+1 rounds. Helpless characters can only move out of the cloud in a random direction. A strong wind disperses the fog in 4 rounds, a greater wind dispersing it in 1 round. The material component is a bit of rotting food, feces, or other foul smelling item.

STONE TELL, Level 6 Wis
CT 10 min. **R** see below **D** 1 tn./lvl.
SV none **SR** n/a **Comp** V, S

This spell allows the caster to speak with stones in the same manner as plants are conversed with via speak to plants. The stones relate to the character who or what has touched them as well as revealing what is covered or concealed behind or under them. The stones relate complete descriptions if asked. Note that a stone's perspective, perception, and knowledge may prevent the stone from providing the details the character is looking for. The character can speak with natural or worked stone.

STORM OF VENGEANCE, Level 9 Wis
CT 2 **R** 450 ft. **D** up to 10 rd.
SV see text **SR** yes **Comp** V, S, DF

Upon invoking this spell, the caster summons and directs a maelstrom of thunder and lightning. Creatures exposed to the storm must make a constitution saving throw or be deafened for 1d4 turns. If concentration ceases, so does the spell. For each additional round the caster concentrates after the first, the storm has the following additional effect. The area of effect for this spell is a 750 foot diameter circle that is 300 feet tall.

ROUND	EFFECT
2	Acid rains down in the area, dealing 1d6 points of acid damage. No save is allowed.
3	The character calls six bolts of lightning down from the cloud. The character decides where the bolts strike. All may be directed at a single target, or they may be directed at up to six separate targets. Each bolt deals 10d6 points of electricity damage, with a dexterity save for half damage.
4	Hailstones rain down in the area, dealing 5d6 points of damage (no save).
5-10	Violent rain and wind gusts reduce visibility. The rain obscures all sight, including special visions. Movement is reduced to 1/4th normal. Ranged attacks within the area are impossible. Spells cast within the area are disrupted unless the caster makes an intelligence check versus the storm-caster's level.

STUN, Level 0 Cha
CT 1 **R** 10 ft./lvl. **D** 1d4 rounds
SV Wisdom half **SR** yes **Comp** V,S

The caster creates a wave of magical energy that stuns a single target. Victims of this spell suffer -4 to all actions and checks and have their movement halved for 1d4 rounds. The victim gets a

Wisdom save against the effect at +2; if successful the penalties and duration are halved, and movement is not affected.

SUGGESTION, LEVEL 3 INT, 3 CHA

CT 1 **R** 50 ft. **D** 1 hr./lvl.
SV charisma negates **SR** yes **COMP** V, M

The caster influences one creature by suggesting a particular course of action (limited to a sentence or two). The suggestion must be worded in such a manner as to make the activity sound reasonable. A small piece of wool must also be rubbed between the fingers as the suggestion is being made for the spell to work. The victim must understand the language of the caster making the suggestion. Any attempt to suggest an act that would be harmful to the victim, or something severely at odds with its behavior, will allow the affected creature to automatically break the enchantment. The Game Master is free to factor in penalties to the victim's saving throw for quite reasonable suggestions, as well as to give the target bonuses to its save for unreasonable or harmful suggestions.

The suggested course of activity can continue for the entire duration. If the suggested activity can be completed in a shorter time, the spell ends when the subject finishes what it was asked to do. The caster can instead specify conditions that will trigger a special activity during the duration. If the condition is not met before the spell expires, the activity is not performed.

SUMMON ANIMALS, LEVEL 4 WIS

CT 1 **R** 50 ft. **D** 1 rd./lvl
SV none **SR** no **COMP** V, S, DF

This spell summons natural wild animals to aid the caster. The animals appear wherever the caster designates within range, and act immediately on the caster's turn in the iniative order thereafter. If the caster can communicate with the animals, the caster can direct them not to attack, to attack particular enemies or to perform other actions. If ordered to do so, animals attack opponents to the best of their ability. Summoned creatures disappear at the end of the spell's duration.

The spell conjures one or more animals with total HD equal to the caster's level. Thus, a 6th level caster can summon one 6 HD animal, or six 1 HD animals. The caster chooses the HD distribution desired, and the spell attempts to accommodate the request. The caster does not choose the specific type of animal summoned, although a request can be worked into the spell's casting. General requests, such as animals that fly, clever animals or fierce animals are more likely to be answered. The animals summoned will come from the region where the spell is cast, and are always determined by the Game Master. A listing of some possible animals include, but is not limited to, the following (this includes giant varieties of each): ape, badger, bat, bear (black, brown, grizzly, cave, polar), bison, boar, camel, cat, cheetah, crocodile, dog (wild), eagle, elephant, frog, hawk, horse (wild), leopard, lion, lizard, manta ray, pugilistey, octupus, owl, rat, raven, shark, snake, squid, tiger, toad, weasel, whale (blue, sperm, orca), wolves and wolverine.

SUMMON BEASTS OR PLANTS, LEVEL 5 WIS

CT 1 **R** 50 ft. **D** 1 rd./lvl.
SV none **SR** no **COMP** V, S, DF

This spell resembles summon animals. The spell conjures one or more beasts or plants with total HD equal to the caster's level. Thus, a 9th level caster can summon one 9 HD creature, two 4 HD creatures plus one 1 HD creature or nine 1 HD creatures. The caster must choose either beasts or plants; not a mixture of the two. The caster chooses the HD distribution desired, and the spell attempts to accommodate the request. The caster does not choose the specific type of creature summoned, but a request can be made (as with summon animals). The types of beasts which can be summoned are left to the discretion of the Game Master.

SUMMON FAMILIAR, LEVEL 1 INT, 1 CHA

CT 1 day **R** n/a **D** n/a
SV no **SR** yes **COMP** V, S, M

This spell calls a familiar, a unique companion and servant, and binds it to the caster. Doing so takes a day and uses up materials costing at least $10. A familiar is a magical, unusually tough and very intelligent version of a small animal or magical beast. The creature serves willingly. A character may have only one familiar at a time.

An empathic link forms between the master and familiars, granting special abilities to the master as detailed below. The empathic link functions only if the familiar is within one mile of its master.

Familiars do not involve themselves in combat. A familiar may fight if its master faces a life-and-death situation, but magical beast familiars, especially those of an evil alignment, might not do so if the familiar feels its own life would be jeopardized. If a familiar dies, or the master chooses to dismiss it, the master loses a level in the class that allowed the spell to be cast and permanently loses the number of hit points the familiar granted the master. A master's experience point total can never go below zero as the result of a familiar's demise. A slain or dismissed familiar cannot be replaced for a year and a day. Slain familiars can be raised from the dead just as characters can be, but do not lose a level or a constitution point when this occurs. If a familiar is raised from the dead, the caster will recover the experience points and hit points lost as a result of the familiar's death.

The type of familiar that responds to the spell is randomly determined, or, some say, is directed by the deities. The Game Master might apply modifiers to the roll to determine the familiar, especially if more than the usual special materials are used in casting the spell. Or, the Game Master may allow the character to choose if certain unusual circumstances are met or are part of the story of the game. The caster may refuse to accept the familiar that is summoned, but the caster will be unable to successfully cast the spell again for one year and a day. Some magical beast familiars serve only a master of a certain alignment. If such a magical beast is summoned by the spell and it refuses to serve the caster, the caster can attempt the spell again after one month and a day has passed.

SUMMONED FAMILIAR TABLE

D20	Familiar	Notes
1-3	Cat	Night vision, superior hearing, move silently, hide
4-6	Hawk	Enhanced vision, distance vision
7-9	Owl	Night vision, superior hearing
10-12	Raven	Enhanced vision, speaks one human language
13-15	Toad	Wide angle vision
16-18	Weasel	Superior hearing and smell, move silently, hide
19	CK choice	One of the above, or another small animal such as a bat, rat, small snake
20	Magical Beast	Roll on magical beast sub-table, or CK chooses.

Some sample stats for the various creatures are included as a basis for the Game Master to build upon.

CAT *(These neutral animal vital stats are HD 2d2, AC14, move 30 feet. Their primary attributes are physical and mental (see below). Cats threaten in combat but the damage of their attack is negligible. See the chart above for special abilities.)*

HAWK *(These neutral animal vital stats are HD 2d6, AC 14/15, move 5/10 feet or 60/80 feet in flight. Their primary attributes are physical and mental (see below). They attack with their talons for one point of damage or beak for 1d2. See the chart above for special abilities.)*

OWL *(These neutral animal vital stats are HD 2d6, AC 14, move 5/10 feet or 60/80 feet in flight. Their primary attributes are physical and mental (see below). They attack with their talons for one point of damage or beak for 1d2. See the chart above for special abilities.)*

RAVEN *(These neutral animal vital stats are HD 2d2, AC 14, move 5 feet or 60 feet in flight. Their primary attributes are physical and mental (see below). They do not participate in combat and flee when danger threatens. See the chart above for special abilities.)*

TOAD *(These small neutral amphibian vital stats are HD 2d8, AC 16, move 10 feet or 20 foot jump. Their primary attributes are physical and mental (see below). They prefer to hide and use their natural coloration for camouflage. Contact with their skin necessitates a constitution save or suffer seizures resulting in death after several days. See the chart above for special abilities.)*

WEASEL *(These small neutral rodent vital stats are HD 2d4, AC13, move 30 feet or climb 20 feet. Their primary attributes are physical and mental (see below). Weasels avoid combat. Their stealthy abilities (see chart above) make them ideal scouts.)*

FAMILIAR BASICS

Use the basic statistics for a creature of its type, as appearing in the bestiary or, if you own it, Monsters & Treasures, except for the following changes:

HIT DICE: Double the hit dice for a normal animal of the type.

HIT POINTS: The familiar's hit point total is added to the master's own hit points, as long as the familiar is within one mile.

Saving Throws: The familiar uses the master's base saving throw bonuses if they're better than the familiar's bonuses.

INTELLIGENCE: Animal familiars are unusually intelligent, and will have an effective intelligence of 1d4+8 (9-12). Magical beast familiars have an effective intelligence of 1d4+10 (11-14), unless a typical creature of its type has a higher intelligence.

SPECIAL ABILITIES: Each familiar has its own special abilities, or enhanced senses, as noted in the table. In addition, the familiar can communicate with animals of approximately the same type as itself, and the communication is limited by the intelligence of the conversing creatures.

EMPATHIC LINK: The empathic link allows the master to communicate telepathically with the familiar for up to one mile. Although some familiars may be able to communicate verbally with their master, telepathic communication is typically better in conveying meaning and intent.

Additionally, the empathic link allows the master to share the familiar's senses as long as the master concentrates on doing so (just like spell concentration). When concentrating, the master shares the familiar's five senses (sight, hearing, smell, taste, and touch). Thus, for example, the master can see through the familiar's eyes. If a familiar has an enhanced sense, like superior hearing, the master gains the benefit of the enhanced sense as well, but only as to what the familiar can sense. In other words, an owl familiar does not grant its master the special ability of superior hearing, the master simply shares and listens through the owl when concentrating on doing so. Sharing the familiar's senses is a somewhat alien process, as a familiar does not always sense in the same way a person does. Some familiars may have a deficiency in one sense, or lack certain body parts, such as ears, that are normally associated with a sense.

The empathic link also allows the master to cast a spell on a familiar that normally can only be cast on the caster alone, without having to touch the familiar (range is up to one mile). At the master's option, the master may cast any spell on himself and it will also affect a familiar (such as shield). If the spell has a duration other than instantaneous, the spell stops affecting the familiar if it moves farther than one mile away. The spell's effect will not be restored even if the familiar returns to the master before the duration would otherwise have ended. The master and familiar can share spells in this way, even if the spells normally would not affect creatures of the familiar's type.

MAGICAL BEAST SUB-TABLE		
D20	**Familiar**	**Special Abilities**
1-12	Magical	Spell resistance equal to magical animal double the familiar's hit dice.
13-14	Demon	See text
15-16	Devil	See text
17-19	Faerie	See text
20	Familiar Dragon	See text

MAGICAL BEASTS

Magical beast familiars are more independent than a normal familiar. Each has its own unique special abilities. The master does not gain the special abilities of a magical beast unless otherwise indicated.

CELESTIAL AND FIENDISH ANIMALS: A celestial (good or holy) or fiendish (evil or unholy) version of an animal. The Game Master should pick a type on the summoned familiar table, or roll again on it to determine the type of celestial animal. A celestial familiar serves only good-aligned characters, and a fiendish familiar serves only evil-aligned characters. These creatures have Spell Resistance of 15 plus their Hit Dice. A celestial or fiendish animal shares its spell resistance with its master as long as the master is within 150 ft.

DEMON: A small demon such as a quasit, or other demon of the Game Master's creation. A demon familiar is one of the most independent types, and it will only serve a chaotic evil or chaotic neutral master. A demon's special abilities are determined by the Game Master or are indicated in the demon's entry in Gods and Demons. They do not share their unique special abilities with their master, and are highly unlikely to fight to save their master's life.

QUAZIT *(These minor demon vital stats are HD 2d8, AC 14, move 40 feet or fly 60 feet. Their primary attributes are physical. They attack with either their claws (1d2) or bite (1d2). They are able to cast the following spells once per day at the 3rd level of ability; protection from good, darkness and pyrotechnics.)*

DEVIL: A small devil such as an imp or other devil of the Game Master's creation. A devil familiar is more independent than normal, for its lawful nature creates loyalty. A devil familiar will only serve a lawful evil or neutral evil master. A devil's special abilities are determined by the Game Master or are indicated in the devil's entry for them in Gods and Demons. They do not share their unique special abilities with their master, and are highly unlikely to fight to save their master's life.

IMP *(These minor devil vital stats are HD 2d8, AC 15, move 20 feet or fly 60 feet. Their primary attributes are physical. They attack with either their bite (1d4) or stinger which causes one point of damage. The stinger administers poison and if a constitution check is not made, the victim suffers 2 points per round for 4 rounds. Imps regenerate one point per round.)*

FAERIE: A small faerie (sprite) such as a pixie, brownie or any other such creature of myth, or one of the Game Master's creation. Faerie familiars can be independent but loyal, annoying but playful. A faerie familiar will serve a master of any alignment, if reasonable for a creature of its type, but most prefer chaotic good, chaotic neutral, neutral good, neutral or neutral evil masters. Most of their special abilities cannot be shared with the master, but those with spell resistance will normally share it with their master.

PIXIE *(These faerie being vital stats are HD 2d4 AC 15, move 20 feet or fly 60 feet. Their primary attributes are physical. They attack with small arrows which do 2-5 points of damage, or another variety that causes sleep for 1d6 turns, or yet another which causes memory loss, unless an intelligence save is made. All arrows have a +4 effective bonus to attack rolls.)*

FAMILIAR DRAGON: A familiar dragon is a very small dragon about 2 to 3 feet in length. Some look like a miniature version of a larger, true dragon, while others have no true draconic counterpart. Their special abilities may mimic a true dragon's, or may more resemble those of a pseudodragon's. Each familiar dragon is unique; and the Game Master determines its details and special abilities, and which of those abilities are shared with the master (if any). They are extremely loyal. A familiar dragon responding to the summons will always be the same alignment as the caster.

FAMILIAR DRAGON *(This magical beast's vital stats are HD 2d8 AC 18, move 15 feet or fly 60 feet. Their primary attributes are physical and mental. They attack with two claws for 1d4 points of damage and a bite for 1d6 points of damage, or a breath weapon (stream of acid) dealing 1d6 points of damage in a 10 foot cone. The familiar dragon may breathe once per round, up to three times per day. Victims may make a dexterity save for half damage).*

SUMMON GREATER MONSTER, Level 7 Int

CT 1 **R** 50 ft. **D** 1 rd./lvl.
SV none **SR** no **Comp** V, S, DF

This spell is like summon monster, save that it summons more powerful monsters to aid the caster. The spell conjures one or more monsters with total HD equal to the caster's level, but no monster can have HD greater than 9. Thus, a 15th level caster can summon one 9 HD monster plus one 6 HD monster, or fifteen 1 HD monsters. For purposes of this spell, monsters include anything that is living and not human.

The caster cannot choose the specific type of monster summoned, although a request can be worked into the spell's casting. More general requests, such as monsters that fly, magical monsters, or fierce monsters are more likely to be answered. The monsters summoned will come from the region where the spell is cast, and are always determined by the Game Master.

SUMMON LESSER MONSTER, Level 3 Int

CT 1 **R** 50 ft. **D** 1 rd./lvl.
SV none **SR** no **Comp** V, S, DF

This spell summons monsters to aid the caster. The monsters appear where the caster designates, within range, and act immediately on the caster's turn in the initiative order thereafter. If the caster can communicate with the monsters, the caster can direct them not to attack, to attack particular enemies or to perform other actions. If communication is not possible, the monsters will attack any apparent enemies of the caster. Monsters attack opponents to the best of their ability. Summoned creatures disappear at the end of the spell's duration.

The spell conjures one or more monsters with total HD equal to the caster's level, but no monster have a HD greater than 3. Thus, a 7th level caster can summon one 4 HD monster plus one 3 HD monster, or seven 1 HD monsters. The caster chooses the HD distribution desired, and the spell attempts to accomodate the request. For purposes of this spell, monsters include anything that is living and not human.

The caster does not choose the specific type of monster to be summoned, although a request can be worked into the spell's casting. More general requests, such as "monsters that fly" or "magical monsters" or "fierce monsters", are more likely to be answered. The monsters summoned comes from the region where the spell is cast, and are always determined by the Game Master.

SUMMON MONSTER, Level 5 Int

CT 1 **R** 50 ft. **D** 1 rd./lvl.
SV none **SR** no **Comp** V, S, DF

This spell is much like summon lesser monster, but the monsters are considerably more powerful. The spell conjures one or more monsters with total HD equal to the caster's level, but no monster can have a HD greater than 6. Thus, a 12th level caster can summon two 6 HD monsters, or two 5 HD monsters plus one 2 HD monster. For purposes of this spell, monsters include anything that is living and not human.

The caster does not choose the specific type of monster summoned, although a request can be worked into the spell's casting. More general requests, such as monsters that fly, magical monsters or fierce monsters are more likely to be answered. The summoned monsters come from the region where the spell is cast, and are always determined by the Game Master.

SUMMON PLANAR ALLY, Level 8 Wis

CT 1 tn. **R** 50 ft. **D** see text
SV see below **SR** see below **Comp** V, S, DF

Beseeching their deity, the caster pleads for aid, prompting the deity to select and send assistance in the form of a number of appropriate elementals or extraplanar creatures totaling no more than 16 HD. The caster may request a known individual creature beholden to the deity, but the deity can ignore this request and send a different creature. If the character serves no particular deity, the spell is a general plea answered by a creature sharing the character's philosophical alignment.

The caster may ask the summoned creature or creatures to perform one task, and a summoned creature may request some service in return (as befits the creature's outlook, alignment, deity and the magnitude of favor asked). If the caster agrees to these requests, the creature performs the task asked of them, reporting back to the character afterward if possible, then returning to their home plane. The caster is honor-bound to perform the return favor, and may lose any or all arcanistal abilities if they fail to do so. This will last until such a point as the caster properly atones, in whatever manner their deity sees fit, for the breech of promise. A creature might accept some form of payment, such as a magic item, in return for its service. The creature might keep it or may deliver the item to another member of the character's religion somewhere else where the item can help the religion's cause.

SUNBURST, Level 8 Wis, 8 Cha

CT 1 **R** 50 ft. **D** instant
SV see text **SR** yes **Comp** V, S, DF

By use of this spell, the caster causes a brilliant sunburst of light to explode soundlessly at a predetermined point. Any creatures within the burst are blinded and take 3d6 hit points of damage. Those making a successful dexterity saving throw avoid blindness and take half the hit point damage. Creatures to whom sunlight is unusual or harmful take double damage. Undead who fail a dexterity save take an additional 1d6 damage per caster level and those who are specifically destroyed or harmed by sunlight (such as vampires) are automatically destroyed.

SYMBOL, Level Level 8 Wis, 8 Cha

CT 10 min. **R** touch **D** see text
SV see text **SR** yes **Comp** V, S, M

This spell allows the caster to scribe, either in the air or on a surface, a variety of mystic sigils and runes. The effects depend on the caster's choice of symbols, but some common symbols are described below. The Game Master is free to add to this list. The material components for this spell are a diamond tipped pen and ink made from some unusual creature. The total value of these items should cost no less than $500.

All symbols are inactive after being traced, and are programmed to activate on a circumstance given to it by the caster. As a guidance, most symbols are triggered whenever a creature does one or more of the following, as the caster selects: reads, touches or passes over the rune; looks at the rune; or passes through a portal bearing the rune.

In this case, reading the rune means any attempt to study it, identify it or fathom its meaning. Throwing a cover over a symbol to render it inoperative triggers it if it reacts to touch. To trigger a symbol, a creature must be within 30 feet of the

rune. The caster can also create a command word that can be spoken prior to any of the above actions, so that the symbol will not activate. Creatures who subsequently meet an active symbol's triggering conditions suffer its effects.

DEATH: One or more creatures within 30 feet whose combined total hit points do not exceed 100 must succeed at constitution save or die. The symbol affects the closest creatures first, skipping creatures with too many hit points to affect. This symbol must be carefully engraved on a surface. Once triggered, the symbol lasts until it has affected 100 hit points worth of creatures.

DISCORD: All creatures with an intelligence score of 3 or higher within 30 feet who fail an intelligence save immediately fall into loud bickering and arguing. Meaningful communication is impossible. If the affected creatures have different alignments, there is a 50% chance that they will attack each other. Bickering lasts 5d4 rounds. Fighting begins 1d4 rounds into the bickering, and lasts 2d4 rounds. This symbol must be carefully engraved on a surface. Once triggered, the symbol lasts 10 minutes per caster level.

FEAR: Living creatures within 30 feet become panicked unless they save versus charisma at -4. Those that fail suffer a -2 penalty on charisma saving throws for 10 minutes per caster level, and they flee from the area. A panicked creature has a 50% chance to drop what it's holding, chooses its path randomly (as long as it is getting away from immediate danger) and flees any other dangers that confront it. If cornered, a panicked creature cowers. Once triggered, the symbol lasts 10 minutes per level.

HOPELESSNESS: All creatures within 30 feet radius must attempt charisma saves at a -4 penalty. If the save fails, the creature suffers from hopelessness for 3d4x10 minutes and submits to simple demands from foes, such as to surrender or get out. If no foes are present to make demands, there is a 25% chance that a hopeless creature proves unable to take any action except hold its ground. If the creature remains free to act, there is a 25% chance it will retreat from the rune at normal speed. In either case, the creature can defend itself normally if attacked. Once triggered, the symbol lasts 10 minutes per caster level.

INSANITY: One or more creatures within 30 feet, whose combined total hit points do not exceed 150, become insane unless they make an intelligence saving throw. Insane creatures behave randomly, either wandering away for 1 minute (unless prevented), doing nothing for 1 round, attacking the nearest creature for 1 round, or acting normally for 1 round until the spell ends. The spell lasts until a restoration, greater restoration, heal, limited wish or wish is cast on the creature. The symbol affects the closest creatures first, skipping creatures with too many hit points to affect. Once triggered, the symbol lasts until it has affected 150 hit points worth of creatures.

PAIN: Creatures within 30 feet suffer wracking pains that temporarily reduce dexterity scores by 2 and impose a -4 penalty on attack rolls, dexterity saves and ability checks. A successful constitution save at -4 negates these effects. The pain lasts 2d10x10 minutes. Once triggered, the symbol lasts 10 minutes per caster level.

PERSUASION: All creatures within 30 feet must succeed at a charisma save at -4 to resist. If the save fails, the creature becomes the same alignment as the caster for 1d20 x 10 minutes. During this time, affected creatures become friendly to the caster. The spell does not enable the character to control the creatures as if they were automatons, but the creatures perceive the character's words and actions in the most favorable way. The caster can try to give the creatures orders, but must succeed at a charisma check (difficulty determined by the Game Master) to convince the creatures to do anything they wouldn't ordinarily do. The creatures never obey suicidal or obviously harmful orders. Any act by the character or the character's apparent allies that threatens the creatures breaks the spell. Note also that the caster must speak the creatures' language to communicate the character's commands, or else be good at pantomiming.

SLEEP: Creatures within 30 feet fall into a catatonic slumber if they have 8 or fewer HD (intelligence save negates). Sleeping creatures cannot be awakened for 3d6x10 minutes. Once triggered, the symbol lasts 10 minutes per caster level.

STUNNING: One or more creatures within 30 feet whose total hit points do not exceed 200 become stunned (constitution save negates). The symbol affects the closest creatures first, skipping creatures with too many hit points to affect. A stunned creature can't act, and loses any dexterity bonus to AC. Attackers gain a+2 bonus while attacking stunned creatures. In addition, stunned creatures will drop what they are holding.

SYSTEM SHOCK, Level 0 Int

CT 1 **R** 50 ft. **D** Instant
SV Constitution negates **SR** yes **Comp** V,S

The caster sends forth a burst of energy that short circuits a target's nervous system. As such, this spell can only be used on living targets that have nervous systems. If the victim fails a Constitution save, he suffers 1d4 points of temporary (subdual) damage and -2 to all actions for the next round. A successful save negates the effects of this spell.

T

TELEKINESIS, Level 5 Int

CT 1 **R** 100 ft. **D** 1 rd./lvl.
SV see text **SR** yes **Comp** V, S

By concentrating, the caster can move an object or creature weighing 25 pound per level of the caster by mental command. Telekinesis can move a creature or object weighing up to 25 pounds per caster level up to 20 feet per round. A creature can negate the effect against itself with a successful charisma save at -4, and against an object it possesses with a successful strength save, or with SR.

The spell lasts up to 1 round per caster level, but it ends if the caster ceases concentrating. The weight can be moved in any direction, but not beyond the spell's range. The spell ends if an object is forced beyond the range.

Alternatively, if the caster chooses, the spell energy can be expended in a single round. The caster can hurl, with massive force, one object or creature (within range toward any target also within range). The caster can hurl up to a total weight of 25 pounds per caster level. To hit a target with a hurled item, caster must succeed at an attack roll using the caster's base attack bonus + the caster's intelligence modifier. Weapons hurled by the spell cause double standard damage (with no strength bonus). Other objects cause 1d6 points of damage per 25 pounds of weight. Creatures who fall within the weight capacity of the spell can be hurled, but they are allowed a charisma save to negate the effect, as are creatures that hold targeted possessions. If a creature is hurled against a solid surface, it takes damage as if it had fallen 30 feet.

TELEPATHIC BOND, Level 5 Int, 5 Cha
CT 1 **R** see below **D** 1 hr.
SV none **SR** no **Comp** V, S

The caster forges a telepathic bond among intelligent creatures. Only one creature per three levels of caster can be effected and they must all be within 30 feet of the caster. All the targets must have an intelligence score of 6 or higher. Each creature targeted is linked to all the others. The bond can be established only among willing subjects. All subjects can communicate telepathically through the bond, regardless of language. Once the bond is formed, it works over any distance, but not between planes of existence.

TELEPORT, Level 5 Int
CT 1 **R** touch **D** instant
SV none **SR** yes (h) **Comp** V

This spell instantly transports the caster, and a certain amount of additional weight, to any designated destination on the same plane of existence. The caster can transport his body and gear, and bring along objects (not held by other creatures) and willing creatures, all of which must not total more than 50 pounds per caster level. The character must have some clear idea of the location and layout of the destination. The clearer the character's mental image, the more likely the teleportation works (see table). Areas of strong physical or magical energies may make teleportation more hazardous or even impossible. Teleportation is instantaneous travel through the astral plane; anything that blocks astral travel also blocks teleportation. To see how well the teleportation works, roll d% and consult the teleport table below. Refer to the following information for definitions of the terms on the table:

TELEPORTATION LOCATION FAMILIARITY				
Familiarity	**On Target**	**Off Target**	**Similar Area**	**Mishap**
Very familiar	01-97	98-99	100	–
Studied carefully	01-94	95-97	98-99	100
Seen casually	01-88	89-94	95-98	99-100
Viewed once	01-76	77-88	89-96	97-100
Description	01-52	53-76	77-92	93-100
False destination	(1d20+80)	–	81-92	93-100

Very Familiar: A place where the caster has been very often and feels at home.

Studied Carefully: A place the caster knows well, either because they have been there often or have used other means to study the place.

Seen Casually: A place that the caster has seen more than once, but with which the character is not very familiar.

Viewed Once: A place that the caster has seen once.

Description: A place whose location and appearance the caster knows only through someone else's description, perhaps even from a precise map.

False Destination: A place that does not exist. When traveling to a false destination, roll 1d20+80 to obtain results on the table, rather than rolling d%, since there is no real destination for the character to hope to arrive at, or even be off target from.

On Target: The caster appears at the desired location.

Off Target: The character appears safely a random distance away from the destination in a random direction. Distance off target is 1d10 x 1d10% of the distance that was to be traveled. The Game Master determines the direction off target randomly.

Similar Area: The caster winds up in an area that's visually or thematically similar to the target area. Generally, the caster appears in the closest similar place, but since the spell has no range limit, they could conceivably wind up somewhere else across the globe.

Mishap: The caster and those teleporting with the caster suffer one of the following: 1-3 scrambled; 4-5 appear above; 6 appear below the intended destination. Scrambled travelers each take 1d10 points of damage, and the Game Master rerolls on the chart to see where the travelers wind up. For these rerolls, roll 1d20+80 and each time mishap comes up, the characters take more damage and must reroll. Characters appearing above do so 1d6x10 feet above the intended destination and suffer appropriate damage if they fall. Characters appearing below do so 1d6x10 feet below the intended destination and either instantly die from teleporting into a solid surface or appear in whatever open space exists underground.

TELEPORTATION CIRCLE, Level 8 Int

CT 1 **R** see below **D** 1 tn./lvl.
SV none **SR** yes (h) **Comp** V, M

By casting this spell, the caster creates a 10 foot diameter circle on any horizontal surface that teleports any creature on it to a designated location. Once the caster chooses the destination, it cannot be changed. The spell fails if the caster attempts to set the circle to teleport creatures into a solid object, to a place with which the caster is not familiar and has no clear description or to another plane. The circle itself is nearly impossible to notice. If the caster intends to keep creatures from activating it accidentally, the circle must be marked in some way. Teleportation is instantaneous travel through the astral plane; anything that blocks astral travel also blocks teleportation. To cast this spell requires a $10 loop of golden thread.

TELEPORT WITHOUT ERROR, Level 7 Int

CT 1 **R** touch **D** instant
SV none **SR** yes (h) **Comp** V

This spell acts just like teleport, except there is no chance the travellers will not arrive at the designated destination. If the caster attempts to teleport with insufficient or misleading information, the spell fails. Areas of strong physical or magical energies may still make teleportation impossible.

TEMPORAL STASIS, Level 9 Int

CT 1 **R** 10 ft. **D** permanent
SV none **SR** yes **Comp** V, S, M

The caster places the target into a state of suspended animation. For the creature, time ceases to flow and it does not grow older. Its body functions virtually cease, and no force or effect can harm it. The onset of poisons and disease halt, and bleeding from mortal wounds ceases. This state persists until the magic is removed by a successful dispel magic spell, or until the caster releases the spell. The caster can release the spell at any time, with a single word of command. To cast this spell requires the use of a $500 diamond.

TIME STOP, Level 9 Int

CT 1 **R** see below **D** 1d4+1 rd.
SV none **SR** see text **Comp** V

This spell causes time to cease flowing for everyone but the caster. The caster is free to act in any manner for the spell's duration, including attacking, casting spells or manipulating objects. All other creatures are frozen in place, unable to act. Creatures with SR can resist the effect. Energy and effects present in the area can still affect the caster. The caster cannot enter an area protected by an antimagic field, or by protection from chaos/evil/good/law, or by a magic circle spell, while under the effects of time stop. Spells cast or damage inflicted

by the caster on another target during a time stop has no effect until the time stop ends. At that time, targets of spells receive a saving throw to avoid or mitigate effects if one is normally allowed. Physical damage, by weapon or spell, also accrues after the time stop ends. Spells cast upon the caster during a time stop take effect immediately upon casting. Durations of spells cast in this way should include the time spent in effect during the time stop. For example, a sorcerer casts shield during the first round of a time stop; the duration of his shield should include the one remaining round of the time stop for the purpose of determining when the spell dissipates.

TINY HUT, Level 3 Int

CT 1 **R** n/a **D** 1 hr./lvl.
SV none **SR** no **Comp** V, S, M

The caster creates an unmoving, opaque sphere of force around his or her self. A small opaque glass ball is fixed in place, and does not move with the caster. The sphere can be of any color. Half of the sphere projects above the ground, and the lower hemisphere passes through the ground. Up to nine other human-size or smaller creatures can fit into the field with the caster and they can freely pass into and out of the hut without harming it. However, if the caster leaves the hut, the spell ends. The temperature inside the hut is 70° F if the exterior temperature is between 0° and 100° F. An exterior temperature below 0 degrees or above 100 degrees lowers or raises, respectively, the interior temperature on a 1-degree-for-1 basis (thus, if it's 20 degrees outside, inside it'll be 50 degrees). The hut also provides protection against the elements, such as rain, dust and sandstorms. The hut withstands any wind of less than hurricane force, but a hurricane (75+ mph wind speed) or greater force destroys it. The caster can dimly illuminate the interior upon command or extinguish the light as desired. Note that although the force field is opaque from the outside, it is transparent from within. Missiles, weapons and most spell effects can pass through the hut without affecting it, although the occupants cannot be seen from outside the hut, and thus have total concealment.

TONGUES, Level 3 Int, 3 Cha, 4 Wis

CT 1 **R** touch **D** 1 tn./lvl.
SV none **SR** no **Comp** V, S.

This spell grants the touched creature the ability to speak and understand the language of any intelligent creature within a 30 foot sphere. The subject can speak only one language at a time, although he or she may be able to understand several languages. This spell does not enable the subject to speak with creatures that do not normally speak. This spell does not guarantee a favorable reaction from any creature addressed.

The reverse of this spell, cipher, garbles verbal communication between all creatures in the affected area. It also counters the effects of the tongues spell.

TRANSMUTE FLESH AND STONE, Level 6 Int

CT 1 **R** 150 ft. **D** permanent
SV wisdom negates (h) **SR** yes **Comp** V, S, M

In but an instant, this spell can transform one creature, and any and all objects it carries, into stone, bereft of sense, thought or the faintest glimmer of life. Alternately, this spell can transform a mass of stone into an equal mass of flesh, though the flesh will possess no bones, organs or life unless the spell is being used to restore a petrified creature. When a petrified creature is turned back to flesh, any damage it or anything it bears has suffered afflicts the creature or object, unless the broken pieces are joined with them as they return to flesh. Only creatures made of flesh may be petrified by this spell. To cast this spell requires the use of blood, clay, dirt or stone.

TRANSMUTE METAL TO WOOD, Level 7 Wis

CT 1 **R** 50 ft. **D** n/a
SV none **SR** yes **Comp** V, S, DF

This spell enables the caster to change one metal object to wood, including weapons, armor and other metal objects carried by creatures. Magic objects made of metal effectively have SR16 plus their bonus against this spell. Artifacts cannot be transmuted. Weapons converted from metal to wood suffer a -2 penalty to attack and damage rolls. Armor converted from metal to wood loses 2 points of AC. Weapons changed by this spell splinter and break on any natural attack roll of 5 or lower, and armor changed by this spell loses an additional point of AC bonus every time it is struck by a natural attack roll of 15 or higher. Only a limited wish (temporary), wish, or similar magic can return an object back to its original state.

TRANSMUTE MUD AND ROCK, Level 5 Int, 5 Wis

CT 1 **R** 150 ft. **D** n/a
SV see text **SR** no **Comp** V, S, M, DF

This spell can transform normal mud or quicksand of any depth into soft stone permanently. Creatures in the mud are allowed a dexterity save to escape before the area is hardened to stone. Alternatively, the spell turns natural, uncut or unworked rock of any sort into an equal volume of mud. Magical or enchanted stone is not affected. The depth of the mud created cannot exceed 10 feet. Creatures unable to levitate, fly or otherwise free themselves from the mud will sink and potentially asphyxiate. If the spell is cast upon the ceiling of a cavern or tunnel, the mud falls to the floor and spreads out in a pool at a depth of 5 feet. The falling mud and the ensuing cave-in deal 8d6 points of damage to anyone caught directly beneath the area, or half damage to those who succeed at dexterity saves. Castles and large stone buildings are generally immune to the effects of the spell because the spell can't affect worked stone and doesn't reach deep enough to undermine such buildings' foundations. However, small buildings or structures often rest upon foundations shallow enough to be damaged or even partially toppled by this spell. Each substance changed remains thus unless natural (evaporation turns mud to normal dirt over a period of days) or magical forces restore its state (but not necessarily its form). Each version of this spell dispels the other, but again, does not restore the original form. The spell can effect two 20 foot cubes per level. The material component for this spell is a piece of clay.

TRAP THE SOUL, LEVEL 8 INT, 9 WIS
CT 1 or see text **R** 10 ft. or see text **D** permanent
SV see text **SR** see text **COMP** V, S, M

This spell forces a creature's material body and life force into a gem (the gem must be worth at least $100 value per level or HD of the creature entrapped). The gem holds the trapped entity indefinitely or until the gem is broken and the life force is released, which allows the material body to reform. If the trapped creature is a powerful creature from another plane, it can be required to perform a service immediately upon being freed. Otherwise, the creature can go free once the gem imprisoning it is broken. The spell can be triggered in one of two ways.

SPELL COMPLETION: The spell can be completed by speaking its final word as if the caster were casting a regular spell at the subject. This allows SR (if any) and an intelligence save to avoid the effect. If the creature's true name is spoken as well, any SR is ignored but the save CL increases by 2. If the save or SR is successful, the gem shatters.

TRIGGER OBJECT: The second method tricks the subject into accepting a trigger object inscribed with the final spell word, automatically placing the creature's soul in the trap. To use this method, both the creature's true name and the trigger word must be inscribed on the trigger object when the gem is enchanted. As soon as the subject picks up or accepts the trigger object, its life force is automatically transferred to the gem without the benefit of SR or a save.

TRUE SEEING, LEVEL 5 WIS, LEVEL 5 CHA
CT 1 **R** touch **D** 1 rd./lvl.
SV none **SR** yes **COMP** V, S, M

The caster confers on the subject the ability to see all things as they actually are. The subject notices secret doors hidden by magic, sees the exact locations of creatures or objects under blur or displacement effects, sees invisible creatures or objects normally, sees through illusions and sees the true form of polymorphed, changed or transmuted things. Further, the subject can see into the ethereal plane. The range of conferred sight is 120 feet. A liquid is used to pour over the eyes to enact this spell. The contents and preparation cost at least $25.

The spell does not penetrate solid objects. It does not cancel concealment, including that caused by fog and the like, nor does it help the viewer see through mundane disguises, spot creatures who are simply hiding or notice secret doors hidden by mundane means. Additionally, the divine version of this spell allows the subject to see auras, noting the alignments of creatures at a glance.

TURN UNDEAD*, LEVEL 1 WIS, LEVEL 3 CHA, LEVEL 6 INT
CT 1 **R** 50 ft. **D** 1 rd./Lvl
SV: Wis Neg **SR** Yes **COMP** V, S, DF

By holding forth a symbol of power (which could be a crucifix, a mandala, a crystal of power, or any symbol of the caster's magical philosophy, and calling upon a deity or the powers of the Earth or Universe, or even just using the force of one's own personality (dependent upon the caster's Primary Spellcasting Ability), the caster can instill panic and fear into undead creatures, or even destroy them outright. The Caster may only target a single group of like undead (skeletons, zombies, etc.) on each casting, and the same specific group (not type, group) of undead may not be attempted to turn more than once per day. The undead make a Charisma-based Saving Throw against the Caster's Spellcraft roll. If they succeed, they are shaken, suffering -2 to hit and damage for the spell's duration. If they fail, the creatures flee as fast as they can for the spell's duration. If the caster has 5 or more levels over and above the undead's hit dice, the creatures are instead instantly destroyed. Per each casting of this spell, the caster can turn 1d6 undead with 1-3 HD, 1d4 undead of 4-8 HD, and but a single undead of 9 or higher HD. Intelligent undead such as Vampires always gain a +3 to their saving throw.

The reverse of this spell, *Command Undead*, enables the caster to assume control of the undead in question, who will obey his every command until destroyed or the spell expires. In the case of intelligent undead, treat the creature as though it were Charmed, meaning that it gains a new saving throw if ordered to perform a suicidal act, or one that goes against its nature.

U

UNDETECTABLE AURA, LEVEL 1 CHA
CT 1 **R** touch **D** n/a
SV none **SR** yes (object) **COMP** V, S

This spell allows the caster to mask a magic item's aura from detection. If the object bearing undetectable aura has identify cast on it or is similarly examined, the examiner recognizes that the aura is false and detects the object's actual qualities. The object so hidden can weigh 5 pounds per level of the caster.

UNSEEN SERVANT, LEVEL 1 INT, 1 CHA
CT 1 **R** 50 ft. **D** 1 hr./lvl.
SV n/a **SR** n/a **COMP** V, S, M

The unseen servant is an invisible, mindless, shapeless force that performs simple tasks at the caster's command. It can run and fetch things, open unstuck doors and hold chairs, as well as clean and mend. The servant can perform only one activity at a time, but it repeats the same activity over and over again if told to do so. It has an effective strength score of 2 for lifting purposes. It can trigger traps and such, but it can exert only 20 pounds of force. Its speed is 15 feet per round. The servant cannot attack in any way. It cannot be killed, but it dissipates if it takes 6 points of damage from area attacks. If the caster attempts to send it beyond the spell's range, the servant ceases to exist. A $1 gem is used to enact this spell.

V

VANISH, Level 7 Cha

CT 1 **R** touch **D** instant
SV none **SR** yes (object) **Comp** V

This spell works exactly like teleport, except only objects can be teleported. The caster can teleport up to 50 pounds or 3 cubic feet of matter per level. Creatures and magical forces cannot be made to vanish. Mishap is possible, just as in the teleport spell.

VEIL, Level 6 Cha, 7 Int

CT 1 **R** 50 ft. **D** 1 hr./lvl.
SV see text **SR** see text **Comp** V, S

The caster instantly changes the appearance of the target creature and then maintains that appearance for the spell's duration. The caster can efect one creature per two levels of experience. The recipients of the spell can not be more than 30 feet apart. The caster makes the subjects appear to be anything the caster wishes. The subjects look, feel, and smells just like the creatures whose appearance the target takes. Affected creatures resume their normal appearances if slain. The caster must succeed at an intelligence check at +6 to duplicate the appearance of a specific individual. Unwilling targets can negate the spell's effect by making intelligence saves. Those who interact with the subjects can attempt intelligence (disbelief) saves to see through the glamour, but SR doesn't help to detect the illusion.

VENTRILOQUISM, Level 1 Cha

CT 1 **R** 50 ft. **D** 3 rd.+1 rd./lvl.
SV intelligence to disbelieve **SR** no **Comp** V, S

The caster can make his voice (or any sound that the caster can normally make vocally) seem to issue from someplace else. The caster can speak in any language the caster knows. Anyone who hears the voice and rolls a successful intelligence save recognizes the sound as illusory (but still hears it).

VISION, Level 7 Cha

CT 1 tn. **R** n/a **D** see text
SV see text **SR** no **Comp** V, S

Vision quickly brings to the caster's mind legends about an important person, place or thing, but produces some strain on the caster. The caster poses a question about some person, place or object, then casts the spell and goes to sleep. If the person or object is at hand, or if the character is in the place in question, the caster receives a vision about it with a successful intelligence check.

If the person, place or object is not at hand, but detailed information is known by the caster, the intelligence check is made at -5, and any information gained is incomplete (though it often provides enough information to help the caster find the person, place or thing, thus allowing a better vision next time). If only rumors are known, the intelligence check is made at -10, and any information gained is vague (though it often directs the caster to more detailed information, thus allowing a better vision).

When completed, the divination brings legends (if any) about the person, place or things to the caster's mind. These may be legends that are still current, legends that have been forgotten or even information that has never been generally known. If the person, place or thing is not of legendary importance, the caster gains no information. As a rule of thumb, characters 10th level and higher are legendary, as are the sorts of creatures they contend with, the major magic items they wield and the places where they perform their key deeds.

W

WALL OF FIRE, Level 4 Int, 5 Wis

CT 1 **R** 50 ft. **D** 1 rd./lvl.
SV none (see text) **SR** yes **Comp** V, S, M, DF

With a single bit of burnt wood, a blazing curtain or ring of shimmering fire springs into existence at the caster's command. The wall can take two forms; either an immobile fiery wall, or a ring of fire surrounding the caster that moves with the caster. In both cases, the wall is 20 feet tall and only 1 foot thick. The fiery wall or curtain of fire measures up to 20 feet long per caster level (up to 100 ft long at 10th level). The ring of fire measures up to 10 feet wide per every two caster levels (up to 50 feet diameter at 10th level).

One side of the wall, selected by the caster, sends forth waves of heat, dealing 2d4 points of fire damage to creatures within 10 feet and 1d4 points of fire damage to those between 10 and 20 feet. The wall deals this damage when it appears, and for each round that a creature enters or remains in the area. In addition, the wall deals 2d6+1 point per caster level of fire damage to any creature entering or passing through the wall. The wall deals double damage to undead creatures. No saving throw is allowed for any of the heat or fire damage.

If the caster evokes the wall so that it appears where creatures are already present, each creature takes damage as if passing through the wall. Each such creature can avoid the wall by making a successful dexterity save. (If the creature ends up on the hot side of the wall, it takes 2d4 points of damage, as normal.)

The caster may maintain the wall indefinitely by concentrating on doing so, or may forgo continued concentration, in which case the wall will last 1 round per caster level.

The wall can be attacked and cancelled by cold spells and damage. If any 5 foot length of the wall takes 20 points of cold damage or more in 1 round, that length goes out.

WALL OF FORCE, Level 4 Wis, 5 Int, 7 Cha

CT 1 **R** 50 ft. **D** 2 rds./lvl.
SV none **SR** no **Comp** V, S, M

This spell creates an invisible, immobile sheet, sphere or hemisphere of force that is immune to damage of most kinds, including spells and even dispel magic. The wall can only be brought down by disintegrate, a rod of cancellation, a sphere of annihilation, or disjunction. Spells and breath weapons cannot pass through the wall in either direction, although

transportation spells and effects can bypass the barrier. It blocks ethereal creatures as well as material creatures. Gaze attacks operate through a wall of force. The material components of this spell are 20 small silver mirrors and a $10 gem.

The caster can form the wall into a flat, vertical plane whose area is up to 10 feet long per caster level, 20 feet tall and 1 inch thick. Alternately, the caster can form it into a sphere up to 1 foot per level in diameter, or a hemisphere up to 2 feet per level in diameter.

WALL OF ICE, Level 4 Int

CT 1 **R** 150 ft. **D** 1 tn./lvl.
SV none **SR** no **Comp** V, S, M

Similar to wall of fire, this spell creates an anchored sheet or hemisphere of ice. Unlike wall of fire, a wall of ice cannot form in an area occupied by physical objects or creatures. Its surface must be smooth and unbroken when created. Fire can melt a wall of ice. Suddenly melting the wall of ice creates a great cloud of steamy fog that lasts for 10 minutes. The details on the two versions follows:

Sheet of ice: A sheet of strong, hard ice appears. The wall may be created either vertically or horizontally/slanting. Vertical walls anchor themselves to the floor, while a horizontal or slanting wall must have two opposite surfaces to anchor itself. The sheet has two possible measurments: (1) up to 10 feet per caster level long, 1 inch per caster level thick, and 10 feet tall/wide, or (2) up to 5 feet per caster level long, 1 inch per caster level thick, and 20 feet tall/wide. A horizontal sheet of ice created in the air without two anchor points acts as a sleet storm spell, but lasts only 5 rounds and covers an area equaling one of the two possible measurements.

Each 10-foot length (for the former) or 5-foot length (for the latter) has 3 hit points per inch of thickness. Creatures can hit the wall automatically, and a section of wall whose hit points drop to 0 is breached. Even when the ice has been broken through, a sheet of frigid air remains that deals 1d6 +1 point per caster level of cold damage to any creature stepping through it. Fire-using creatures passing through this cold air suffer double damage, while cold-using creatures suffer no damage.

Hemisphere of Ice: The wall takes the form of a hemisphere of ice over the caster or a designated target. The hemisphere has a maximum possible diameter of 2 feet per caster level. It is as hard to break through as the sheet of ice, but it does not deal damage to those who go through a breach. The caster can create the hemisphere so that it traps one or more creatures, though these creatures can avoid being trapped by making successful dexterity saves.

WALL OF IRON, Level 5 Int

CT 1 **R** 50 ft. **D** permanent
SV see text **SR** no **Comp** V, S, M

The caster causes an anchored, vertical iron wall to spring into being. A piece of iron once used in a wall of a fortress is necessary to enact this spell. The wall cannot be conjured to occupy the same space as a creature or another object. The wall inserts itself into the surroundings, anchoring itself if possible. The wall must always form a flat plane, though the caster can shape its edges to fit available space. Like any iron wall, this wall is subject to rust, perforation and other natural phenomena.

The wall of iron is 1 inch thick per four caster levels, and up to 5 feet x 5 feet per caster level. The caster can double the wall's area by halving its thickness. Each 5 foot square of the wall has 30 hit points per inch of thickness. Creatures can hit the wall automatically, but it is so hard that the first 10 points of damage from each blow are ignored. A section of wall whose hit points drop to 0 is breached.

If the wall is created where it cannot anchor itself, either vertically resting on a flat surface or in the air, it falls on creatures beneath it. An unanchored vertical wall is 50% likely to tip in either direction if left unpushed after 2 rounds. It can be pushed with a strength check (CL 10). Creatures with room to flee the falling wall may do so by making successful Dex save. Creatures who fail take 10d6 points of damage.

WALL OF STONE, Level 5 Int, 6 Wis

CT 1 **R** 150 ft. **D** permanent
SV see text **SR** no **Comp** V, S, M

This spell creates a wall of rock that merges into adjoining rock surfaces. To enact this spell requires a piece of tone from a wall. The wall is 1 inch thick per four caster levels, and up to 5 feet x 5 feet per caster level. The caster can double the wall's area by halving its thickness. The wall cannot be conjured so that it occupies the same space as a creature or another object.

The caster can create the wall in almost any shape. The wall need not be vertical, nor rest upon any firm foundation; however, it must merge with and be solidly supported by existing stone. It can be used to bridge a chasm, for instance, or to form a ramp. For this use, if the span is more than 20 feet, the wall must be arched and buttressed. This requirement reduces the spell's area by half. The wall can be crudely shaped to allow crenellations, battlements and so forth by likewise reducing the area.

Each 5 foot square area of the wall has 15 hit points per inch of thickness. Creatures can hit the wall automatically, but the wall is so hard that the first 8 points of damage from each blow are ignored. A section of wall whose hit points drop to 0 is breached. It is possible, but difficult, to trap mobile opponents within or under a wall of stone, provided the wall is shaped so it can hold the creatures. Creatures avoid entrapment with successful dexterity saves.

WALL OF THORNS, Level 5 Wis

CT 1 **R** 150 ft. **D** 10 min./lvl.
SV none **SR** no **Comp** V, S, M

This spell creates a barrier of very tough, pliable and tangled brush, bearing needle-sharp thorns as long as a person's finger that is 10 cubic feet in size per level of the caster. A simple

thorn is used to enact this spell. Any creature forced into or attempting to move through the wall of thorns takes 25 points of damage per round of movement minus 1 point for each point of the creature's AC that is granted by armor. Dexterity bonus to AC does not count for this calculation.

Creatures can force their way slowly through the wall by making a successful strength check (challenge level 10). A successful creature moves a number of feet equal to its strength divided by 3 (round down). Of course, moving or attempting to move through the thorns incurs damage as described above.

Any creature within the area of the spell when it is cast takes damage as if it had moved into the wall, and is caught inside. In order to escape, it must attempt to push its way free, or it can wait until the spell ends. A creature trapped in the thorns can choose to remain motionless in order to avoid taking any more damage. Creatures with the ability to pass unhindered through overgrown areas can pass through a wall of thorns at normal speed without taking damage.

A wall of thorns can be carefully breached by slow work with edged weapons. Chopping away at the wall creates a safe passage 1 foot deep for every 10 minutes of work. Normal fire cannot harm the barrier, but magical fire burns it away in 10 minutes.

WALL OF WIND, Level 3 Wis

CT 1 **R** 150 ft. **D** 1 rd./lvl.
SV none **SR** no **Comp** V, S

A 10 x 20 foot high invisible vertical curtain of wind appears. It is 2 feet thick and of considerable strength. The roaring blast is sufficient to blow away any bird smaller than an eagle, and tear papers and similar materials from unsuspecting hands. Small flying creatures cannot pass through the barrier. Loose materials and cloth garments fly upward when caught in a wind wall. Arrows and bolts are deflected upward and miss, while any other normal ranged weapon passing through the wall suffers a -6 to hit and -2 points of damage. Massive ranged weapons like catapult boulders, are not affected. Gases, most gaseous breath weapons, and creatures in gaseous form cannot pass through the wall (although it is no barrier to incorporeal creatures). While the wall must be vertical, the caster can shape it in any continuous path along the ground.

WARP WOOD*, Level 3 Wis

CT 1 **R** 50 ft. **D** n/a
SV no **SR** yes (object) **Comp** V, S, DF

The caster causes wood to bend and warp, permanently destroying its straightness, form and strength. One cubic foot of material can be effected by this spell. Boards or planks can be affected. Warped weapons are useless. Wood that is already enchanted or somehow innately magical is not affected. The reverse of this spell, straighten wood, reforms to original shape, straightness and strength any wood that has been warped by this spell or by other means.

WATER BREATHING, Level 3 Int

CT 1 **R** touch **D** 2 hrs./lvl.
SV constitution negates (h) **SR** yes (h) **Comp** V, S, M, DF

The recipient creatures can breathe water freely. Any number of creatures can be affected by touching them in turn, but the duration is divided evenly among them. A straw like instrument is used to enact this spell.

WEB, Level 2 Int

CT 1 **R** 50 ft. **D** n/a
SV see text **SR** no **Comp** V, S, M

This spell creates a many-layered 20 x 20 x 10 foot thick mass of strong, sticky strands resembling a giant spider's web, that trap objects and creatures caught in them. A strand or wad of web from a spider's web is used to enact this spell. The webs must be anchored to two or more solid and diametrically opposed points or else it collapses upon itself. Creatures caught within a web or simply touching its strands become entangled among the gluey fibers. Anyone in the spell's area of effect when it is cast must make a dexterity save or become stuck. An entangled creature suffers a -2 penalty to attack and damage rolls, a -4 penalty to effective dexterity and can't move. An entangled character cannot cast spells with somatic components. A stuck creature can break loose by succeeding at a strength check.

Once loose (either by making the initial dexterity save or a later strength check), a creature may progress through the web very slowly at a rate of 5 feet per round. Each 5 feet of movement requires a new strength check to avoid becoming stuck again.

The webs are flammable and fire burns 5 square feet in 1 round. All creatures in the webs take 2d4 points of damage from the flames.

WEIRD, Level 9 Cha

CT 1 **R** 150 ft. **D** n/a
SV intelligence **SR** yes **Comp** V, S

This spell acts like phatasmal killer, but it affects all creatures within a 25 x 25 foot area. The caster causes a manifestation, in the targets' minds, of the most horrific creature imaginable. This creature is the formulation of all the subconscious fears of each target, brought into a very convincing and deadly illusion. Only the caster and the targets can see the killers. The killers make illusory attacks upon the targets, who must make a successful intelligence saving throw or instantly die from fear and psychic damage. A successful saving throw results in 8d6 damage and stuns the targets for 1 round. The killers cannot be damaged, and will pass through all physical barriers to reach the targets. The killers cannot pass through magical protections such as a minor globe of invulnerability, or through any area of antimagic.

Likewise, if the arcanist casting the spell is killed before the effect reaches the target, the spell ends. In rare circumstances, such as when the target makes a successful saving throw and is wearing a helm of telepathy, the target can turn the killer back upon the caster just as if the target cast the spell in the first place.

WHIRLWIND, Level 9 Int
CT 1 **R** 450 ft. **D** 1 rd./lvl.
SV see text **SR** yes **Comp** V, S, M

This spell creates a powerful cyclone of raging wind that is 10 feet wide at the base, 30 feet tall and 30 feet wide at the top that moves through the air, along the ground or over water at a speed of 60 feet per round. The caster can concentrate on controlling the cyclone's every movement or specify a simple course of motion (that cannot be changed once set). The whirlwind moves during the caster's turn in the initiative order. If the cyclone exceeds the spell's range, it moves in a random, uncontrolled fashion for 1d3 rounds possibly endangering the caster or the caster's allies before it dissipates (the caster can't regain control of the cyclone even if comes back within range).

Any creature less than 40 feet tall/long that comes in contact with the whirlwind must succeed at a dexterity save or take 3d6 points of damage. Medium-size or smaller creatures who fail their first save must succeed at a second one or be picked up bodily by the whirlwind and held suspended in its powerful winds, taking 1d8 points of damage each round with no save allowed. The caster may direct the cyclone to eject any carried creatures whenever the caster wishes, depositing the hapless souls wherever the whirlwind happens to be when they are released.

The material component of this spell is a $100 ornate Oriental fan, which is not consumed in casting.

WIND WALK, Level 6 Wis, level 8 Cha
CT 1 **R** touch **D** 1 tn./lvl.
SV n/a **SR** yes (h) **Comp** V, S, DF

The caster's body becomes a cloudlike vapor, allowing movement through the air at great speed. The caster can also use the spell to affect additional creatures, each of which acts independently. The caster can add one creature per 3 levels of experience. A magical wind wafts a wind walker along at up to 600 feet per round, or as slow as 5 feet per round. Wind walkers are not invisible, but appear misty and translucent. A wind walker can regain physical form as desired, and later resume the cloud form (during the spell's duration). Each such change requires 5 rounds.

While in vaporous form, subjects gain immunity from physical harm, though they may sustain damage from high winds (as determined by the Game Master). No spell casting is possible in vaporous form. For the last minute of the spell, a wind walker automatically descends 60 feet per round (for a total of 600 feet) unless the wind waker concentrates otherwise, although descent may be faster if desired. This descent serves as a warning that the spell is about to end.

WISH, Level 9 Int
CT time it takes to word wish **R** n/a **D** n/a
SV see text **SR** yes **Comp** V

By speaking aloud, the caster alters reality with this most powerful of spells. Even wishes, however, have limits. The caster may wish for anything conceivable, but the wish must be precisely stated. The longer and more complicated the wish, the more dangerous the spell becomes. A wish gives the opportunity to fulfill the caster's request, but the spell, for whatever reason, may pervert the caster's intent into a literal but undesirable fulfillment or a fulfillment with unseen consequence. A wish never restores a level or constitution loss from being raised, resurrected or reincarnated from the dead. The caster of a wish spell always ages due to the debilitating effects of the spell upon the body. The caster must make a constitution save (challenge level 9) or age 3 years. Success means the caster ages only 1 year. Typically, a wish can aid one creature but, multiple subjects can be affected if, for example, they are all cured of the same type of affliction. In such a case, the caster can affect one subject for every three caster levels.

Generally, a wish can do any one of the following, if worded correctly, with little danger of misfortune:

- Duplicate a spell of 9th level or lower that the character knows and has cast, or duplicate any other spell of 6th level or lower that the character has seen
- Undo the harmful effects of other spells
- Create a valuable item, even a magic item, of up to $1,500 in value
- Permanently raise or lower an attribute by +1 or -1
- Remove injuries and afflictions
- A wish can bring a dead creature back to life by duplicating resurrection
- A wish can revive a dead creature whose body has been destroyed, but the feat takes two wishes, one to recreate the body and another to infuse the body with life again.
- A wish can lift one creature per caster level from anywhere on any plane and place these creatures anywhere else on any plane regardless of local conditions. An unwilling target gets a Cha save to negate as well as SR
- A wish can undo a single recent event. The wish forces a reroll of any roll made within the last round. Reality reshapes itself to accommodate the new result. The reroll, however, may be as bad as or worse than the original roll.

Duplicated spells allow saves and SR as normal. When a wish duplicates a spell with a material component that costs more than $1,000, the character must provide that component.

WORD OF RECALL, Level 7 Int
CT 1 **R** unlimited **D** n/a
SV see text **SR** yes (h) **Comp** V

This spell teleports the caster instantly to the caster's sanctuary when a command word is uttered. The caster must designate the sanctuary when the spell is prepared. It must be a very familiar place. The actual point of arrival is a designated area no larger than 10 feet by 10 feet. The caster can be transported any distance within a plane but cannot travel between planes. The caster can transport, in addition to himself, objects and creatures weighing up to 50 pounds per caster level. Exceeding this limit causes the spell to fail. An unwilling creature can't be teleported by word of recall. Unattended, nonmagical objects receive no saving throw.

BOOK FOUR: ASTONISHING STORIES

ATTRIBUTE CHECKS

The primary method of task resolution in ***Amazing Adventures*** is the Attribute Check, also called the SIEGE Check. Whenever something needs to be done whose outcome is in doubt or unclear, a check must be made to see if the character succeeds at his task. Every check has an associated attribute. Whenever one of these checks is made, 1d20 is rolled by the player. Attribute and level modifiers are added to this roll, if applicable; other factors such as Backgrounds, Knowledge Skills, and Traits may also add or subtract to this roll. If the final result is equal to or greater than a number generated by the Game Master, called the challenge class (CC), then the attribute check is successful.

The challenge class is a number generated by the Game Master that represents the degree of difficulty for performing that action. The challenge class is generated by the Game Master adding or subtracting the challenge level (CL) to the challenge base (CB), which is 12 if the ability score in question is Primary (Prime), or 18 if it is Secondary. The challenge level represents the degree of difficulty the Game Master believes appropriate for the action being taken. This usually ranges between 0 and 10, but can go higher. The sum total is the CC, and the player must roll higher than that to successfully perform the action. Remember, if the Attribute in question is Prime, the CB is 12, while if it is Secondary, the CB is 18.

For example, a 3rd level Gumshoe with 15 Wisdom (+1 modifier) as a Prime attribute attempts to track a pair of wily second-level hooligans to their hideout deep in the city, using his Cat and Mouse ability. Since Wisdom is a Prime, the Challenge Base (CB) for the task is 12.

The challenge class is the combination of the CB and the Challenge Level (CL) assigned by the GM. In this case the GM gives a bonus of +3 to the hooligans as the trail is only a few days old and they haven't been very careful. He then adds the hooligans' average level of 2 to the CL, for a total CL of 5.

Adding this CL to the gumshoe's CB of 12 gives us a final CC of 17.

The player rolls 1d20 and adds the raider's level (+3) and attribute modifier (+1) to the roll. The die comes up 15, to which the player adds 3 for his level and 1 for his Wisdom attribute modifier, and gets a total of 19. This is greater than the 17 necessary, so the raider successfully tracks the hooligans to their dark and foreboding hideout at the docks.

If it seems simple, that's because it is! All contests, actions, attempts, and tasks in the system are handled using these Attribute Checks, save for combat, which uses a slightly modified version of the same resolution system, substituting the character's BtH bonus and special class-based abilities for the character's level and/or Prime bonus.

In combat, a player will roll a d20, adding their Base to Hit (BtH) and appropriate Attribute modifier (usually Strength for melee and Dexterity for ranged), plus situational bonuses, and tries to equal or beat the target's Armor Class, or AC.

ACTIVE AND PASSIVE OPPOSED CHECKS

Some checks represent a contest between two people. There are two ways to handle these sorts of contest–one way assumes one party is passive, the other active. One requires only one die roll; the other is more dynamic. It's up to the GM to decide which works better for her game.

The Passive Method

The Passive Method of opposed checks is the default for most SIEGE engine games. Under this method, the CL of any check is set by the level or hit dice and appropriate ability bonus of the target. The example above of the gumshoe hunting the hooligans using Cat and Mouse is an example of a Passive method opposed check.

In the example, the GM knows the Hooligans have an average hit die of 2 and decides that Intelligence is the appropriate

ability to cover their tracks, but that the hooligans are just about average, so they have no Intelligence bonus. All they have is their +3 for their 3-day head start.

The gumshoe needs to make a CL 5 check, which adds to his CB of 12 for a total CC of 17 to track the Hooligans. This method is faster playing, but by removing a die roll the players may feel that they have lost some control in situations where the NPCs are making checks.

The Active Method

Under the active method of opposed checks, if the abilities of a "defender" can affect the outcome, both parties make an Attribute Check, with whichever party succeeds by the widest margin winning the contest. In this case, both parties simply use their Challenge Base as the total Challenge Class.

In the example above, if the gumshoe's quarry were actively attempting to cover their tracks, they might roll an Intelligence check, gaining a +3 bonus from the GM due to the 3 days' time between their passage and the gumshoe's arrival. The GM decides also that the group of Hooligans has an average level of 2 and they're not that bright–Intelligence is not a Prime for them and they don't have an attribute bonus for that score.

In this case, instead of the gumshoe's CC being set at 12 + 3 for the passage of time, the GM simply uses the Challenge Base for both parties (12 for the gumshoe and 18 for the hooligans). He then compares the margin of success for the gumshoe's check of 16 against the result of the hooligans' check.

Let's say the GM rolls for the hooligans and the die result is 15. Adding +3 for their 3-day head start bonus, and 2 for their level, the final result is 20. Their margin of success is two (Check result of 20 – Challenge Class of 18 equals 2).

The gumshoe, on the other hand, achieved a result of 16. Since his Challenge Base was only 12, his margin of success is 4 (Check result of 16 – Challenge Class of 12 equals 4). Again, the gumshoe tracks them to their lair.

AIDING OTHERS

Attribute Checks can also be used to represent multiple people working together. When this occurs, decide who the leader of the attempt is. That person will make the Attribute Check that will determine the final outcome. Before this, all those attempting to aid make Attribute Checks. If they succeed, they add +1 to the leader's check. If they succeed by more than 5, they add an additional +1 for every five points by which they succeed. Thus, if a pilot and co-pilot are trying to steer a bomber through German anti-aircraft fire, the pilot would be the leader, making a Dexterity check to steer the plane. His co-pilot, however, could also aid him–let's say the GM rules through Wisdom, to spot openings in the wall of flak ahead. The co-pilot, who has Wisdom as a Prime makes his Wisdom check and scores a 20! He would add +2 to the pilot's Dexterity check: +1 for making the basic success of 12, and +1 for a superior success of 5 above the base. If the co-pilot had scored 22, he would add +3 to the pilot's check.

EXPLODING AND IMPLODING DICE

Any time a player rolls a test of 1d20, if the result of the roll is 20 before modifiers are added (a "natural 20"), roll an extra d6 and add it to the total. Continue the process until the die comes up a number other than 6. So long as you keep rolling 6, keep adding to the total. This is called an Exploding result.

For example, Luke is making a check against his 3rd-level character's Strength of 18, a Prime for his character. He throws the bones and rolls a 20. He now rolls an extra d6 to add to the total, and it comes up as 6, too! His next d6 roll comes up 4. He's now rolled a total of 30 (20+6+4). He then adds his Strength bonus (+3), and his level (+3) for a whopping total result of 36! He would articulate this as "36, with an Exploding 30."

Game masters are encouraged to adjudicate exploding results as extraordinary successes.

Conversely, if a roll result comes up with an unmodified result of "1," roll an extra d6 and subtract it from the total. If the result of this bonus die is 6, subtract six and roll again. Continue in the same manner as with an exploding result, subtracting the total as long as the additional dice come up 6. This is called an Imploding result. GM's should adjudicate imploding results as disastrous failures or in the case of an imploding result that still succeeds, some sort of nasty complication. Generally speaking, at lower levels, a single roll of "1" is going to result in a failure, but when characters get to higher levels of play, it might require several successive implosion results to cause failure!

SAVING THROWS

The only difference between a normal Attribute Check and a Saving Throw is that generally, an attribute check is made to attempt to do something, while a saving throw is made to attempt to avoid something happening. Regardless, the system is virtually identical: the player rolls a d20 and adds her attribute bonus, character level, and any situational modifiers against a CC set by the Game Master.

TYPES OF SAVING THROWS

There are six different kinds of saving throws each corresponding to an attribute. The situations and effects that trigger a saving throw generally fall into one of the following categories. This list is not definitive but should provide a template for Game Masters to determine a saving throw category for something not listed here.

SAVE TYPE	CATEGORIES
Strength	Paralysis, Constriction
Dexterity	Breath Weapon, Traps
Constitution	Disease, Energy Drain, Exhaustion, Fatigue, Poison, Transformation
Intelligence	Magic, Illusion
Wisdom	Confusion, Gaze Attack, Petrification, Psionics
Charisma	Death Attack, Charm, Fear
Variable	Spells

BREATH WEAPON (Dexterity or Constitution): Any character caught in the area of effect of a breath weapon must make the appropriate saving throw or suffer the breath weapon's full effects. The type of saving throw necessary is described with the monster or spell which causes the saving throw. Generally, the character must dodge the effects of a breath weapon, so a dexterity check is appropriate, but on occasions gaseous clouds require a constitution saving throw.

CHARM (Charisma): Charm spells or spell-like abilities allow a charisma saving throw to avoid being overcome by the charm. A failed save means the character suffers the effect of the charm spell.

CONFUSION (Wisdom): Confusion spells or spell-like abilities allow a wisdom saving throw to avoid being overcome by confusion. A failed save means the character becomes confused for an amount of time as specified by the spell or ability.

A confused character's actions are determined by a 1d10 roll, rerolled each round with the following results: 1 wander away (unless prevented) for 1 minute (and don't roll for another random action until the minute is up); 2-6 do nothing for one round; 7-9 attack the nearest creature for one round; 10 act normally for 1 round. Any confused creature who is attacked automatically attacks the attackers on the next turn.

DEATH ATTACKS (Charisma): Death attacks are rare and only a few monsters and the rare artifact have them. In most cases, death attacks allow the victim to make a charisma save to avoid the affect, but if the save fails the character will die instantly.

DISEASE (Constitution): When a character is injured by a disease attack such as from a ghoul, touching an item smeared with diseased matter or consumes disease-tainted food or drink, the character must make an immediate constitution saving throw. If the character succeeds, the disease has no effect, for the immune system has fought off the infection. If failed, damage occurs after an incubation period. The description for each disease will give the details on the effects following the incubation period. It is recommended that the Game Master roll these constitution saving throws for the player so that he doesn't know whether the disease has taken hold.

ENERGY DRAIN (Constitution): An energy drain attack takes away levels or attribute scores from the victim unless a successful saving throw is made. Most energy drain attacks require a successful melee attack. Mere physical contact is not enough. The full effect of an energy drain, such as the number of levels taken away, is specified in the monster, magic item or spell description causing the drain. If it is not specified, one level is removed.

A character who loses a level this way suffers the effects of the drain immediately. The character loses one hit die of hit points of the appropriate class, and all other class abilities are reduced to the new level. If a familiar or companion creature has abilities tied to a character who has lost a level, the creature's abilities are adjusted to fit the character's new level. The victim's experience point total is immediately set to the midpoint of the previous level.

Characters drained below 1st level become a 0-level character with no class or abilities. A character drained below 0-level is instantly slain. Depending on the creature that killed the character, the character may rise the next night as a monster of that kind. If not, the character may at the GM's option rise as another type of undead creature.

Lost levels or attribute scores remain until removed by spell, such as restoration, or other means. Sometimes, level or attribute loss is temporary and will return to normal in a day's time.

A creature gains temporary hit points each time it successfully uses a natural energy drain ability. Unless specified otherwise, the creature gains the amount of hit points that the victim loses. Energy drain through spell or magic item does not grant temporary hit points unless their description indicates otherwise.

FATIGUE OR EXHAUSTION (Constitution): Pushing the body beyond its limits, contracting diseases, or being hit with certain spells or energy drain effects can cause the character to drop from sheer exhaustion in his tracks. For more information on how this works, see "Fatigue and Exhaustion," below.

FEAR (Charisma): Spells, magic items and certain monsters can affect characters with fear. The character facing a monster who emanates fear or who has a spell cast upon him makes a charisma saving throw to resist the effect. A failed roll means that the character is affected by the fear, as detailed in the spell or monster description.

GAZE ATTACK (Wisdom): Each character within range of a gaze attack must attempt a saving throw each round at the beginning of his turn. Generally the character can avoid the gaze with a successful wisdom check. In many instances, the situation is more appropriately handled without a saving throw through narrative and role playing. If necessary, the

Game Master may require a saving throw. Failure indicates the character was unable to avoid the gaze and suffers its effect.

MAGIC/ILLUSION (Intelligence or Wisdom): This category is for spells cast by creatures or from scrolls. It is a catch all for magic not covered by one of the other saving throw categories.

Arcane or divine spells cast by a magic item or other object, or a spell-like ability possessed by a creature or item usually allow a saving throw to negate, lessen, avoid or resist their effect. If the type of magic is arcane, then an intelligence saving throw is made. If divine, then a wisdom saving throw is made.

In some cases, the specific effect of the spell calls for another type of saving throw. All charm spells, whether cast by creature, item or spell-like ability make a charisma saving throw (see above). Other saving throw categories not covered by this catch all would include paralysis, polymorph, energy drain, death attack and fear.

PARALYSIS/ CONSTRICTION (Strength): Some monsters and spells have the supernatural or spell-like ability to paralyze or hold victims, immobilizing them through magical means. Paralysis works on a character's body, but a character can usually resist it with a strength saving throw. The effects of spell, monster constriction and/or paralysis are discussed above in the spell or monster ability descriptions.

PETRIFICATION/ POLYMORPH (Wisdom): Arcane and divine magic can cause creatures and characters to change their shapes, sometimes against their will. The victim may make a wisdom saving throw to resist the polymorph. Polymorphed creatures retain their own minds, but have new physical forms.

A petrified character is not dead if a majority of the body is intact. No movement or actions of any kind can be made, not even mental ones while petrified. Strength and dexterity scores are effectively (but not actually) reduced to 0. There is no awareness of what is occurring since all of the senses have ceased operating. If a petrified character cracks or breaks but the broken pieces are joined with him as he returns to flesh, he is unharmed. If the character's petrified body is incomplete when it returns to flesh, the body is also incomplete.

POISON (Constitution): When a character takes damage from a poisoned weapon, an item smeared with contact poison, consumes poisoned food or drink or is otherwise poisoned, he must make a constitution saving throw. If he fails, he suffers the poison's initial damage (usually ability damage). Even if he succeeds, he typically faces more damage a short time later. Sometimes, the additional damage allows for another saving throw.

SPELLS (Variable): Magic spells sometimes allow a saving throw to negate, lessen, avoid, or resist the effect. Each spell description indicates the type of saving throw including those spells cast from scrolls, wands, rings or other magical devices.

TRAPS (Dexterity): When a character sets off a trap, a dexterity saving throw is allowed to avoid all or some of the effects of the trap. Each trap is unique and the effects of a successful or failed saving throw should be designated beforehand. The CL for avoiding a given trap is generally equal to the level or hit dice of the adversary who set the trap, though at the Game Master's option, the CC can be set by having the adversary make an Intelligence check (for setting the trap). The result of this check, minus 12, can be used as the CL instead of adding the trap-setter's level to the normal challenge base. This makes characters with Intelligence as a Prime much deadlier at setting traps than other characters.

For example, a 5th level hooligan sets a trap. A 7th level gumshoe with a 9 dexterity walks into the trap. A saving throw is required to determine whether or not the gumshoe sets off the trap and suffers the full effects of it. The gumshoe's Prime attributes are strength, constitution, and wisdom. Thus, he will have to use a Challenge Base of 18 for this check. In this instance, the trap was set by a 5th level hooligan, so the gumshoe succeeds on a 23 or better.

The player rolls 1d20 and adds the gumshoe's level of 7 to the attribute modifier for traps (dexterity). The gumshoe has no dexterity modifier. Thus, if the result of the 1d20 roll plus the character's level is 23 or higher, the gumshoe makes his saving throw and dodges the trap.

FATIGUE AND EXHAUSTION

Fatigue and Exhaustion are conditions every adventurer strives to avoid; they are temporary but debilitating conditions that can in some situations mean the difference between life and death. In general, a character can become fatigued if he suffers 75% of his current hit points (round down) in damage, or if he fails a Constitution check for any reason related to pushing the body beyond its normal limits. Many diseases (GM's discretion) and all Energy Drain attacks result in fatigue if the character fails her attribute check against the effects of the affliction.

The exact effects of fatigue and exhaustion are explained below.

EXHAUSTED

An exhausted character moves at half speed and takes a -4 penalty to Strength and Dexterity, and must make a Constitution check at the end of each round in which any sort of strenuous activity occurs, with a cumulative penalty of -1 per consecutive round of strenuous activity. Failure means the character passes out. After 1 hour of complete rest, an exhausted character becomes fatigued. A fatigued character can become exhausted by doing something else that would normally cause fatigue.

FATIGUED

A fatigued character can neither run nor charge (can only move up to his base movement rate) and takes a -2 penalty to Strength and Dexterity. Doing anything that would normally result in fatigue can cause the fatigued character to become exhausted. After 8 hours of complete rest, fatigued characters are no longer fatigued. The only exception to this is in the case of diseases that cause fatigue. In such cases, diseased characters generally remain fatigued until the disease is treated or cured.

AVOIDING FATIGUE AND EXHAUSTION

A character reduced to 25% of his total hit points is entitled to a Constitution save with a Challenge Level of 3 to avoid becoming Fatigued. Thereafter, he must make additional Constitution saves when his hit points drop to 20% and 10% of their total, with the CL increasing to 5 and 10 respectively. Failing this save means the character has become fatigued.

Avoiding exhaustion means making a Constitution save whenever a fatigued character does something that would result in exhaustion (see "Fatigued" above). This save has a CL equal to an exhaustion save for the current Hit Point level, plus 5. In addition, Constitution saves against exhaustion are made at -2.

For example, a character dropped to 25% of his total hit points who has become fatigued and does not have Constitution as a Prime attempts to run. He must now make a Constitution save with a CL of 8 (saving for fatigue against 25% of current hit points has a CL 3; we add 5 to that total) for a total CC of 26. Since he is already fatigued, his save is made at -2. If he fails, he becomes exhausted.

COMBAT

Much of the excitement in playing ***Amazing Adventures*** occurs during the character's combat with monsters. Whether a gadgeteer battling a horde of Nazi cultists, a gumshoe facing off with a nefarious crime boss or an arcanist facing down an ancient mummy, combat is often the climax of many roleplaying sessions. Combat is also the nexus of many rules in ***Amazing Adventures***. Managing combat is often a challenging affair as the Game Master must not only know the rules, but must also know how to apply the rules fluidly to maintain a sense of excitement through description and action.

To facilitate this, the rules for combat have been kept as simple as possible with much maneuver room left for the Game Master. The rules are designed to organize the action of combat. Yet, as the essence of combat is its narrative, they also enable the Game Master to manipulate the rules in support of the narrative. Narrative development is as equally important to the game as any combat's results. The rules of combat and its narrative development are discussed below.

BASIC OUTLINE OF A COMBAT ROUND

When a combat occurs, each participant will want to take action. The most common action will be an attack on a foe, but might also include, for example, drinking a potion or casting a spell. To facilitate when a character or monster can act, combat is broken into a series of time measurements called rounds. Each participant in a combat generally gets one action each combat round.

Each participant acts during the round in an order established by the roll of a d10. This is called initiative. The character with the highest initiative acts first, and each character in turn performs an action until the last character with the lowest initiative roll has acted. If a character attacks during a combat round, the character's player rolls 1d20 to determine if the character hits the opponent. If the resulting number rolled plus the character's class bonus to hit and any attribute modifier totals are equal to or greater than the opponent's armor class, the character has successfully hit the opponent. A successful hit results in damage to the opponent. Monsters and non-player characters follow the same procedure and rules as characters, but the Game Master manages their actions. After all participants have acted once in the combat round, a new round begins.

SAMPLE COMBAT ROUND

With a furious scream and sword in hand, Captain Spirit, a gadgeteer, charges a Nazi scouting near his campsite. To resolve the combat, Captain Spirit's player rolls initiative for Captain Spirit, and the Game Master rolls initiative for the villain. Captain Spirit rolls a 7, and the Nazi rolls a 4. Thus, Captain Spirit acts first.

Captain Spirit, a 5th level gadgeteer with 14 strength, attacks

the Nazi with his sword. The player rolls a 1d20 and the result is 15. Captain Spirit adds his base to hit bonus (+1) and his strength bonus (+1) to get a total attack roll of 17. The Nazi's SS trench coat imparts an armor class of 12. Captain Spirit's attack roll of 17 exceeds the Nazi's armor class of 12, thus Captain Spirit has successfully hit the Nazi with his sword. The sword inflicts 1d8 hit points of damage, so Captain Spirit's player rolls a d8 and adds Captain Spirit's strength bonus (+1) to the roll. Captain Spirit rolls a 6, for a total of 7 hit points of damage. The nefarious villain only had 6 hit points, so Captain Spirit has defeated it in one mighty swing of his sword.

If Captain Spirit had only inflicted 2 hit points of damage, the villain would have survived the attack. He then would get to perform an action, perhaps an attack on Captain Spirit with his Luger pistol. If both Captain Spirit and the Nazi survived the first round of combat, then a new combat round would begin, started by a new initiative roll. This sequence would repeat until either Captain Spirit or the Nazi were victorious.

COMBAT TERMS

Amazing Adventures uses a set terminology to describe combat. The following are the most common terms of which the Game Master, and eventually the players, need to understand to successfully run a combat.

ACTION: During each combat round, a character or monster may either attack, cast a spell, move, use an ability, use an item, or simply perform some other non-lethal action such as talking or standing still.

ARMOR CLASS: This is an abstract representation of the difficulty in hitting a defender. An attacker's attack roll must be equal to or greater than a defender's armor class to cause damage. All creatures have an armor class. In most cases, it is determined by the type of armor being worn. Armor class normally ranges from 10 to 20, but can extend higher than 20.

ATTACK: Attacks generally refer to the use of a weapon, whether a melee weapon or a ranged weapon, or an unarmed attack. Weapon attacks are made by the attacker rolling 1d20, adding or subtracting the appropriate modifiers, and comparing it to the defender's armor class. There are other forms of attack, like spells, class abilities such as turn undead, or magic items, but each of them are actions that generally have their own rules for determining the result of their attack.

ATTACKER: The term used to refer to the character or monster making an attack on their turn during a combat round.

BASE TO HIT BONUS: This feature is distinct to each class and is listed in the appropriate class table. The listed modifier is added to the attacker's die roll during combat. All monsters possess a bonus to hit equal to their number of hit dice. For example a 5 HD monster has a +5 bonus to hit in combat.

COMBAT ROUND: This is the amount of time it takes for all those involved in combat to take a single action. A combat round lasts approximately 10 seconds. Six consecutive combat rounds equal a turn, which is thus roughly equal to one minute.

COMBAT MANEUVER: These are actions taken by characters during combat to avoid being hit. These usually result in armor class adjustments.

DAMAGE: If an attack is successful, the defender takes damage, typically in the form of hit points. The amount of damage inflicted depends upon the weapon or attack used by the attacker. Weapon damage is listed next to the weapon in the equipment lists. Other attack damage is detailed in the class, spell, magic item or monster description.

DEFENDER: The term used to refer to the character or monster being attacked.

HIT DICE: This term has dual meanings. First, it indicates what type of die is rolled to determine a character or monster's hit points. For example, a sorcerers gains 1d4 hit points each level earned. Second, it indicates the level, and thus, the number of the type of die rolled to determine hit points. For example, a 5th level gumshoe will have rolled 5d10 over the course of the character's history to determine hit points. A monster's description details its hit dice. For example, a monster may have 5d8 HD. To determine the monster's hit points, the Game Master rolls a d8 five times, adding the numbers rolled together to get the monster's total hit points.

HIT POINTS: Hit points represent a body's ability to withstand damage. A creature's hit points equals the amount of damage it can take before being killed or knocked unconscious. An object's hit points equals the amount of damage it can take before being broken.

INITIATIVE: This roll is used to determine the order of action in a combat round among the combat's participants. Initiative is determined by the roll of a d10 by each individual or each group in a combat, as determined by the Game Master.

SURPRISE: This is the act of one party or individual catching another party or individual unaware. The party gaining surprise gets one free combat round to act against the surprised party, who may do nothing.

COMBAT ROUND

One combat round is ten seconds long. During this round, all the characters, monsters and non-player characters should get a chance to act. Generally, only one action is allowed, such as making a melee attack or casting a spell. The types of actions are discussed ahead.

It is important to remember that each round is an abstract measurement. The actions and activities that occur in a round are not meant to take place during specific seconds or

segments. It should be viewed as a short range of time during which many things happen. Although each character or monster must wait their turn to act as determined by initiative, they do not necessarily act in that same order in a narrative sense. The moment of occurrence is not necessarily equal to the initiative roll. Abstract consideration of the combat round allows for a more fluid and expansive narrative.

SURPRISE

Before combat begins, the Game Master determines if one or the other party is surprised. Surprise is a situation in which the adventuring party happens upon monsters and neither is aware nor expects the other. Surprise establishes who becomes aware first. The group that successfully surprises the other gains a free combat round in which to act. Those that are surprised get no action. After the surprise round, combat proceeds normally.

Surprise may involve a situation where two characters or groups are unaware of each other, or a situation where one group is attempting to surprise another. Before any surprise roll is made, the Game Master must determine if surprise is possible. A group that is aware of another's presence cannot be surprised. Situations often arise in which one group is not able to surprise another, such as if they have to pass over a hallway strewn with dead leaves that crack and pop when stepped on, thus warning the inhabitants of the room down the hallway.

Even in those instances in which surprise is possible, there is always a chance something could go awry and the surprise fails to occur. If a party can be surprised, a standard wisdom attribute check is made by the individual in the group with the best chance of succeeding at it, or by each member of the group individually. If the check is successful, that party or individual is not surprised. Failure indicates surprise.

When two separate parties could be surprised, both groups or individuals in the groups must make the wisdom check. If both groups fail the check, they are both surprised and nothing occurs as they stare at one another in a moment of stunned silence. Initiative would be rolled as normal to begin combat.

The chances for surprise can be mitigated by many circumstances. If a party is well hidden or camouflaged and awaiting a group of poorly perceptive thugs on a brightly lit road, the Game Master may decide to penalize the wisdom check for the thugs. In general, the bonus or penalty should remain within a range of -5 to +5, although it might be greater in extraordinary situations.

Returning to the example of Captain Spirit and the Nazi, suppose that Captain Spirit came upon a group of Nazis and they were unaware of his presence. He decides to leap off a narrow ledge into the Nazis, landing amidst them, reigning blows left and right as they scratch and claw to get away from his deadly blade. In such an instance, the Game Master would roll a wisdom check for the Nazis to determine if they are surprised. If surprised, Captain Spirit would get a free round to attack them. If not, Captain Spirit and the Nazis would roll initiative and combat would proceed.

INITIATIVE

The order of action in a combat round is determined by an initiative roll. Every creature or character participating in the combat round rolls a d10 to determine their initiative each round. Those with the highest roll take their action first, and the actions of others descend from there. In the case of a tie, the one with the highest dexterity goes first. In the case of equal dexterity, a simultaneous action occurs.

This method of establishing initiative may seem chaotic at times, especially with large groups of creatures or characters. In those cases, the Game Master may find it necessary to require a group initiative instead, with the winning party acting before anyone in the opponent party.

There is one exception to initiative: when a creature uses a weapon with a reach of greater than 10 feet against an opponent with a weapon with less than a 6 foot reach, or when a large creature is fighting a medium or smaller sized creature. In the first round only, the creature with the more lengthy reach or of larger size is allowed to attack first, even if the creature with the shorter weapon or the smaller creature won the initiative roll. This rule only applies if the creature with the shorter reach or smaller creature approaches within ten feet. Such action counts as the action for that round for the larger creature or the one with the longer weapon.

For example, The Midnight Avenger draws his knife and charges a rabid gigantopithecus who just crushed his companion with a small tree trunk. Screaming in a rage driven by revenge and loss, the Avenger leaps forward to attack. He rolls a 9 initiative, and the ape rolls a 3. The ape is large and the Avenger is medium. Thus, when the Avenger moves within 10 feet of the ape, the ape is allowed to swing first even though the Avenger won initiative.

COMBAT ACTIONS

In a combat round, characters can perform a wide variety of actions. Every possible action, however, can be categorized in one of the five types of actions that may be performed during combat, which all have a chance of failure. The five possible actions are attack, cast a spell, move, use an ability or use an item.

ATTACK

A character or monster is allowed one attack each round unless they possess a special ability allowing them to exceed the limitation. Attacks include melee attacks, either armed with a weapon or unarmed, and ranged attacks with a missile weapon. An attack allows a character or monster to move up to one-half their movement rate. Moving farther than one-half movement rate negates the ability to make an attack.

CAST SPELL

A character or creature is allowed to cast one spell each round. Some spells require two or more rounds to cast, in which case the character must wait until the following round for the effect of the spell to take place. The magic section fully details how spells are cast and when they take effect. A character may not move any distance and cast a spell in the same round unless the spell description states otherwise.

MOVE

If no other action is taken, a character or monster can walk a distance equal to their full movement rate. Full movement also includes jogging (twice the normal move rate) and running (quadruple the normal move rate).

USE AN ABILITY

A character or monster may perform one class or special ability each round. Some abilities, like spells, take more than one round to complete. Some monsters can perform more than one ability per round. Ability may involve movement, but in most cases the movement will not exceed the normal movement rate. Otherwise, the Game Master retains discretion as to whether any ability use involves movement.

USE AN ITEM

An item that is carried and readied can be used. The most common actions in this category are using or activating a magic item or piece of equipment. Such actions include, but are not limited to, drinking a potion, using a wand, casting a spell from a scroll,or casting a grappling hook. In most cases, no movement will be involved or allowed when using an item. Readying an item is not difficult, as long as it is easily accessed. Usually, the item must be on a belt or hanging from a pack, and readying it should not take more than a few seconds. Whereas, if an item is in a backpack, it would take at least a round to take off the pack, dig through it,and retrieve the item. The Game Master and players must use common sense in deciding whether an item is readily available. In some cases, the Game Master may require the players to indicate on their character sheets which items are readily available or how and where an item is being carried.

IMPROVISED AND NON-PROFICIENT WEAPONS

Each character class has a list of weapons allowable to that class. These weapons are those in which a member of said class is typically proficient, or trained to use. That doesn't mean, however, that someone untrained in the use of firearms can't pick up a gun and pull the trigger. It does, however, mean that lack of training will make it harder for him to effectively use the weapon. If a character attempts to use a weapon that is outside of his class's allowed weapons list, he suffers a -4 penalty to hit with that weapon, due to lack of training.

NON-LETHAL AND MULTIPLE ACTIONS

There is of course another broad category encompassing non-lethal or otherwise mundane actions such as talking, standing still and doing nothing or picking up an item. Such actions typically have no chance of failure, however, so they are not considered combat actions.

No matter the type of action attempted, it is up to the Game Master to adjudicate how long any action takes and whether it can be performed in a single round. Most actions occur in a single round, or if they take longer, the rules for the specific action usually detail just how many rounds the action takes to complete. The Game Master may allow more than one action per round under special circumstances (if a character has a haste spell cast on him, for example). Also, some non-combat actions a character may take might not consume a full round. This latter aspect is important and the Game Master must use common sense and reason to determine if an action takes a full round. Drawing a sword would not take a full round. Tossing someone an item may not take a full round. As a rule of thumb, simply think of how long such an action would take in real life. If it takes just a couple of seconds to perform a non-combat action, then the character should be allowed another action, be it combat or non-combat in nature. The Game Master can, and on occasion should, impose an initiative penalty for some of these actions.

MOVEMENT IN THE COMBAT ROUND

Once initiative or surprise is determined, each character or monster involved in combat is allowed an action. One allowed action is movement. Movement, like the combat round, is an abstraction. It is a manner of establishing the distance that can be moved in a given period of time. Movement can be in a straight line, a curve or around a corner. Humans have a base movement rate of 30 feet per round. Base movement rates for monsters are listed in each monster description. The listed rate is the distance in feet that can be moved in one combat round. Movement can be increased by jogging (double the movement rate) or running (quadruple the movement rate). Drop all fractions when figuring movement rates (minimum of 1 foot). To translate the movement rate into inches, hexes or squares, divide the movement rate by 5.

An attacker can move one-half their movement rate and still attack. No attack is allowed if a character exceeds one-half their movement rate. The only exception to this rule is when a charge is attempted. Charging allows for an attack and full movement, but the special rules for charging apply. The Game Master has the option of reducing the movement rate due to terrain, obstacles, injuries or other circumstances. Generally, the movement rate should not be reduced by more than three-fourths (0.75). The Game Master should always allow a character to move at least 5 feet in a combat round, unless the character is restrained or otherwise unable to move.

CHARGING

Charging is a special, movement-based combat maneuver. When charging, a character precedes a melee attack by jogging or running, with the intent of using the gained leverage and momentum to inflict greater damage on a defender. A successful charge attack results in a +2 bonus to damage inflicted, but imposes a -4 penalty to the attacker's armor class for the entire combat round. The charge must be announced prior to the character moving.

When charging, a character is considered to be jogging or running. The character must minimally move the full distance of their normal movement rate. The charge must be in a straight line. The total distance moved while charging cannot exceed the character's jogging movement rate. For example, Una the mentalist announces that she is going to charge a cultist standing across the room. Una's base movement is 30 feet, and thus, her jogging rate is 60 feet. As long as the cultist is at least 30 feet away, but no more than 60 feet, Una may attempt the charge maneuver.

When charging, the attacker suffers a -4 penalty to armor class for the combat round. The penalty applies even if the charge attack is not successful. The penalty also applies if the defender attacks first due to size or weapon length, or by ranged attack. If a defender scores a successful hit upon a charging character, the charge is negated. If a charge is negated, the attacker is still allowed their movement and attack, but a successful hit does not deal any extra damage.

MELEE COMBAT

Melee occurs when two creatures engage in hand-to-hand combat. The attacker rolls 1d20 and adds the basic to hit bonus plus any strength modifier. A monster's basic to hit bonus is equal to its total number of hit dice (a 3d8 hit dice creature adds a +3). If the total is greater than or equal to the defender's armor class, the attacker has successfully hit the defender and inflicts damage as determined by the weapon used. Unarmed combat is a type of melee attack, but it is addressed separately below.

It is important to note that a melee attack, like the combat round and movement, is also an abstraction. Though a character usually makes only one attack per round, it should not be considered a single swing. A melee attack involves a series of parries and thrusts, along with attack and defensive maneuvers that sometimes result in damage to the defender. The damage could be from one blow or could be representative of a series of blows or fatigue.

There are many other bonuses and penalties which may affect a melee attack to hit roll. These include, but are not limited to, class ability modifiers, spell effect modifiers, and situational modifiers.

RANGED COMBAT

Ranged combat is much like melee combat except it occurs when an attack is made with a missile weapon against a defender some distance away. Dexterity is the attribute that modifies a ranged attack to hit roll. If the total of the 1d20 roll plus the character's basic to hit bonus and dexterity modifier is greater than or equal to the defender's armor class, the attacker has successfully hit the defender and inflicts damage as determined by the missile weapon used.

There are two types of ranged weapons: thrown and propelled. Thrown weapons are those whose momentums are dependent upon the strength of the character or monster throwing it. These include javelins, daggers, spears and the like. Propelled weapons are those whose momentum and thrust are dependent on the mechanism which propels them forward. This includes bows, stones from a sling and similar devices. When attacking with ranged weapons, the attacker's dexterity modifies the to hit roll. Additionally, a character's strength modifier is added to the damage of thrown weapons, but not propelled weapons.

Ranged weapons also have range increments, and they have a maximum effective distance equal to three times the listed range increment as detailed in the equipment list. The listed range increment is considered to be close range. Twice the range increment is medium range and three times the increment is long range. Medium range results in a -2 penalty to the ranged attack roll, and long range imparts a -6 penalty to the attack roll.

Ranged weapons that miss their target continue on their path and can potentially hit another target within close range. If the target of the attack is missed, the projectile continues in a straight line and can hit anything in its path. For each ten feet traveled within close range, the attack accrues a -1 penalty.

Point Blank Shots in Melee

It's not easy while engaged in fisticuffs or pick-sticking matches to simply put a gun into your opponent's face and pull the trigger. Your opponent naturally will do all he can to grab your wrist or otherwise knock the weapon away. Any character attempting to use a ranged weapon while engaged by an opponent in melee combat suffers a -4 penalty to hit, as his opponent will naturally struggle to knock the firearm or other ranged weapon away. However, if the character manages to hit his target, treat the result as a Critical Hit, adding exploding d6's (up to 3d6; see "Critical Hits and Fumbles," p. 178) to the weapon's damage due to the point blank range hit.

FIRING INTO MELEE

Attempting to fire a ranged weapon into melee combat is dangerous business. There is always a risk of hitting an ally when attempting such a maneuver. Make a roll to hit as normal, subtracting -3 for each ally or other creature currently in melee combat with the target. If the roll would normally hit

the target, but misses due to the penalty imparted by allies, then the shot hits an ally or other combatant.

For example, Bucky Newson, Gadgeteer Extraordinare, takes aim with his Radium Homing Pistol at a vampire who currently happens to be in melee combat with Bucky's allies, Savage Steve McDermott and Tennessee O'Malley. Because Bucky has two allies in combat with the vampire, he suffers -6 to hit. He rolls and scores a 21, which would normally hit the vampire, but the -6 from his allies drops this to 15. Since he normally would've hit, and missed only because of the melee-based penalty, his bullet strikes an ally. Bucky throws a die to determine which: odd for Steve, even for Tennessee. The result is odd, and Steve takes an unfortunate shot in the back. If Bucky's original roll to hit before the -6 penalty had been less than 20 (meaning he'd have missed regardless), then the shot misses clean and nobody gets hit.

At the GM's option, such shots may only do damage if the original roll (before the penalty) would've defeated the ally's AC, but this adds an extra level of bookkeeping and can potentially slow down combat (however slightly).

FIREARMS

People often complain that firearms in game systems should do more damage than swords. As much as we'd like to believe it, this just ain't so. Imagine the damage from smacking someone at the base of the neck and shoulder with an overhanded swing from a broadsword. Now imagine that same person taking a hit from a .40 caliber bullet. The sword does just as much, if not more, damage (and it's a lot gorier, to boot). Firearms are just a lot harder to counter, have a greater range and accuracy than ancient weapons do, and may have the advantage of firing off multiple rounds, fast.

Firearms are listed with a rate of fire (RoF): 1, 2, or 3. Some are designated Automatic (A). The way these work is simple. Weapons may fire one projectile per rate of fire, per attack; however, additional shots suffer a cumulative recoil penalty indicated on the chart as "Rec."

For example, Dirk pulls his Walther PPK and fires three shots (it has a ROF "3"). The first shot he fires suffers no penalty. Since the gun's recoil (REC) is 2, the second is at -2, and the third is at -4 as the recoil increases with each quick shot.

Fully automatic weapons may fire in bursts of 3, 5, 10, or 50 shots. A burst of 3 or 5 rounds imparts a +3 or +5 to hit, respectively, and for every increment of 5 above the target's AC the attack roll achieves, an additional bullet strikes home.

For example, Dirk whips a Tommy gun out of a violin case and opens up with a 5-round burst on Big Tony. Big Tony has an AC of 14. Dirk fires, adding +5 to his roll from the burst, and hits with a 24! Since he beat Tony's AC by 10, two increments of 5, a grand total of three bullets hit home. Tony's probably hurting a lot.

Firing bursts of 10 or 50 shots is treated as an area effect attack. A 10-shot burst is called "hosing" a target and deals damage to a 5' path in a straight line up to the weapon's maximum range (or until it hits a solid enough object to stop the hail of bullets); all characters make a Dexterity check for half damage, adding any cover bonuses they may have as a bonus to the Dexterity check. The CL of this check is equal to the attacker's "to hit" roll, minus 10. Rules for multiple hits apply as per 3- or 5-burst fire, above.

A 50 shot burst is called "spraying" an area and is treated the same as a 10-shot burst, but effects a 10' wide path. In this case, the CL of the Dexterity save is equal to the attackers "to hit" roll, minus 5. Rules for multiple hits apply as per 3- or 5-burst fire, above.

For a hosing or spraying attack, if full cover is available (i.e. the target can dive behind a wall or car), the target's Dexterity save can completely negate damage, but this also results in the target being "pinned" and unable to act for one full round (i.e. the target loses their next action).

SHOTGUNS

The default assumption for shotguns is the solid slug. If using solid slugs, treat a pump-action shotgun as any other single-action gun (See RoF for individual models, p. 55). Slugs do normal damage at any range increment. Emptying both barrels of a double-barreled shotgun loaded with solid slugs results in double-damage, but requires a full round to reload the weapon. Loading the weapon with bird or buckshot does double damage at point blank range, normal damage at first increment, and half damage beyond the first increment. Finally, when using shot, the weapon's accuracy rating increases by +2 - the tradeoff is less damage at ranges beyond point blank, since the shot scatters. Emptying both barrels of a double-barreled shotgun loaded with shot is treated as a 50-shot "spraying" burst (see above), keeping reduced damage for range increments in mind.

UNARMED COMBAT

Unarmed combat is similar to armed combat, only the attacker is not using a melee weapon, but natural weapons instead, such as claws, hands, fangs or even the whole body. Many monsters employ unarmed melee attacks, as do pugilist characters. In most cases, the success of these attacks are determined as with a normal melee attack. The attacker rolls 1d20 and adds the basic to hit bonus plus any strength modifier. A (nonhuman) monster's basic to hit bonus is equal to its total number of hit dice (a 3d8 hit dice creature adds a +3). If the total is greater than or equal to the defender's armor class, the attacker has successfully hit the defender and inflicts damage as determined by the class ability or monster description.

There are also special unarmed attacks of an entirely different nature and effect: grappling, pummeling, overbearing and touch

attacks. Each type follows the same basic principle but with different modifications to the to hit roll and damage inflicted. For example, characters who are not of the pugilist class who wish to punch or kick are attempting a pummeling attack.

GRAPPLING

Grappling involves grabbing and holding a defender, as with classical wrestling or a snake constricting its body around its prey. Grappling is directed at holding an opponent and subduing them. The attacker rolls 1d20 and adds any strength modifier. The Game Master may or may not deem the basic to hit bonus an appropriate modifier.

The armor class of a defender in an overbearing attack is different than normal. A standard armor class of 15 is used for all defenders, as armor has little effect on the capacity to defend against this type of attack. The armor class is modified by the strength and the dexterity modifier of the defender, as well as the size difference between the two opponents. For each size difference larger, add +2 to the defender's armor class. For each size difference smaller, a -2 penalty is imposed on the defender's armor class.

For example, a giant gorilla attacks a socialite to grab her to carry her up the Empire State Building. The socialite has an armor class of 15 and, due to a strength of 14 and a dexterity of 14, adds +1 to each for a total of 16. But the great ape is two sizes larger, so a -4 adjustment to the socialite's armor class results in an armor class of 12.

Should an attack be successful, the defender is held and cannot act except to attempt to break the hold. The defender is considered prone and defenseless. The defender can break the hold by making his own successful grappling attack.

PUMMELING

Pummeling involves the use of fists, feet, knees, elbows or other body parts to inflict damage on an opponent with the intention of knocking them out or otherwise incapacitating them. The attacker rolls 1d20 to hit, adding any strength modifier plus any other modifier the Game Master deems appropriate. The Game Master may or may not deem the basic to hit bonus an appropriate modifier. If the total equals or exceeds the defenders armor class, the pummeling inflicts 1-2 hit points of subdual damage. Damage is modified by strength.

A pugilist's unarmed combat ability and monsters' natural weapons are not considered pummeling attacks. Characters who are not pugilists who wish to use hand-to-hand combat are subject to the pummeling rules.

OVERBEARING

This type of attack is used to knock an opponent down. This is a tactic used in wrestling and other types of hand-to-hand combat, as well as when an animal charges and knocks someone over. The attacker rolls 1d20 to hit and adds any strength modifier or other modifier that the Game Master deems fit. The Game Master may or may not deem the basic to hit bonus an appropriate modifier.

As with grappling, a standard armor class of 15 is used for all defenders. For overbearing, however, only strength and size difference modifies the standard armor class. For each size difference larger add +2, and for each size difference smaller subtract -2.

If a hit is successful, the defender is knocked prone for the remainder of that round. An attacker cannot knock over a defender two sizes larger. In addition, the defender takes 1-2 points of subdual damage.

An attacker attempting to overbear suffers a -2 penalty to armor class because they are more exposed than usual. The penalty remains to their armor class for the combat round.

TOUCH ATTACK

A touch attack is one in which an attacker is simply trying to touch an opponent. This often occurs with spells that require a touch to be successful. With a touch attack, a standard armor class of 10 is used for all defenders, adjusted only by dexterity of the defender (or hit dice, if no Dexterity score is listed) and special modifiers resulting from, for example, magic items or spells.

SITUATIONAL MODIFIERS

Situational modifiers are somewhat nebulous and, for the most part, those that the Game Master deems appropriate. There are often those situations which are impossible to set a rule or would involve such complex rules as to fill up an entire tome. In these instances, the Game Master must use reason, common sense or narrative development to determine what modifier is applied to the to hit roll. For example, should a hooligan, after a long night of carousing, be barreling across town hanging out of his car window, driving with one hand and brandishing a Tommy gun with the other, decide to take a spray at a rival crime boss as he drives by, the Game Master must decide upon the appropriate modifier to the to hit roll (or an attribute check to determine if it is even possible to make the attack).

In general, combat to hit modifiers can be broken down into three categories: easy, difficult and heroic. For tasks that are easy, up to a +/-5 modifier should be imposed. Difficult tasks would range from +/- 6 to 10, and heroic acts would range from +/- 11 or above. The instance described above may seem ridiculous, but players attempt all manner of actions with their characters - something which should be encouraged. However, the Game Master is left with the task of deciding the modifier to be applied to a situation. What the hooligan in the example above is attempting is not heroic, but it most certainly is not easy. In this instance, the Game

Master should probably err on the high side of difficult since the hooligan is inebriated. A -10 to the attack roll would not be unreasonable.

Some situational modifiers can be applied with regularity. These are listed below and can be used to help in making decisions about other unusual situations. Concealment includes those circumstances where nothing physically blocks an attack, but there is something that interferes with the attacker's accuracy. The other modifiers should be self explanatory. The modifiers are cumulative. In all instances, attackers must know of a defender's presence, though not their exact location. Also, the Game Master should add to this list and keep track of decisions which are made in the game in order that they can be made with some regularity and consistency.

SITUATIONAL COMBAT MODIFIERS	
Defender prone or blind:	+5
Defender prone and defenseless:	+10
Defender at lower elevation:	+1
Defender stunned or cowering:	+2
Defender invisible or attacker blind:	–10
Melee attack from mount or unstable platform:	–2
Ranged attack at point blank range (within 3 feet):	+2
Ranged attack from mount or unstable platform:	–4
Ranged attack into melee combat:	–4
Defender 1/4 concealed (light fog):	–2
Defender 1/2 concealed (dense fog):	–4
Defender 3/4 concealed(near darkness):	–6
Defender completely concealed:	–10

ARMOR CLASS

Armor class is representative of a defender's ability to avoid damage. Armor class results from a combination of armor, dexterous avoidance of attacks, and ability to absorb the shock of a damaging blow or roll with it. Armor class takes into account an active defense (aware of the attacker), the armor worn and a general ability to withstand or avoid attacks. It does not represent armor alone. In ***Amazing Adventures*** it takes into account your character's signature outfit and the clothes she's wearing as well! Indeed, for game purposes, outfit is the primary determinate of armor class, as it is the most easy to quantify.

In game terms, the Armor Class (AC) of a character is the target number required to hit a character in combat. Armor class begins at 10. A person wearing "normal" clothing has a 10 armor class. Armor class can increase as much as modifiers allow. In rare cases, modifiers can result in an armor class less than 10, though never below 1. The following rules should be taken into account when determining the armor class of a defender. It is not an exhaustive list and the Game Master is encouraged to develop her own adjustments as needed.

ARMOR: Each piece of pulp clothing's adjustment is described in the equipment list. A trench coat, for example, has a +3 adjustment to armor class. This gives the individual wearing it a 13 armor class (10+3).

SHIELDS: At some point, someone might grab a small chair or table, or trash can lid and hold it up to help fend off an attack. This is a primitive shield. Every shield has a +1 modifier to armor class, but the size of the shield determines how many opponents the +1 modifier applies against. Small shields only offer the adjustment against one attacker, medium shields against two attackers and large shields against three attackers.

DEXTERITY: Dexterity modifies a character's armor class if that character can physically react to an attack. Characters lose their dexterity modifier when they are surprised, unaware of an attacker or when they are restrained or otherwise rendered immobile. Dexterity does not apply, for example, when a character is attacked from the rear.

COVER: Characters will often take cover behind objects such as tables, doors, chairs or other structures in order to gain some protection. Cover confers an armor class bonus to the character as follows:

1/4 cover:	+2 AC
1/2 cover:	+4 AC
3/4 cover:	+6 AC
Full cover:	+10 AC

Although cover is primarily used as protection against missile or ranged weapons, it can also be used in melee combat. For example, when the arcanist Lady Raven finds her spells useless against a golem, she decides to jump behind a large column in an attempt to avoid being smashed by its massive fists. This action offers 3/4 cover from the golem's attacks. When cover is used in melee attacks though, the cover applies to both the attacker and defender until one or the other move out from behind it. In some cases, the Game Master may rule that the character seeking cover may not attack.

It should also be noted that a character engaged in melee combat has cover for purposes of firing at him with a ranged weapon. Each person with whom he currently battles provides 25% cover. If the missile misses the character by less than the cover bonus provided by the other combatants, at the Game Master's option, another combatant is struck instead.

MAGIC: There are numerous other modifiers that can be applied to armor class. Spells, magic armor and rings, or other unique items and situations can increase or decrease armor class. A character's condition, such as being stunned poisoned, or fatigued may affect the armor class. In general, magical rings, robes or other protective devices and spells affect armor class for touch attacks. Magical armors do not effect touch attacks.

SITUATION AND CIRCUMSTANCE: There are innumerable situational modifiers which can also adjust armor class. These are too numerous to list, but the Game Master should always bear in mind the current situation or circumstances. For example, a rusted suit of armor may suffer a -1 to its overall armor class adjustment. It is, as always, incumbent on the Game Master to use common sense when making these adjustment. Always err on the side of safety. It is a game, after all.

COMBAT MANEUVERS

Players try all manner of inventive actions during combat, from using chairs as shields, trying to dodge opponents blows or running haphazardly away from some monstrous beast. It is impossible to enumerate and describe all the possibilities and it is unproductive to try and do so. These generally fall into a category of combat maneuvers.

Some of the more common combat maneuvers and their effects are listed and described below. These rules can be considered optional as they are not necessary to gameplay. They are provided to allow the Game Master and players more options in combat and to introduce the concept of amending and adding rules to fit a group's style of play. They should be introduced slowly and with practice to insure that they meld with the style and tempo of play desired by both the players and Game Master.

AIM

A character might decide to take his time and get a very careful bead on his enemy before firing, in an effort to get a more accurate shot. In game terms, taking careful aim delays a character's shot until the end of the round, but confers a +2 to hit his target. This +2 remains in effect even when accounting for recoil penalties with guns that have a rate of fire greater than one. For example, a gun with a rate of fire 3 and a recoil penalty of 2 would normally fire at 0, -2, -4. But if the character takes aim, the gun would fire at +2, 0, -2 instead.

DODGE

In this case, a character can dodge up to three attacks in a round that originate from an attacker(s) which they are facing and are aware of. If dodging, the character sacrifices their action in that round. The character cannot attack, cast spells, move or use an ability or item. To dodge, the character makes a standard Dexterity check, and uses that check to replace their normal AC for the round. Armor bonuses to AC do not apply when dodging. A character can dodge every round should they desire. A dodge can be declared at any time in a combat round as long as the character has not taken any other action.

DISENGAGING FROM COMBAT

Disengaging from combat is a dangerous maneuver since it exposes the character to attacks. If disengaging, a character can take no other action. The character is only allowed a movement, which is part of the two types of disengagement. Monsters and non-player characters can disengage from combat. They can also opt to follow those disengaging from combat.

A hasty disengagement is one in which the character or monster attempts to leave combat and expends all effort to do so. A character disengaging hastily may move as far as possible up to their maximum running distance, but they suffer a -2 to armor class and their opponent gets an attack against them as they run away. This is a free attack and does not count against the opponent's other action in the round, although the opponent may not make a second attack against the fleeing character. The armor class adjustment lasts throughout the combat round and applies to every attack against the fleeing character.

A fighting disengagement is a more carefully executed withdrawal from combat. By performing a fighting disengagement, the character moves one-half their movement rate or less away from their opponent and they can disengage from combat. The character suffers no penalty to armor class, but they cannot take any other action in the round.

DISARM

A character can disarm an opponent. The character must successfully hit an armor class equivalent of 18 plus the hit dice or level of the defender to successfully disarm them. For example, a Raider would need to hit an armor class of 23 to disarm a 5 hit dice creature or 5th level opponent. The defender receives a dexterity bonus to this armor class, if applicable.

ACTIVE DISARM

If the GM wishes to make resisting a disarm attempt more active on the defender's part, the defender can make a Dexterity save to avoid being disarmed. The CL of this check is equal to the hit dice of the attacker.

The attacker makes a standard attack roll against the Defender, using 10 plus Hit Dice or Dex Bonus (if any) as his target AC. Both results are compared, and whoever succeeds by the highest margin wins. For example, a 3rd Raider attacks his 5 HD opponent who has Physical Primes. The Raider makes a roll against AC 15 (10 plus the opponent's hit dice) and scores a 21. The opponent makes a Dexterity save, rolling d20 +5, and gets a result of 18. The CL for the check is 3 (a 3rd level Raider). The Raider succeeded in his attempt to disarm by 6. The opponent resisted with a successful save, but only beat his Challenge Class of 15 (12 for Physical Primes, plus 3 for the Raider's level) by 3. The Raider wins and disarms his opponent.

EVADE

This maneuver is a desperate attempt to avoid being hit and involves using all one's energies to dodge and parry blows but remains engaged in combat. The character doing this is allowed to evade one opponent they are facing. Evade confers a +4 bonus to armor class for that round against that opponent, but results in -2 to armor class against all other opponents.

FIGHTING DEFENSIVELY

Fighting Defensively is a combat maneuver that allows a character to remain cautious while in combat, keeping his guard up and taking only the most well-considered attempts to injure his opponent. Fighting Defensively normally provides +2 to the AC of the character, while inflicting a -4 penalty to attacks the defensive character makes that round.

FLANK ATTACK

This is an attack that takes places to one or the other rear sides of a defender. When using flank attack rules, they should be used consistently for monsters and characters alike. The defender may or may not be aware of the attack, but in any case, is less capable of defending against the flank attack than those from the front. A flank attack confers a +1 bonus to hit.

REAR ATTACK

An attack to the rear of an opponent gives the attacker a +2 bonus to hit. The hooligan does not get this in addition to her back attack bonus, as it is already considered in her class abilities.

TWO-FISTED FIGHTING

At some point, characters will attempt to fight with a weapon in both hands. This is a difficult skill to master, and it takes much experience to do it well (see the pugilist class). When using two weapons, the player must designate which hand is used for the primary attack and which is the off hand attack. Typically, this is determined by the handedness of the character, either right handed or left handed. The character is allowed to swing with both weapons, thus gaining two attacks in a single round, but the attack with the primary hand is at -3 and the attack with the off hand is at -6. These penalties are affected by the character's dexterity modifier. The character's strength modifier only applies to damage inflicted. These penalties can be offset with the Two-Fisted Generic Class ability (see Chapter Two)

RUNNING COMBAT

A clear understanding of the rules is essential to running a smooth combat. A competent grasp of initiative, movement and allowed actions allows the Game Master to react to circumstances, answer questions and resolve issues that arise during the course of any combat. But a technical understanding of combat does not necessarily create a successful combat.

Combat is an essential part of the ***Amazing Adventures*** experience. It is all-too-often that combat degenerates into rules manipulation, dice rolling and forays into number crunching that more resemble an economics course than a heroic encounter. Combat should be the epic struggle between good and evil, law and chaos. Combat pits the raider against the mummy lord, locks the mentalist in deadly struggle with a manipulative cult leader and aligns the arcanist in magical opposition to abyssal creatures threatening his world. ***Amazing Adventures*** often revolves around such struggles, and it is the Game Master's duty to make certain that combat resolution is balanced and challenging, but most of all fun. The Game Master must engage the players, make them forget the rules and draw them into the whirling maelstrom of the bone crunching maw of the T-Rex. This is combat through narrative.

There are several ways to achieve a successful narrative in your game's battles. Vivid descriptions can capture a group of the most lackluster players and keep them engaged. There is a vast gulf between entering a room with "three punks with revolvers, sitting at a table drinking," and entering a room where "three burly men are ranged around a table doing shots like there's no tomorrow; they're a foul-looking lot, with scars and pock-marks crisscrossing their skin, spindly limbs, wide eyes and mouths full of yellowed, crooked teeth emitting a putrid breath; the gang is armed for war with handguns the size of cannons."

Once the players are captured, the Game Master must keep hold of them. Battle can be the most exciting part of the game, and the most memorable. Compare the following two descriptions of an attack in combat. "The hooligan swings at you. He hits, and you take 3 points of damage" vs. "The gang member twists about, bringing his razor-sharp knife across your shin, where you have no armor. The gleaming blade slices the cloth of your trousers effortlessly to score through flesh and blood, biting to the bone for 3 hits points damage."

Good descriptions help pace a combat, and keep players lively and excited. It is important to note that characters should be allowed to participate in the narrative description. A Game Master who spends 15 minutes describing or setting up a scene can easily lose a hard-won audience. Players should be allowed and encouraged to bring their own descriptive subtext to combat. The best and most common example of this is the called shot. If a character wants to strive for the heroic chance against all odds, they should be allowed to do so. Calling a shot, or any extraordinary act such as leaping out of your biplane into the empty copilot's seat of the one below, generally throws out all the rules and the Game Master must wing the encounter, allowing for chance, while seeking to achieve the most dramatic narrative possible.

Many factors must be considered, from the reasonable chance of success to the character's ability to do so, from the needs of the party to the game's need for realism, consistency and fun. This is where the art of running a good

combat reaches its most demanding height, and where the rules are utterly subject to the narrative. The Game Master must decide what is best for the game, the group and the individual player. A bored, frustrated player can be won back in seconds by a good call from the Game Master. Even if Luther the gumshoe misses with his called shot, his bullet may knock over a lamp that encumbers or trips the enemy, casting them to the ground and thus buying precious time for the rest of the party to act. Leaping from one plane to another is no easy task and is perhaps the most deadly of maneuvers, but even if a character attempts such a thing and fails miserably, it may be the distraction needed for the rest of the party to retreat and survive to fight again another day.

It is important to note that the Game Master must be careful not to run one-sided fights. Characters can do the same damage that monsters do. When Luther's bullet strikes home it "pierces the very eye of the sneering villain, driving him backwards and to the floor in an explosion of red mist and gray matter!" Running a combat in a narrative fashion is difficult, but fun. Engaging the players and keeping them such is one of the most rewarding experiences a Game Master can have, but doing so means that the Game Master must understand the rules and when to bend them.

HIT POINTS

Hit points represent the amount of damage, physical and mental, a character, non-player character or monster can take before passing out or dying. A character's hit points are a mere abstraction and are not a numeration of the character's physical being. It is generally a representation of the overall health of the individual. The higher the hit points, the healthier the individual.

Hit points are determined by a character or monster's hit die. There are several hit die types: d4, d6, d8 and d12. Class descriptions list the hit die type for that class. Monsters have various hit die types also. These are listed with the monster descriptions as given in the Bestiary.

Hit points for the classes are acquired by level. At each level, the hit die type is rolled and added to the previous levels total. The constitution modifier is added or subtracted from this roll. At 10th level, all classes acquire hit points at a specified rate. Constitution modifiers are added to or subtracted from this. In all cases, a character gains at least 1 hit point for each level advanced.

Monster hit points are specified in the monster description. Monsters receive a number of hit die types for hit points. Some rolls are adjusted. For example, 3d6 indicates that three, six-sided dice are rolled and added together for that monster's hit point total. A 3d12+4 indicates that three 12 sided dice are rolled and 4 added to each die rolled.

In some instances, such as with a socialite's inspire ability, characters or monsters can gain temporary hit points. Temporary hit points are added to a character's current hit points. In combat, temporary hit points are the first to be reduced due to combat, spells or other instances in which damage occurs. When all temporary hit points are gone, they are removed from the character's normal hit points. For all intents and purposes, temporary hit points act as real hit points as long as the spell or ability is in effect. The only exception is that temporary hit points cannot be healed or cured.

Hit points can be reduced by weapons, magical spells, exhaustion and poisons amongst other things. These are detailed in the following section. Once damage is taken, it must be healed for the hit points to be restored to their maximum level. Hit points can never be healed beyond what they were before taking damage.

In general, when 0 hit points is reached, the character or monster passes out. They are not dead, but rather incapable of acting while passed out due to blood loss and physical or mental damage. The character or monster is unable to act and is unconscious or gravely wounded. Those so wounded can do little more than crawl from the battlefield or call out for help. Those with 0 hit points recover consciousness in 1d6 hours, after which they can move at 1⁄2 their normal move rate, but cannot participate in combat, cast spells, turn undead or any other strenuous or demanding action. The full effects of magical healing of characters reduced to 0 hit points is immediate.

At –1 to –5 hit points, the character or monster is unconscious and grievously wounded. They require bed rest to recover, unless magically healed. A character so wounded must rest 24 hours before the process of healing begins, unless magically healed (See "Healing", p. 178).

At –6 to –9 hit points, the character or monster is mortally wounded and loses one hit point per round after reaching -6 hit points. Aid administered to the wounds (as with the Medicine generic class ability or Knowledge skill; see Chapter Two) stops the hit point loss. This takes at least one full round, during which no hit point is lost. After 24 hours have passed, the normal healing process as described for -1 to -5 hit points begins.

At –10 hit points death occurs immediately. Only powerful and forbidden magic (or bribes to the Game Master) can remedy death.

DAMAGE

If a hit is successful, damage is assessed for the opponent and its hit points are reduced. Damage delivered from a blow by a weapon depends on the weapon being used or as described in the monsters description. Damage is applied immediately. If a character or monster dies as a result of damage inflicted, it gets no opportunity to swing, cast spells or anything else. There are several categories of damage that need examining. From this, the Game Master should determine the type

and nature of any damage inflicted on a character if not specifically described in the rules.

Damage takes its toll in a variety of ways: a sword cutting an arm, a club bruising an arm, a flesh wound from a Saturday night special, or simply physical exertion during the course of a difficult or long combat. The Game Master should not automatically assume that damage causes flesh to be shorn from limbs and bones crushed. Four points of damage to a 3rd level raider could simply be bruising on the arm, a series of small cuts or exertion. Alternately, it could be a mortal blow that fells a character. In general, it is not wise to break bones, lop off limbs or inflict significant organ damage, as healing times for these types of wounds are significant and complete recovery often impossible. Being creative with the type of damage inflicted should enhance combat rather than detract from game play. Be sure to keep it that way.

WEAPON DAMAGE

The amount of damage inflicted is determined by the type of weapon being used or natural weapons such as the claws of a lion, the fist of a golem or the bite of a giant rat. Weapon damages are listed in the equipment chart. Damage from melee weapons is adjusted by the strength modifier, and other factors or adjustments if applicable. Natural weapons and their effects are described in the appropriate monster description or combat rule. Any modifications to damage are noted in the descriptions.

MAGIC DAMAGE

Damage caused by spell effects are applied in the same manner as those by melee weapons or natural weapons. Special considerations are described in the appropriate spell. Of special note though, damage caused by illusions can be real. Though not real in a material sense, the viewer of the illusion believes the damage to be real and suffers psychic and mental shock as if it were real. The spell descriptions list the details of damage form illusions, but in general, it can be said that damage received from illusory attacks is, in reality, subdual damage and the characters follow all the rules for subdual damage with the following exception. Characters or monsters reduced to -10 hit points by illusory damage die from the psychic shock to the system, which is too great to withstand.

SUBDUAL DAMAGE

This type of damage is generally not fatal, though on occasion it can be. Subdual damage is more the bludgeoning one receives in a fist fight than the slashing, gashing bone breaking combat of swords and firearms. It may hurt and even knock one unconscious, but rarely draws blood and usually results in damage that heals quickly.

Subdual damage is usually caused in unarmed combat with natural weapons. However, many monsters use natural weapons that cause normal damage. If a monster's attack causes subdual rather than normal damage, the monster description will note it. Otherwise, damage from monsters should be considered normal damage. A pugilist's unarmed attack is normal damage, unless he chooses to subdue as if using a weapon.

An attacker can use weapons to deliver subdual damage but it does so at varying rates. When being used for subdual, weapons inflict normal damage, but it is mostly temporary damage. Minimally, these weapons deliver one point of normal damage. All subdual damage delivers some normal damage. For every five points of subdual damage inflicted, one point is considered normal damage. Attempting to use bladed weapons to deliver subdual damage imparts a -2 to the to hit roll, as it is awkward to use these piercing and slashing weapons to deal non-lethal damage. Unless they are using special ammunition (a shotgun loaded with rock salt, for example, or plastic bullets in a more modern game), firearms cannot be used to deal subdual damage.

Subdual damage heals faster than normal damage as it is not usually fatal. It heals at a rate of 1 hit point per every 10 minutes. The normal damage inflicted as a part of subdual damage heals as previously described. At the Game Master's discretion, when a character reaches -10 hit points or more of subdual damage, they have taken severe enough bludgeoning damage to an internal organ to cause death or permanent incapacitation. Otherwise, they should be considered unconscious for 24 hours and do not begin healing until gaining consciousness.

FALLING DAMAGE

Falling damage occurs when a character or monster falls from a height of five feet or more. Falling can be very deadly and players should be made aware of the potential hazards of a fall prior to beginning a climb.

If a character falls from a height of six to ten feet, a dexterity check must be made. If the check is successful, the person falling takes no damage. If the check is not successful, the person takes 1d6 points of damage. From heights greater than ten feet, damage accrues significantly. For every ten feet fallen, the number of d6 used for damage increases by one. The damage for each 10 feet fallen is cumulative.

For example, if a character falls 18 feet, they take 1d6 damage for the first ten feet and 2d6 damage for the next 10 feet for a total of 3d6 damage. If a charcter were to fall from a height of 45 feet, they would take 1d6 damage for the first 10 feet, 2d6 damage for the second 10 feet, 3d6 damage for the third 10 feet, and 4d6 damage for the last 10 feet, for a total 10d6 points of damage.

CRITICAL HITS AND FUMBLES

Whenever an attack roll comes up an Exploding result (see p. 164), this is a critical hit. The attack automatically hits, regardless of the armor class of the opponent. In addition, the value of all exploding dice is added to the total damage from the attack.

For example, Luke rolls a d20 to attack his opponent and it comes up 20! This is a critical hit. Luke continues rolling; his first exploding die comes up 6. His second comes up 6 again! His third comes up 3. Luke would add 15 to his total damage.

Likewise, when a character rolls a natural 1, this is a fumble. The GM should adjudicate this as any other imploding result: a disastrous failure, though at very least it should cost the character one round of action from being thrown off balance, dropping (or throwing) his weapon, or something similar. For truly horrible results that roll down more than once, weapons could break, guns could explode, etc, at the GM's option.

POISON

Poisons come in five varieties, varying in intensity from minor to lethal. Someone subjected to poison must make a constitution save. A successful save halves the listed damage for first round effects and there are no effects in the following rounds. A failed save on the first round delivers the damage indicated below and the character becomes ill, suffering a -1 to all physical attribute checks and a -1 to hit and damage for ten minutes. First round effects always occur immediately.

Ten turns, or 10 minutes after the initial ingestion, another constitution save must be made to avoid the further effects of the poison. A successful save indicates the poison has been fought off. A failed save causes the onset of the effects listed below and the character must make daily saves thereafter until the poison is successfully fought off or runs its course–or the character dies.

Type	Save CL	First Save	Second Save	Duration
1	0	1d2	1d2,double effects of illness	1 week
2	2	1d4	1d4, triple effects of illness	1 week
3	4	1d6	1d6, quadruple effects of illness	1-2 weeks
4	5	1d8	1d8, incapacitated	1-4 weeks
5	10	1d10	Death in 2-8 rounds	not long

A failed save indicates that the effects listed continue for another day. Additionally, the character loses 1 point of constitution. The same "second save" process is followed for each successive day until the character successfully saves and fights off the poison. For every five points of constitution lost, one point is lost permanently. Should a character's constitution ever reach zero, it is dead.

Game Masters are cautioned to carefully adjudicate the use of poison, as deadly toxins such as cyanide and strychnine are cheap and readily available in the pulp era, though certainly the technology exists to identify and trace these substances. More exotic, untraceable substances are likely far less available and may be prohibitively expensive.

DISEASE

The game effects of disease are identical to those of poison (see p. 179), though the duration is longer. The first save should be made upon exposure to the disease, determined by the GM rolling percentile dice against a disease's estimated communicability rate; some examples are listed below:

Disease	Type	Communicability
Influenza	Type 2	75%
The Common Cold	Type 1	80%
Pneumonia	Type 3	0%*
Tuberculosis	Type 2 (CL 10 save)	22%**
Malaria	Type 4	0%+

*results from 3 failed saves vs. Influenza or cold

**increases to 70% on sexual contact

+results from mosquito bite

Saves should be made weekly, rather than daily, except in the case of Type 5 diseases, for which saves are still made daily, and to recover, the victim must make three consecutive daily saves to fight off the disease, or death occurs. Type 5 diseases represent ailments like botulism or ebola, which kill ugly and fast.

HEALING

Hit points heal at a rate of one point per day plus a character's constitution bonus, if any, so long as the character is resting, well fed, kept warm and the wounds tended to. After seven days, the rate of healing increases to include the character's level. After 14 days, the rate of healing doubles and after thirty days, it triples. Rates of healing can be adjusted by magical healing, herbs, diet, level of care or other factors the Game Master deems applicable.

If a character is below zero hit points, magical healing can only restore hit points to 0, after which healing proceeds normally.

For example, a pugilist is mauled by a werewolf and reduced to -1 hit points. Before healing begins, the pugilist must wait 24 hours. However, a local priest, an arcanist of goodly intent with knowledge of mystical healing decides to share the grace of his god with the gallant warrior, and casts cure light wounds. The cure is for 8 hit points, but the pugilist is only brought back up to 0 hit points. However, healing can proceed as normal thereafter and any further magical healing utilized will have full effect.

Attribute damage suffered via poison, disease, or a monster's special attack, will heal at one point per day.

Also, do not forget the "Second Wind" use of Fate Points, which can greatly decrease the amount of time it takes for a character to heal from grievous injury.

MOVEMENT

Movement is a fairly abstract necessity in any game. The movements rates listed for characters, monsters and NPCs is an estimation of how far that creature can move at a normal pace in a ten second round. In general, jogging is twice that movement rate, while running is four times the movement rate. As this is a ten second movement rate, a full minute would be six times the movement rate. Movement outdoors equates to movement indoors. For movement outdoors, it should be noted that at an average walking pace for normal person is about 2 miles an hour.

Moving silently occurs as per class description. Moving silently does not mean that the character is moving without making a sound. Moving silently means that the character is attempting to move and make as little noise as possible. If successful, this means that the character has moved in such a manner that no one within hearing range has heard him. Some creatures have a more acute sense of hearing so adjustments to the roll might be necessary. For example, a wolf can hear better than a human, so the Game Master may want to adjust the challenge level by +2 or more. Further, it is easier to move silently in certain areas. For example, moving silently across a carpet is much easier than moving silently across a dry forest bed full of leaves and twigs, so adjustments can be made for this environment also if the Game Master chooses.

In much the same manner, moving while invisible does not mean the character cannot be detected. If the character makes noise, this can be heard. Further, all creatures smell and the odor of a sweating body can be detected. Bear in mind, many creatures use sonar or other abilities to determine the location of prey and this can reveal the presence of an invisible creature. An invisible creature does not leave a heat signature.

SPELL RESISTANCE

Spell resistance is a special defensive ability. A defender's spell resistance is like an armor class against magical attacks. If a spell is being resisted by a defender with spell resistance, the caster of the spell must make a check (d20) at least equal to or greater than the creature's SR for the spell to effect that creature. Spell resistance applies even if a given spell also allows a creature a saving throw. The effects of spell resistance, if any, are applied first, and then the creature may also make a saving throw. In most cases, spell resistance applies only when a resistant creature is targeted by the spell, not when a resistant creature encounters a spell that is already in place, such as a wall of iron.

VISION

Light sources provide vision for creatures unable to see in the dark. The radius of vision depends on the light source.

Match or lighter: 5 feet

Torch: 40 feet

Lantern: 30-60 feet

Campfire: 20-40 feet

Some creatures have the ability to see in the dark or in spaces where normal human vision does not work. There are five gradations of vision: normal, deepvision, twilight vision, dark vision and dusk vision.

DARKVISION: In a similar manner to deepvision, some creatures can see in complete darkness for up to 60 feet. Darkvision produces images that are in shades of gray, but it is otherwise like normal sight. These creatures can function well with no light at all. Bright lights, such as from a lantern or other light source, spoil darkvision. A creature requires one turn to adjust his or her eyes when a light source is extinguished before gaining full use of darkvision.

DEEPVISION: Ages spent beneath the earth, and in the dark and quiet places of the world have imbued certain creatures with the ability to see into darkness that a human would find impenetrable with the naked eye. This vision extends up to 120 feet in even the darkest of nights and deepest of tunnels. Colors tend to erode with deepvision, and objects appear in many shades of gray. It is otherwise like normal sight, and creatures can function well with no light at all. Bright lights, such as from a lantern or other light source, spoil deepvision. A creature requires one turn to adjust his or her eyes when a light source is extinguished before gaining full use of deepvision.

DUSK VISION: Nocturnal creatures, often equipped with large and piercing eyes, can see in starlight and moonlight just as a human can at dusk. They retain the ability to distinguish color and some detail under these conditions, though everything is cast in shadows. They have no enhanced vision underground, under torchlight or in similar conditions of poor illumination.

TWILIGHT VISION: Even under starlight, moonlight or torchlight these creatures have exceedingly good vision. They can distinguish color and detail under these conditions for up to one mile when outside.

TIME

In ***Amazing Adventures***, time is represented in two simple equations: a round is 10 seconds and a turn is one minute. This allows the Game Master a logical solution to the unfolding of events in combat or roleplay. That said, the Game Master should be flexible in his interpretation of the round. In normal circumstances, actions are pretty simple. Greg the pugilist attacks Sly the hooligan. Greg wins initiative and swings. Sly takes his swing. Both being high rollers they crack each other on the head. But throw in parrying, dodging, other combatants, the register of gunfire, spells and psychic powers; not to mention the shouting that innovative players do, the calls for help or curses upon the unlucky blade, the wounded and dying and it all adds up to one chaotic ball of action, consequence and inaction.

The Game Master has to be very flexible and willing to move with events and the actions of their players. Tracking off

seconds of the round can slow the pace of a well run combat and disconcert players who are immersed in the cacophony of sound and sight described by the Game Master. Greg is struck hard by Sly, with what appears to be a mortal blow. On the next round, Greg tries to bandage his wounds, swing his meaty fist and trip Nard. Needless to say this is far too many actions. But if Greg wants to roll and throw up his sinewy arm to ward off the blow at the same time, though he's lost initiative, such an action would not be impossible and might earn him some bonus AC points from the Game Master.

VEHICLE COMBAT

What's a pulp game without gangsters speeding by the hideout of a rival syndicate and blasting away with Tommy guns? Or hotshot pilots zooming to the rescue of their heroic mercenary squadron? In order to handle these elements, it's necessary to have in place a set of vehicle rules. Combat between two vehicles works exactly the same as combat between two characters. A vehicle has Dexterity and Constitution scores, and AC and Hit Points, just like characters do. Vehicles also have a fourth Attribute, Speed. A vehicle's Speed (Spd) attribute works exactly like a Player Character Attribute, using the same table for bonuses and penalties. It's a rough representation of the real-world speed comparison between any two vehicles. It's not a direct conversion of actual miles-per-hour. If you really need to find out the mph (or kph, in Europe) of a vehicle, a web search should fix you up, fine. It shouldn't be necessary for this game.

Most tasks in vehicular combat are going to be resolved with Dexterity rolls by the driver or pilot of the vehicle. When piloting a vehicle, a character uses either his Dexterity score or the vehicle's, whichever is higher. However, if the vehicle has a negative Dexterity score, this negative acts as a penalty to the character's Dex.

For example, a player with an 18 Dexterity (+3) piloting a Motorcycle (Dexterity +2) would use his Dexterity bonus of +3 when making piloting rolls. However, that same character piloting a Ford Model T (Dexterity -1) would gain only +2 on piloting rolls, as the -1 reduces his own Dexterity.

Combat proceeds between two vehicles exactly as in normal combat, rolling a d10 and adding Dex bonus for initiative, and using d20 and Dexterity for ranged attacks from the weapon. In this manner, player characters can interact seamlessly with vehicle combat. Remember, the pilot of a vehicle uses his Dexterity score or the vehicle's, whichever is higher.

FIRING FROM A VEHICLE (GROUND VEHICLES ONLY)

Player characters in a car may attempt to fire their guns at other vehicles or at pedestrians on the street. To do this the players simply lean out the window and open up! This requires a Dexterity Save with a CL equal to the vehicle's Speed bonus (to avoid falling out!). If successful, the player characters may freely attack with any ranged weapons they have, albeit at a penalty equal to the vehicle's Speed Bonus.

ACCELERATING AND DECELERATING

A vehicle does not have to travel its maximum speed all the time. It may voluntarily reduce its speed to as low as 1 (if a ground vehicle), representing a dead stop. Each round, a vehicle may increase its speed attribute by 1d6 (for ground vehicles) or 1d8 (for aerial vehicles), all the way up to its maximum.

Deceleration can safely be performed at the same rate. However, a vehicle can "brake slam" to decelerate suddenly; this requires a Dexterity check by the pilot and a Dexterity save by the passengers, all at a CL equal to the vehicle's current speed bonus. Failing this save means taking 1d4 points of damage times the current speed bonus, from getting violently bounced around and hurled forward. Post-1949, wearing a seat belt negates damage from sudden stops.

When applying penalties based on the current speed bonus, apply speed penalties as bonuses.

For Example, Ricardo is engaged in a wild chase with the Feds. He decides to skid to a halt, and allow his boys to open up with their Tommy Guns. He makes his Dexterity Check to pull off the sudden stop. His car is currently traveling at a speed of 17, a +2 bonus. He makes his check at a CL of 2. He rolls and the result is 17, just barely successful. His boys also make their checks, so they take no damage. His car skids to a sudden halt, and is now considered to have a speed attribute of 1. The feds come speeding up. His boys, now at a stable platform, turn the -4 speed penalty of his car (the speed attribute of 1 is a -4 penalty) to a +4 to their rolls to hit the feds. It's much easier to fire from a set position than a moving one!

A SENSE OF SCALE

In the interest of keeping things simple, vehicle combat does not take place on a different scale than character combat; some vehicular weapons just do a lot more damage, and some player character weapons are unable to damage vehicles. In general, for aircraft newer than 1950, a player cannot harm the aircraft with a handgun or any sort of archaic weapon. For tanks and artillery, only other tanks and artillery, or aircraft with bombs or rockets, can harm them. Any vehicle-mounted weapons other than machine guns suffer -6 to their to-hit roll when trying to target player character-sized targets.

DAMAGE

When a vehicle hits 0 hit points, it's severely damaged, but not necessarily out of the action yet. It loses its Dexterity bonus to AC, but may make a Constitution save (CL = damage below zero the vehicle currently is) to keep going. When the vehicle hits -10 hit points, it's rendered inoperable. If it takes enough damage to reduce its hit points to its constitution score below zero, it's completely destroyed.

CINEMATIC PHYSICS

In vehicle combat, it can be fun to include options that may not exist in the real world but happen in fiction all the time. We call these "Cinematic Physics." For example, why not allow a character to explode a canister of gasoline (or car) with a well-placed gunshot to the tank? In the real world, shooting a car's gas tank just makes the gas leak. In movies and pulp fiction, however, vehicles explode almost on cue. Cinematic damage can keep a game wild and fun, but only apply it when it is dramatically appropriate.

VEHICLE COMBAT MANEUVERS

Here are a few easy combat maneuvers that pilots of vehicles can attempt, with rules for each and any restrictions or exceptions listed. Unless otherwise stated, these maneuvers take one standard action to accomplish.

PLAYING CHICKEN

Two vehicles head straight for one another. After the game is initiated, both pilots must make a Wis save each round at a cumulative CL of 2 per round after the first. Pilots, if recognized by their foes, may also add their Reputation bonus (see below) to the CL of their opponent's check. Failure means one pilot or the other breaks off. While the two craft are heading towards one another they may freely fire upon each other at no penalty. The GM should secretly roll a d6; this is how many rounds before the vehicles must break off, or hit one another, destroying both vehicles and dealing 1d10 damage times the vehicle's Spd bonus to all occupants. Cars or aircraft may play chicken.

KAMIKAZE

While we're on the subject, if a player or NPC decides to be suicidal, they can simply drive their vehicle into another one. Make a Wisdom check. If you succeed, you've got the guts to pull this off. Make a Dexterity check opposed by your opponent's Dexterity check. If you win, you drive (or fly) your vehicle into your opponent, and both vehicles (and all occupants inside) suffer 1d10 damage times the ramming vehicle's Speed bonus to all occupants. A Constitution or Dexterity save halves this damage; in aircraft, a Dexterity save indicates you've managed to bail out (if you've got a parachute).

BOOTLEG STOP

This maneuver can only be performed in a ground-based vehicle. It's when a pilot attempts to skid to a sudden halt, turning his vehicle broadside as he does so, often to give passengers a chance to open fire on an oncoming vehicle, or to dive out, presenting that vehicle with an immanent collision. This maneuver calls for a brake slam, as detailed under "Acceleration and Deceleration," above, increasing the CL of the Dexterity check by double its normal brake slam level. Thus, for a car traveling at speed 15 (+1), the Dexterity check would be at CL 2. A car traveling at speed 16 (+2) would invoke a CL 4.

Success means the passengers immediately get one free action, be it to fire on their opponents or to dive out of the car! Oh, and the oncoming pilot had better hope he can decelerate fast enough to avoid hitting his target!

BOOTLEG TURN

This is when two vehicles are heading towards one another and one vehicle attempts to spin around and get into another's blind spot for a combat advantage. The attacker attempting the Bootleg makes a Dexterity Check, opposed by his opponent's Wisdom Check. If the opponent wins, the attacker is unable to bootleg. If the attacker wins, he's on the opponent's "six" (if in the air) or in his blind spot (if ground-based) and may make one round of free attacks, against which the attacker cannot defend (the vehicle loses its Dexterity bonus to AC). However, when a vehicle performs a bootleg turn his vehicle's current speed is immediately reduced by 3d6, to a minimum of 1.

SAMPLE VEHICLES

Below we present some sample vehicles, their attributes, AC, hit points, armament, and general era of use. Attributes are listed by their attribute bonus, rather than their full 3-18 attribute, for ease of reference and use. If you need to know the exact attribute of a vehicle, assume it falls in the middle of the range. For example, a Ford Model T has a +1 Con bonus. Since 13-15 is the +1 range for an Attribute, assume the Model T has a 14 Con.

Game Masters should feel free to come up with others based on these quick templates. Note that a designation of "[Year]-?" under "era" denotes that a vehicle begins in the year listed, but is still in fairly common use into the 1950's.

Vehicle	Dex	Con	Spd	AC	HP	Weapons	Era
Ford Model T	-1	+1	-1 (8)	18	30	n/a	ALL
Jeep,Military	+1	0	+1 (11)	13	20	Machinegun 2d10*	1930's-?
Mercedes Benz	0	+1	0 (13)	17	25	n/a	1930's-?
Motorcycle	+2	0	+1 (14)	10	15	n/a	1930's-?
1950's "Muscle" Car	+1	+1	+2 (16)	17	30	n/a	1950's
WWII Fighter	+3	+1	+3 (18)	15	40	Machineguns 2d10, Rockets 5d10	1940's-?
Tank	-2	+5	-1 (8)	23	80**	Artillery 5d12	1930's-?
WWI Biplane	+2	0	+2 (16)	12	20	Machinegun 3d6	1920's-1940's

*Civilian models exist–without the machinegun, of course

**Can only be damaged by rockets, explosions or other artillery

EXPERIENCE AND ADVANCEMENT

EXPERIENCE POINTS

After characters defeat monsters or acquire treasure, they earn experience points (xp). The Game Master is free to award experience points in whatever manner desired, but the following is a recommended general method.

MONSTERS

The Game Master adds the value of all monsters defeated or overcome on the adventure. Each monster has a base xp value, and a bonus can be given if a specific monster was greater than normal for its type. The total xp are then divided by the number of characters that defeated the monsters.

MONEY

Although not all Game Masters do so, some award xp for non-magical treasure. The Game Master should award 1 xp to the party for every $1.00 value of non-magical treasure such as money, gems, art and other items acquired during the adventure.

STORY

The Game Master should assign an xp value to each adventure and award that total to each character who completed the adventure successfully. An easy way to determine the story xp value is to compare the adventure to a monster of a hit dice that is challenging to the party. The Game Master can then award xps as if the party overcame that monster.

ROLEPLAYING

The Game Master can also award specific characters xp bonuses for good roleplaying (or penalties for bad) in a specific situation or over the course of an adventure. A good range to award is 25 to 250 xps, depending on the level of the character.

GAINING LEVELS

Characters gain levels as they adventure. Gaining levels equates to becoming better and more experienced at one's chosen profession. With new levels, the character gains more abilites and greater chances of performing abilities successfully. Hit points increase as does bonus to hit.

To gain a level, the character must accumulate enough experience points to meet the next level's experience point progression (XP or EPPs). The EPPs for each class are located in the appropriate class description. Experience points are gained by successfully completing an adventure, killing foes, successfully performing actions, collecting treasure and as rewards for good roleplaying. The Game Master awards experience points as described in the rules but always has the right to add or subtract experience points for whatever reason.

Monster experience points are located in the monster manual. Experience points awarded for treasure acquired is equal to the dollar value of all the treasure picked up in the course of adventuring. Optionally, the Game Master may not allow this or only some percentage of the treasure's value, as this may speed up the rate of level progression depending on the amount of treasure acquired. For experience points awarded for defeating monsters and roleplaying see the Bestiary. Bear in mind that the Game Master does not have to award this amount if the player did a poor job of roleplaying, but can if he wants to.

Once enough experience points are acquired to advance a level, the character must train for the number of weeks equal to the level reached before receiving the benefits of that level. For example, a 6th level arcanist, upon acquiring the experience points necessary to reach 7th level, must train for 7 weeks before receiving the benefits of that level. Once training is completed, the character gains the extra hit points, spells or abilities which that level confers upon the class.

TREASURE

Treasure can consist of any, some or all of the following: money, jewels, art objects, mundane items, treasure maps, ancient codices and scrolls, even magic items. Treasure can be found in lost tombs, hidden in a crime lord's mansion, or serve as the goal of a chase across the world.

BOOK FIVE: SPINNING STRANGE TALES

INTRODUCTION

This section will function as a Game Master's guide to running a pulp game. It will carefully lay out a "formula" for creating pulp adventures, and follow that with a complete scenario to get you off and running!

In a moment we'll get to the method by which you can create an adventure, but first there are important factors to consider. The first thing to do is decide what kind of game you want to play. This takes preparation and careful thought. Are you planning, for example, a one-night beer-and-pretzels game, or a world-spanning campaign that will last for years and see your characters grow from green novices to experienced veteran heroes who have time and again beat back the darkness? What will the rewards be–is this a game of gold or glory, or both? What are the mood, tone, and pace going to be? All of this depends largely upon you, the Game Master, and for a novice it can be an overwhelming thing.

As Game Master, it's important to remember that your relationship with the players, while adversarial in the sense that you control the main villains and challenges your players will face, is not one of competition. Your job, above everything else, is to structure a story that will enable everyone at the table to have a good time. What you want, in the end, is for your players to be talking about your game years from now, and not because you were so heavy-handed that you angered a player into leaving the table. No, you want them to tell the kinds of stories you generally hear when one recaps a great action-adventure movie to their friends.

Setting, pace, theme, mood...these are all integral to the game as the style is. There are many sub-genres of pulp, from gritty, Sam-Spade-style noir stories to rousing tales of adventure raiding the tombs of Egypt looking for the Lost Ark of the Covenant or King Solomon's Mines. There are tales of eldritch horrors from beyond the pale–tentacled monstrosities out to consume all of mankind. There are heroic tales of 17th-century pirates, Musketeers, and wandering Puritan heroes whose sole purpose in life is to destroy the minions of Hell. There are stories of brave Confederate soldiers during the Civil War who are swept off to other worlds of fantasy and romance, of four-armed green Martians and stunning, sensuous, red-skinned princesses. All this and more is at your fingertips with ***Amazing Adventures***; you just have to make the right decisions and perhaps a few easy tweaks to the available character classes and rules options.

STYLE AND MOOD

There are as many styles of play as there are game players out there, and no two tables at which a player sits will be exactly alike. Of paramount importance to a Game

Master is to, firstly, find a group of players whose play style matches the style you want to run, and to figure out what kind of game will provide your players the most enjoyment. Some players, for example, prefer games that are high on role playing and political intrigue, games that border on the theatrical where character motivation is what it's all about. Often, these games tend to be light on combat, and when a fight does happen, it's deeply personal (for the characters–hopefully not for the players!) These games also tend to be lighter on the dice, where players will actively substitute roleplaying for things like diplomacy, which otherwise might resort to a Charisma check. Games like this set in the pulp era would likely deal with subjects like the decline of the British Empire, wherein the players are stationed at a British encampment in India, and have to negotiate the mysteries of that strange country, dealing with the political movers and shakers of the region. Intrigue and mystery would be the order of the day in games like this, and characters will see themselves engaging in adventures such as solving the mystery of a diplomat's murder to save (or destroy) the reputation of a local government official. These types of games may see mass battles take place, wherein the PCs have to play a major role, either as commanders, or engaging in specialized espionage to aid their allies.

Games of this sort rely heavily on the GM's decision making skills, and carry a certain danger to them. The GM, you see, must always remain absolutely neutral in adjudication of a game, and when the game relies on the rules so little, when it becomes an exercise in freeform storytelling with the GM as judge, personal bias and feelings can come into play all too easily. If, for example, you've had a really bad day and are just in a foul mood, these feelings can threaten to influence your judgment in game and it's important to be able to remove yourself from this problem before you begin to run. Likewise, if a player has his character do something clever that nevertheless goes against your plans or threatens to upset your carefully crafted story, making a snap decision that overrides the player's stated actions just because you don't like them is something you should always avoid. Nor, however, should you simply throw your hands in the air and say, "Fine! You win!" Neither is an acceptable outcome for you or the players. Neutrality is of paramount importance, as is the ability to think on your feet. More on the latter in a bit, but for now, if you think you'll have a difficult time remaining neutral in the face of personal feelings, a heavy theatrical style game may not be the best option for you.

On the far other end of the spectrum lies the tactical gaming group. These are people who like their rules, their miniatures, and their grid- or measurement-based combat. Roleplaying is often had in games like this, but they tend to be combat-heavy and depend on the rules-as-written, and as good as it may be at times, roleplaying is what tends to happen between combats. Games like this are fast-paced and action-oriented. There are few deliberations and these groups have little time for investigation and puzzle-solving. They would much rather solve diplomatic situations with a roll of the dice, and get to the next part of the scenario where they can go in guns-a-blazing.

These sorts of games run a different kind of danger than the heavily theatrical ones. In tactical games, there tends to be a heavy reliance upon rules, which can bog the game down and lead to combats that last for hours. Newer GMs in this case may want to restrict themselves to the bare bones of combat rules until they get the hang of running it. Then, gradually, you can add in more rules and even house rules like critical hits, parting shots (when someone runs away from combat), and tactical movement (what happens when a player moves his character's miniature figure across the table, inch-by-inch). A game like this will truly be enhanced as the GM and players work together to find just the right balance of rules and encounters to make the game their own.

Most games, however, lie at neither of end of these spectra, but somewhere in the middle. Most games are a mix of heavy roleplaying and action-oriented combat. Too much combat can become boring after awhile, losing its excitement and flavor in an endless procession of die rolls. Too much heavy role playing can become onerous to someone who is emotionally drained from a tough week at work.As you play with your group, as you get to know them and their tendencies, you'll begin to see which way to lean on any given night, and in fact, in any given set of campaign notes that you set up, you'll discover there are options and ways to beef up one or the other aspect to appeal to your group as need be. If, for example, the game is going very heavy on the role playing side, and you notice that Bill over to your left is starting to doze off, why not have some ninja kick in the door and attack? A quick skirmish or two will often not only inject some excitement and interest back into the game, but will sometimes force you to figure out just why the heck those ninja were there in the first place, which can sometimes take the game off into a whole new and exciting direction! Likewise, perhaps half the session has been dominated by a massive battle with a vile Sheik who seeks to spread a dark religious cult dedicated to the Old Ones across the world. Afterwards, while the players' heads are spinning from the battle, provide a chance for them to role play the aftermath. Let them brag about their exploits, or hit them with an ironic twist that elicits a collective groan (again, more on this later), but hand them something that lets them role play what happens next. They will often view this as a reward for a hard-fought battle, and it can provide some much-needed entertainment as Tennessee O'Malley berates Savage Steve McDermott for a particularly foolhardy action during the battle (McDermott, you see, isn't all that bright), while Natalya "The Fox" Abramova sticks up for the simple pugilist. In the meanwhile, perhaps Bucky Newson wins the affections of the very girl Tennessee was out to rescue!

As you can see, style and mood are extremely important in defining the kind of game you and your players want to play. Creating the proper mood is an art form as well as a science—learning who your players are, what they like, and reading their mood on any given night is something you'll learn as you go along, but the better you get at it, the more second nature it will become, and the more successful all of your games will be.

MAINTAINING PACE

After setting and controlling the style and mood of your game, maintaining the pace is next in importance. In order to keep your players involved and interested in the game, you have to keep the story moving along. The best way to do this, proven over decades of gaming, is to keep changing things up. You want a good mix of combat, role playing, and problem solving. This isn't something that comes easy; you'll need to figure out and establish the perfect mix for your group, but once you get the hang of it, it will improve your game overall.

One of the best ways to determine the pace to set for your game is to get to know not only your players, but their characters. When you begin to design game sessions so that each character gets a chance to stand in the limelight without boring the other players, you'll have found the right sense of pace for your group. The trick is, while one player

is taking the lead, letting his or her characters' talents shine, the other characters should also have something meaningful to contribute to the situation at hand, be it a Socialite's speech that distracts the enemy, a well-placed knife in the back from the Hooligan, the Raider deciphering hieroglyphs at just the right moment, or the clever disguise the Gumshoe cooks up in a pinch.

This is not to say there won't be situations where not all the players are involved. Such a scenario, in fact, is nigh inevitable, and can be difficult to manage. For example, while the Gumshoe is off chasing down leads with his Cat and Mouse talent, what are the rest of the players doing? It's important, in these situations, to cook up a way to keep the other players invested, be it through "scene switching" to what the other characters are doing in the meanwhile, or through allowing the characters to kibitz at the table, contributing encouragement and ideas to the player in the spotlight. Some GMs are very strict about not allowing participation from players whose characters are not present, but being too heavy-handed like that can indeed cause players to lose interest in the game when their characters aren't directly involved in the action.

Combat and Pace

Combat is at the crux of many games; the players investigate, solve puzzles, dodge and juke their way through traps, but at the end of the day, it's all about defeating the bad guy, and that usually involves a throw-down fight. This is fine; the problem comes when there's a combat that arises which involves one of the players, but not the rest. Again, this will probably happen from time to time, but the trick is to make sure such a battle does not dominate the game. Try to keep these combats quick so they don't try the patience of the other players, and if they do start to drag out, find a way to switch over to the other characters' actions. Gaming is an inclusive hobby, and that's paramount to maintaining the pace of a game.

When combat works as intended, you should keep it rapid-fire. Make sure it moves fast. Give vivid (even lurid) descriptions of the action—try not to boil it down to, "You hit. Roll damage. Okay, he takes six. He rolls a 12 to hit you back. What's your AC?" This is the type of thing that can become rote, and if numbers are your game, then great! For most, however, it's far better to describe the hit (especially hits that take down enemies) and keep the combat moving at breakneck pace. Try not to allow rules issues to slow things down—make a logical ruling about something that's unclear, and move on. You can always look up the "canon" answer after the game session is over. Likewise, don't allow players to take forever to decide what they're going to do. They're in the thick of battle. They need to make snap decisions or lose their turn. At first some players may be overwhelmed or even irritated by this, but you'll find that after you give it a go a few times, they start to think on their feet and you might even have a tough time keeping up with them!

The Death of a Gumshoe

Killing off a PC is not an easy thing with which to deal. It shouldn't ever be done lightly, flippantly, or as an act of vengeance because the player ticked you off. Players often put a great deal of time and effort into building their characters, and have a lot invested in them, and the loss of a character needlessly can result in (sometimes justifiable) anger on the part of the player. This is why it's so important for the GM to always remain fair, balanced, and impartial in adjudicating the game.

That being said, characters do die in games, and survival should *never* be a given. While pulp heroes tend not to die in stories, they do find themselves in great and mortal peril all the time, and in a role playing game, the best way to keep the dramatic tension going is the knowledge that characters don't have the kind of plot immunity that their fictional counterparts may have. Fate Points go a long way towards balancing the scales and keeping characters alive, but if a character enters combat, the chance of death is always there, and the player should understand that.

If a player character dies in combat, succumbs to poison, disease, or a trap, or otherwise takes the ghost train to the netherworld, you should allow the player to make a new character immediately (while you go on with the game, of course) and introduce that new character to the game as soon as is humanly possible. There are many ways to do this—if the characters are in a city somewhere, the possibilities for meeting a new ally are many. If they happen to be plumbing an ancient tomb, why not have them stumble across the new character, either a caged victim of the PCs nemesis, or stumbling around in the wilderness, half-starved and sick from being lost? Be creative and spontaneous; you'll find a way to get the new character in the game.

The new character, in most cases, should probably be created with either the same amount of experience that the deceased had, or with the average amount of experience points for the entire party. This will maintain parity across the board and avoid repeated character deaths when the challenges are too great for the new character's low level.

SCOPE OF THE GAME

As stated earlier, if you know your group and the style of play they prefer, this will make it easier for you to decide what kind of game to run. The standard unit around which games are generally centered is the adventure module (or, if you prefer to be more pulpy, the "episode.") An episode or module is generally a self-contained story with a beginning, middle, and end that can be played between one and four sessions of a game. However, often a GM will prefer to create a campaign or "series" from a set of linked modules,

with each story leading into the next and so on, all the while building a larger mystery or deeper plot. Series of this nature can take characters from their novice days as adventurers all the way into high levels of play and have been known to stretch over decades and incorporate many different levels of interconnected plot threads, themes, metaplot, and epic stories with characters sometimes going on to affect events at the worldwide level. Sticking with the episode-and-series terminology, such series would be broken down into sub-series chunks that could be referred to as "seasons" or "serials."

However, you need not set out to plan a gigantic, multi-serial series with hooks and plot threads galore right out of the gate. Indeed, for the novice GM this would be a daunting task! Rather, it's best to start with a basic adventure or two, perhaps unrelated, perhaps with a recurring theme or villain. Observe your players, watch the direction they take the game, see how they like to play, and listen to the things they say, especially when they're trying to puzzle out what's going on. Their speculations can give you great ideas for future scenarios. If they're making offhanded references constantly, for example, to Lovecraftian themes, it might be a good idea to drop a few tentacled horrors or other viscous, fetid beasts of the Outer Dark in at some point. In the end, if you watch how your players react to the themes you introduce in a couple of early, largely unrelated, adventures, you will find ways to further connect your themes and in this way, a few nights of play can extend into a long and epic struggle against the forces of darkness that you and your players will talk about for years to come.

RULES VS. RULINGS

You can't have a game without rules. Clearly, the very reason you picked up this book was to have a set of rules to define how to run a pulp game with your friends. Rules help to maintain the game's balance, establish a fair and impartial baseline by which to adjudicate how the story plays along, and keep the players or GM from gaining too much power.

Perhaps the best example of this is that of two kids playing Cowboys or War. One boy points his (orange-tipped and brightly-colored) cap gun at another and yells, "BANG! I GOT YOU!"

His friend, then, says, "No, you didn't! You missed!"

"Did not!"

"Did so! And I'm wearin' armor, anyway!"

"Who said?"

...and so on.

This is an example of role playing without rules. Now, while we'd all like to think that as teens and adults we're beyond those sorts of arguments, take a minute to think about it: how would you know without rules, if your shot hit the enemy in game? After all, tabletop role playing is just talking, and while some groups may be capable of the type of freeform gaming that requires no system for adjudicating combat, they're rare, and probably wouldn't be looking at this book to begin with, nor any other published game, for that matter.

That's not to say that the rules are the be-all, end-all of the game. Rather, they're a starting point, a means by which you can maintain consistency and balance in play. Deviating from the rules as written can be fun and even necessary to the style of game you want to play. Rule zero in any role playing game is, "throw out the rules you don't like." However, it is necessary to *have* rules. Rules mean consistency–that when a player does the same thing he did last week, it will have similar results (sometimes modified by a die roll). Consider that if the GM makes random judgement calls constantly, without ever referencing the rules or keeping track of the rulings he made last week, the game will be chaotic, inconsistent, unfocused, and will suffer from a lack of player investment and willingness to participate or be engaged.

You'll discover that this becomes less of a problem as you gain more experience behind the screen, but for now, remember that consistency is important. It's sometimes good and even necessary to make rulings when a game rule seems unclear, there is no rule to cover a given situation, or you simply don't agree with the rules as written. What is important, however, is that you are consistent about applying your rulings. If you rule on how a situation works in a different way than the book suggests, you would be wise to make a note of that ruling so you don't forget it later on. Also, you should always be willing to listen to your players' thoughts on rulings that you make after the game session is over. Any time you implement a new rule or system, discuss it with your players so that everyone is in agreement about how it should all work. However, and this cannot be stressed enough, these discussions should be held away from the table, before or after or between game sessions. Never allow rules-based debates to slow down or interrupt your game.

RUNNING *AMAZING ADVENTURES*

Above, we gave some tips and advice for new game masters, and refresher advice for experienced GMs on how to run a game, how to decide on scope and scale, how to learn what your players like and anticipate their actions, and generally a primer on the basics of Game Mastering. This section is of use to those more experienced Game Masters, especially those familiar with ***Castles & Crusades***. In order to better mimic the themes and tropes of pulp literature, film, and gaming, ***Amazing Adventures*** has some specific rules in play that don't exist in prior iterations of the SIEGE Engine. In this section we'll look at some issues specific to ***Amazing Adventures*** and the specialized rules herein.

Fate Points and the GM

Fate Points are an important tool in ***Amazing Adventures***, and using them can and will change the entire tenor of your game. There are two specific things you need to keep in mind when tracking the use of Fate Points in your game.

The first thing is, you need to give them out to your players. Characters get only a limited number of Fate Points per level, and you'll find that you will be the final arbiter of how fast they get spent. The harder your game is, the more challenges you put forward for the characters to face, the more frequently they'll have to call on Fate Points to pull their bacon out of the fire. As such, Fate Points shouldn't only be gained each level. Rather, the GM should award Fate Points a couple per session, based on how well the players do. Situations in which Fate Points can be awarded are as follows:

- If a player is role playing his character particularly well, especially if he role plays a Trait or established personality quirk to his character's detriment, give him a Fate Point as a reward for his troubles.
- If another player makes a joke at the table that is appropriate to the game or situation at hand, while also making everyone else laugh–a clever one-liner spoken by his character, for example–a Fate Point award should result. This award should only be given if the joke is appropriate, however–players who are constantly wisecracking to the detriment of the mood of the game should never be rewarded for such antics.
- If a player sees his character throw herself in front of a bullet to save an innocent NPC or even another PC (or the entire group, taking on a major villain alone to buy the others time to escape), Fate Points should be awarded for the heroic sacrifice. If the sacrifice actually results in the death of the character, by all means, the player's new PC should be awarded bonus Fate Points for the player's actions.
- If–and this one is a tricky one–you need the plot to turn a certain way, and it requires one or more characters to take it on the chin as a result, you can award a Fate Point or two in compensation, often with a shrug and a bashful apology ("Sorry, dude. You got clubbed from behind. You never saw it coming. But have two Fate Points for it.") This particular situation is not recommended as a regular thing; the very last thing you want is for your players to feel like they're being railroaded through your story. But every once in a great while it allows you, the GM, to throw a plot twist in that throws the players for a loop. If you do this and they complain, remind them that they, too, have the ability to use Fate Points to influence the story through minor plot twists using Providence Smiles.

Secondly, never, ever forget that if the players can do it, so can the GM. What this means is that *your monsters and villains should have Fate Points, too.* For general monsters, like your average thug, zombie, ghoul, or cultist, give them maybe two Fate Points each to allow for shrugging off wounds.

If it's a major villain, give him or her Fate Points equal to 5 plus one half of their hit dice (round up or down as you see fit). Thus, if your adventure's Big Bad is a 10 HD vampire who bathes in the blood of virgin girls, she should have ten fate points (5 plus half her ten hit dice). The reason villains of this sort don't have the full fate points that their hit dice might indicate (ten plus each of their levels or hit dice) should be obvious: this would result in a nigh-unkillable enemy with dozens of fate points. Consider, ten to start, plus half their level for each level up to ten...the vampire above would have 35 fate points per the rules for player characters gaining fate points on page 52. It has to be assumed that over the years of its life, the creature has spent some fate points to get where it currently is. Thus, it gets a limited subset of the normally-expected total.

Wealth

The Wealth system in ***Amazing Adventures*** is intended to be very intuitive and easy to use, falling back on the familiar SIEGE check system for implementation. Each character has a Wealth score based upon their character class, which translates roughly to an ability check bonus in terms of scale (generally, +1 to +3). When a character needs to make a purchase, a Wealth check is made to see if funds are currently available, this check being a standard SIEGE check (d20 plus Wealth bonus, plus character level). The Wealthy Generic Class Ability (p.62) essentially allows a character to declare this ability as an additional Prime, granting +5 to Wealth checks.

Events in game can come into play that will, at the GM's discretion, change this score for the better or worse. If the game is running through the Great Depression, characters may see their wealth scores severely penalized, even halved, due to the worldwide financial crisis. If the characters gain fame and fortune through discovering the lost treasure of Coronado, laying claim to it, and selling it to a museum, they could all gain a pretty big bonus to their wealth scores, be it a permanent or long-term temporary bonus (perhaps dependent upon what the players state they're doing with their new money–invest or squander?)

The key thing to keep in mind with the wealth system is that it is not intended to bog down the game with additional die rolls. In fact, it's intended to speed up the game by removing the need to track the exact dollars and cents available to your characters at any given time. Use common sense when applying this system. If a player wants her character to buy a pack of gum or a carton of cigarettes, no wealth check should be needed. If a player wants to buy a car, on the

other hand, what is her wealth score? If it's +3, she might not need to make a roll. If it's +1 or +2, perhaps a roll is in order. If she's Wealthy, it's likely she can afford that car and no roll should be made. Also, as characters increase in level, it's assumed that they gain more means as their fame and fortune as adventurers gets higher. Thus, while a first level character with a +1 wealth score may not be able to afford much, a tenth level character with a +1 wealth may be able to actually buy a car without needing to make a roll (he's starting with a +11 to his check, anyway, at this point).

Basic guidelines are given for the CL of wealth checks on p. 79, but use your own judgment based on each individual character's combined score and level bonus to decide if a roll really needs to be made.

Sanity

Sanity rules are expressly optional in ***Amazing Adventures***, but nevertheless require certain considerations when choosing to implement them in game. The biggest tip you can keep in mind if you want to use the Sanity rules (p. 64) in your game is that you need to commit. Sanity is a brutal thing, and if you're going to make it a game element it needs to be a presence. Any time a sanity check could be called for, call for one. There are two approaches you can take–the first is the long, slow slide into madness, and the second is the full-blown, committed, sanity-blasting campaign.

The Long, Slow Slide

In this type of game Sanity will be whittled away bit by bit until the players eventually go completely mad, but until this happens there will be little indication of the encroaching darkness as the players will lose only a few points at a time. Remember, in order to experience a psychotic (or other kind of) break from sanity on a temporary basis, a PC must lose more than half her Wisdom score from a single scene. If you're going easy on the sanity checks, this might not happen. For example, let's say the heroes encounter a group of zombies. The GM calls for Sanity Checks on the initial encounter, and then moves on. It's likely that even those who fail won't take the amount of loss needed to suffer a break from reality (though it might happen, this will be somewhat rare).

More likely in this type of game would be Indefinite Insanity, wherein a player loses significant SAN points in the space of a few hours of game time. However, if you're keeping it light and slow on the SAN loss, even this won't happen very often. Rather, you probably won't really see the effects of sanity loss until players start to reach a SAN of 0, and at that point, the game is going to be pretty dark indeed! Going light on sanity checks is a viable approach and will result in a more heroic style game wherein players have a good chance to beat back the forces of darkness, raging against the dying of the light (said "light" being their own mental stability). In this sort of game, ancient tomes of forgotten and forbidden lore are tools to use against the forces of darkness, often containing spells for containing evil as well as for summoning it.

The Sanity-Blasting Approach

If you're going to use the sanity rules to their fullest measure, you may want to commit to the idea of having a dark game to begin with, and as such you should be calling for pretty frequent sanity checks. In the example above, the first check upon encountering the zombies is all well and good, but the first time a zombie actually *bites a chunk out of a player character, and starts to chew on the flesh with relish,* another sanity check would be called for. If a PC is grappled by a zombie while two others bear down on him, you could be justified in calling for a third check (especially if said PC has failed the first two).

This brings up a good point–keep track of which characters fail a sanity check at the beginning of an encounter. These PCs should be called upon more often to make further checks that scene than those who succeeded in their check and are thus better able to process what's happening to them. Remember that failing a sanity check means that your mind is reeling from the encounter; you can't really process what you've seen and every instinct in you is crying, "Run! Now!"

This type of game, which features frequent checks, will see many more episodes of temporary and indefinite insanity, and may see players lose more than one character to permanent madness. It's appropriate for full-on Lovecraftian horror games, where the protagonists are desperately trying to make their way in a nihilistic world of chaos and entropy, caught up inexorably in forces with which they can neither contend nor comprehend. Unlike in the Long, Slow Slide style of gaming, in this style ancient tomes of forbidden lore carry their own sanity cost just for reading them and are as likely to corrupt and drive characters mad who try to use the knowledge within, as they are to help. GMs may even decide in games like this to place sanity costs on spells cast by Arcanists, making magic itself a corrupting and maddening otherworldly force.

Reputation

Like Sanity, these rules are expressly optional, but require some work to properly implement and represent some additional bookkeeping by the game master. They may be particularly advantageous in games where one or more players are running Socialite characters, whose reputation may influence their ability to use their Connected class ability. While this isn't explicitly laid out in the earlier rules, it's something that GMs may want to keep in mind.

DESIGNING A PULP SCENARIO

Lester Dent, creator of Doc Savage and one of the foremost pulp adventure writers in history, wrote an essay containing a "master plot" formula for a 6,000-word pulp story that according to him, never failed to produce a yarn that didn't sell. There is absolutely no reason why his formula cannot be adapted to writing adventure scenarios for role playing games, and that's exactly what the formula we're giving you here is based upon and inspired by. For anyone wishing to read Dent's original article, we direct you to http://www.miskatonic.org/dent.html where the article is reprinted in its entirety.

ESTABLISH THE ADVENTURE

The first thing you need to do to create a pulp adventure is establish your primary hook. Every adventure has to start with a hook, and an obstacle for the heroes. This obstacle should consist of at least two of four possible elements: An unusual crime, an unusual item or artifact that the villain seeks, an exotic location, or a grand and shadowy threat of some sort.

The "unusual" or "exotic" need not necessarily be completely unique; rather, it could be a twist on a common theme. Take, for example, your unusual crime. A shooting in the city is not unusual. But what if the shooting was performed with a poisoned blowgun dart akin to those used by South American cannibal tribes, and nobody saw the shooter?

How about combining that with your unusual location? A restaurant is not unusual; at least, not if it's your everyday greasy spoon. But a posh nightclub where the wealthy and elite of society mingle, with a Caribbean theme? Suddenly the mundane becomes exotic.

What about an unusual item? A pen is about the most mundane item one can imagine, but what if it were the gold-plated favorite pen of Nicola Tesla, and rumor has it he's hidden plans inside it for an energy source of such vast power that it could become a doomsday device in the wrong hands?

Now, just to throw all four elements in, a shadowy menace: the shooting victim–who of course supposedly had Tesla's pen on his person–suddenly gets up and begins eating people as a ravenous, mindless zombie! The poison on the dart was a type of burundaga powder from the Caribbean that has a mystical element, raising the bodies of the dead.

Put those four elements together, and set your scenario in, say, New York, 1935, and suddenly you've got the setup for a fantastic adventure.

THE FOUR ACT PLOT

Now it's time to work that setup into an adventure. Every adventure has four sections, each one filling a niche in the story arc and furthering the plot towards its explosive

conclusion. Remember, this is a pulp story, so action should be paramount. We'll look at each act below, what it should include, and how it breaks down. After this exploration, we'll include an example of how it all fits together in the form of a complete introductory scenario: The Heart of Yhtill.

Act One: Setup

Act one introduces all the main characters, usually by dumping a mess of trouble on the head of the hero. There are many ways to do this: begin in media res, with the hero up to his eyeballs in conflict, or have it start with someone walking up to the hero to deliver the trouble. This trouble does not have to be the main mystery. It can be a smaller conflict that leads into the main plot point; the idea is to start things off with a bang. Often, a good way to do this is what is sometimes known as "boxed text," a "cut scene" or, in TV and movie terms, a "pre-credits sequence." This is a block of text that you read aloud to your group which sets the scene for what is to come. Since you want things to focus on your PCs, this introductory boxed text shouldn't be more than a couple paragraphs at most; you don't want to lose your players by having them think you're just there to read them a story!

Following this setup, quickly introduce the other characters to the situation. In a game scenario this could mean that one character witnesses the crime, or is at least nearby when

everything goes down, and is drawn to the scene. The others may be passers-by, specialists called in to take a look at what's gone down, or they could encounter other problems related somehow to the main conflict.

Once all the characters are involved, you need to take things off at a break neck pace. Some sort of conflict should arise, quickly...that means combat; a skirmish with thugs is probably your best bet at this point. But this conflict leads you to your first transition: a clue, revelation, or plot twist that is unexpected or surprising in some way.

The keys to this first act are suspense, danger, and menace.

Act Two: Complication

The clue, revelation, or plot twist encountered at the end of act one should lead the characters directly into the next stage of their adventure: grief. Not grief as in "mourning" or "sadness." Grief as in, "problems dumped on the heads of our intrepid paragons of justice." Something about the revelation or clue in Act One has marked our PCs as wanted, dangerous, or a threat to someone involved with the situation, and that someone wants them out of the way. Act two is where things begin to go downhill, where the heroes (though not the players!) start to think it's going to be a long night.

Be careful, however, not to make things too dark. Not yet, at least. There needs to be a sense of hope at the end of it, or at least something that drives the heroes to determination. They might be patriotic, heroic, or just downright pissed off, but something needs to be there to push them forward so they don't get frustrated or hopeless and quit.

In the end, their struggles lead them to a second physical confrontation. This one should further the plot even more, leading the adventurers to a revelation or another plot twist, this one more major, that puts them squarely on the road to resolving the problem (or so they think, at least).

The key to act two is to build the suspense and sense of menace even further. Make sure the characters know they're in it neck deep, and the only way out is forward.

Act Three: Caught in a Web

Act three is where things get their darkest. Troubles keep growing for our PCs, and the villain's menace seems unconquerable. At this point the heroes are struggling because they don't have much other choice. The bad guy clearly wants them out of the picture and is willing to do almost anything to make that happen. And yet, the heroes make progress. Perhaps they finally discover who the shadowy figure is behind the menace, or track the villain to his secret hideaway. They corner him after battling or sneaking their way through all his various henchmen. Bravado is shown, speeches are made, and insults exchanged.

Then, just when the heroes think they have their nemesis on the ropes...throw another plot twist at them. This one needs to give it to them hard. Stick a proverbial knife in their guts and turn it a few times. Who knew, for example, that the villain had a pet: the last tyrannosaurus in existence? The beast charges in, the walls slam down, and the heroes are trapped.

Needless to say, the villain escapes, apparently on the brink of victory, and the heroes find themselves hopelessly trapped, perhaps looking at the supposedly dead body of someone they were supposed to protect or rescue. This is the point where the game hits its darkest point. If there were a serious cliffhanger, this is where you'd put it, though to be honest, every act should end with some sort of minor cliffhanger. But to use old Saturday morning serial terms, this is where the hero is literally hanging by one hand from a cliff and the branch on which he's hanging is pulling away from the ledge. Or the hero and his best girl are tied to the railroad tracks with a train speeding towards them, unaware of their plight. This is the big one, the "how will they ever get out of this one?" moment.

To Fight another Day

"But how," you're wondering, "can I ensure that the villain escapes without railroading the players?"

Good question. The answer is that there's no real foolproof answer. You can't prepare for everything your heroes are going to do, and if they do something brilliant that ends the scenario early, run with it! As long as everyone's had a good time, that's what's paramount. But, should you want to carry things on a little longer, something to remember: there is no reason and nothing in the rules that says bad guys can't have Fate Points, too. It may seem like a cheap trick, but it's not. It's fair play, all around. There's an old adage in gaming: if the players can do it, so can the GM.

This is probably a good place for an aside. Turning your players' tricks back upon them is not to say by any means that tabletop role-playing gaming is adversarial. Quite the opposite is true, in fact. In most role playing games, the GM's job is not to be antagonistic towards the players, it's to foster a good time for all. We'll deal with that a little later, but that's why being a game master is such hard work. Even though you're running the bad guys, you're not out to kill the player characters off. You're out to provide a challenge for them to overcome, but only to the end that everyone has a great time telling a great story together. Some have complained that the current trend in games is that it's too hard to kill off player characters. But in the end, it should be hard to kill off PCs. How often do the main characters in great novels or television series die off? Not often: it happens, but it's far from a regular occurrence, and generally when it does happen it's a major plot development, never just the consequence of a random combat.

This is a very difficult line for a GM to walk. You don't want to throw your PCs bones every die roll of every session.

There must be a sense of danger and excitement. The players must realize that their characters are not immortal and can be killed, but at the same time, said characters are pulp heroes. You'll need to learn to put them into dangerous situations that they'll need to use all of their wits, skills, and talents to escape, but from which there is, in fact, a means of extrication. Every so often, it may be necessary to let the dice fall where they may and allow a character to meet his end to hammer home the gravity of the situation, but if you're killing off characters by the six-pack, then you have probably ramped your game's threat level up a bit too high. All of this comes with practice, with trial and error, and with paying attention to your players, the comments and suggestions they make, and their style of play. If they'll just run in and attack eight T-Rexes at second level without batting an eye, you've probably been too easy on them. Likewise, if they're suspicious of a random cat on the side of the road, you may have been a bit too harsh with the danger.

Act Four: Climax and Resolution

This is where everything comes together. Everything the scenario has been building to wraps up explosively in this act. The heroes' first task is to get out of their predicament, and it should be their own unique talents and skills that allow them to do so. Avoid deus ex machina in this bit. This is where the heroes show their stuff and get to really shine and overcome a serious, major obstacle. That's not to say they won't see something that they can use, but sticking with the tyrannosaur idea from above, the beast shouldn't just trip and fall into a pit. Rather, the characters struggle for awhile before the gadgeteer, buzzing about like a mosquito with his rocket pack, manages to lure the beast onto a grate above which a heavy chandelier hangs. Encouraged by the socialite, one well-placed shot from the gumshoe drops the chandelier, which combined with the weight of the dinosaur collapses the grate, dropping the beast into a deep well, where it drowns. All the while, the hooligan in the group works at the locks on the doors, his unique talents as a locksmith freeing the heroes from their prison. Your job here, as GM, is to set the scene and provide options, then let the players and their characters come up with clever ideas to use their own talents to get out of the jam they're in.

By the same token, don't forget the rules are there for a reason: the players are not their characters and no matter how well you set the scene, they might miss something that would be plain and obvious to someone in the situation you've laid out. If the players seem stumped, don't be afraid to call for Intelligence or Wisdom checks which yield hints if successful. For example, a successful Intelligence check from the gadgeteer yields, "Gee, that dinosaur seems irritated with you, swatting at you like a fly. You're driving it to distraction." A Wisdom check by the gumshoe reveals, "Hey, there's a huge, iron chandelier hanging just above that grate. You'd bet the grate couldn't hold both the dinosaur and the chandelier..."

Now it becomes a race against time to solve the problem before everything goes south. The characters fight their way through scads of bad guys or chase the villain through an exotic locale: through the mountains, across rooftops, etc., to a final conclusion. There should be one big reveal left at this point, something that's been held over till now. The villain isn't who he appeared to be, or works for someone even higher up. The treasure turns out to be more or less than originally thought, or just something completely different. Hit the characters with one last big plot twist, a real, "Wow, that was cool!" or even a (light hearted) "Man, that sucks!" moment.

Shortly after this big reveal, the villain is defeated, and the episode winds down, but there should always be a punch line to end things. If a more lighthearted game, the hero kisses the girl or rides off into the sunset. If a darker, more sarcastic, or even comical game, the hero never gets his just due. Someone makes a snide remark that the hero was probably the cause of the whole mess, or someone else gets credit. Or, the punch line could be one more clue that the villain they just defeated was only a little fish in a big pond of badness, and there's dark clouds on the horizon. Whatever direction you go, make sure to end it on a note that gets either a cheer or a collective (again, light hearted) groan.

THE SPIRIT OF EXPLORATION

Of the four elements listed above, the one that perhaps most commonly leaps out in pulp stories (at least of the type we're talking about) is the unusual location. Pulp stories are full of stalwart adventurers stumbling upon (or seeking out) ancient ruins, vast underground caverns, lost cities tucked in the mountains or deep in the jungles, or ancient temples of lost and forgotten cults.

In many respects, these adventures aren't much different than your typical fantasy dungeon crawl. In fact, what is a dungeon crawl if not an exploration of an underground tomb, cave network, lost city, or other mysterious locale? The genre of pulp shares many tropes with the type of fantasy gaming to which players the world over have become accustomed. There are two things that will make a typical fantasy dungeon crawl into a pulp adventure story. The first is the introduction of more modern characters carrying things like guns. You'd be amazed at how fast that changes the feel of an adventure—when a herd of ghouls emerge from the shadows and a two-fisted Raider opens up with both of his six-shooters, the whole playing field changes immediately.

The second thing that alters your typical fantasy crawl into a pulp story falls more into the purview of the GM, and that is the sense of *otherness*, or alien-ness of the place. For a fighter in a fantasy game, a wet, moldy dungeon wall and that rancid ooze that might just be a Black Pudding is commonplace—it's part and parcel of his world, expected. In a pulp scenario, the world (in general) is the world of the mundane. There are movies, crime-ridden streets, Universities, radios, and though a bit more primitive than our modern day, all the comforts of industrialized home. Entering a forgotten city for these folks is quite literally stepping into a different world, one where

the rules bend, break, or don't apply at all. When running a pulp scenario of the exploration variety, description is paramount–you need to really hammer home the cold and dank (or hot and dry) corridors, the stench of old death, that strange substance on the walls. The more detailed you can make your descriptions, the more atmosphere you will create, and pulp is all about atmosphere.

Other than that, however, it's not difficult to pull any old dungeon crawl or fantasy adventure off the shelf and adapt it to a pulp scenario.

PLOT VS. RAILROAD

This is an important issue to address, especially when dealing with a formulaic structure for creating adventures. Never, ever forget the cardinal rule: your players will think of things you did not. They will attempt tactics you did not anticipate. You absolutely, positively must be able to think on your feet. Don't ever force them on a path they don't want to take. Don't ever make them feel like they have no choice or can't have an effect on your world.

That's not to say that players always do have a choice. As much as some new-school gamers might like to think so, it is absolutely not the job of the GM to passively sit there, throw an NPC at players, and react to whatever they do. It's absolutely not a crime for you to have a story in mind, or a preferred sequence of events. You merely need to be prepared for your group to step outside that story, and you need to always maintain at very least the illusion of choice on their part.

What this means is, if you intend your players to drive across country and find themselves beset by enemies when they stop for the night, but they decide rather to take a train, let them! Your sequence of events isn't remotely compromised. Just move the confrontation with the enemies on board the train, which can set up an even more exciting battle including a chase through (and even on top of) rail cars. If they instead fly, you can if you're feeling plucky have an encounter on board a passenger plane, which could result in all kinds of chaos, or you can simply have the enemy encounter take place in the airport before they leave or after they arrive at their destination. Think fast; adjust events according to your players' actions, but never blatantly force them on a course of action.

Even still, you will find after you game with your group for a few months, that you can anticipate their probable course of action in almost any given situation... provided, of course, that they play their characters consistently. As you get to know your players and their characters, you will find yourselves making notes such as, "They will likely choose this path. But if they don't..." and "When they inevitably do this," and the longer you play with your group, the more often those little notes will be correct. Even still, it never hurts to include a "Troubleshooting" section in your notes that deals with several different avenues the characters might take, and even then you'll find you need to think fast as they make choices that you didn't account for, no matter how many avenues and possibilities you prepare in advance. But as long as you are able to roll with their choices and have a good time with it, you will be doing your job properly.

There you have it! Sure, this method is a formula, but it is a tried and true one that has worked not only for storytellers for thousands of years, but one that has worked for Game Masters as long as role playing games have existed. Just remember, your primary job as GM is to facilitate a good time for everyone, and that includes yourself. That does not mean if a game isn't fun that it is necessarily your fault; it does mean that if people are not enjoying themselves, it is time to step back, assess the situation, see where the problem lies, and address it, often with the cooperation of your players. You are the group leader, as it were, but not the group emperor. Keep your eyes and ears open, and always listen to your players' concerns and ideas. Really, in the end it's not that difficult if you're open minded and creative...and both of those factors are skills that can be learned with practice.

TWEAKING THE RULES

It's also possible to make minor tweaks in the rules to subtly alter the feel of play. There are many different ways to express and modify the probabilities that are represented in the SIEGE engine, all without substantially changing play.

For example, changing the d20 for attacks and ability checks to 3d6 maintains the general scale of play, but introduces a "bell curve" result, meaning the vast majority of checks on the dice will fall into the average range of 9-12. This creates a feeling of predictability where the characters' actual abilities mean more than the dice, but where exceptional successes and dismal failures are all the more dramatic as they become rarer. As an added bonus, by switching to solely d6's, the game can be played using dice from any old standard board game you've got laying around.

Expressing Probabilities as a Percent

It can help to understand the probabilities behind how the SIEGE engine works. In the standard SIEGE engine, the challenge base (CB) for any primary attributes is 12, and for secondary attributes the CB is 18. This equates to a first level character having a 45% chance of success when attempting a task with a primary attribute, but only a 15% chance of success when attempting to do something with a secondary attribute. These percentages do not take into account level or attribute bonuses. An attribute of 18 with a +3 bonus, combined with a +1 from level 1, increases the percentage chance of success on a given chance by roughly 20%, so a first level character with an 18 attribute now has a 65% chance of succeeding on a prime task, and a 35% chance of succeeding on a secondary task.

Now that we understand the probabilities, other minor system alterations are possible as well.

Expressing as 18/+6

Some GMs prefer to use a flat challenge base of 18 and give +6 for primes. This maintains the same general probabilities and game play, but removes a step of calculation out, as the CB always remains static.

The onus, then, falls on the players to calculate their roll by adding +6 to those checks that are made with primary attributes, whereas in the standard system, the player would note his roll result, indicating whether it was with a primary or secondary attribute, and the GM would then calculate the success or failure of the roll based off of the appropriate challenge base.

For example, in the default rules, let's say that Eric is making a Charisma check for his socialite, Mackie Gleeson, to charm a door man. Since Charisma is a primary attribute for Mackie, Eric rolls and gets a 14. He would properly express this as, "I rolled a 14 for Mackie, prime." This tells the GM that he needs to calculate the task's success using a CB of 12.

In the 18/+6 scenario, Eric would make the same roll, but since Charisma is a Prime, he would add +6 to the roll. In this case, the result would be 20, and the GM would calculate the success or failure based on a flat challenge base of 18.

You could even, if you want, use a flat 20 as a Challenge Base, adding +8 for primary attribute checks and +2 for secondary, or use a 15 Challenge Base, adding 3 for primary attributes and imposing a -3 penalty to secondary attribute checks. The probabilities across the board remain similar and the point is that it's your game! You can and should feel free to add, excise, alter, or expand the rules any way you see fit for your game; just always do so consistently, make sure that there is a good reason for altering the rules, and always attempt to maintain the balance so that one aspect of the rules (or characters, or monsters, etc.) doesn't overshadow or overpower the others. It's your game; read the rules, adapt them to your taste, and run wild! In the end, you're the one who knows what evil lurks in the hearts of men...

WHY CHANGE BACK?

The first printing of the ***Amazing Adventures*** game used a similar system to the 18/+6 expression, but used a 15/+5 expression. Primary attributes added a "Prime Bonus" of +5 to rolls using that ability, and the Challenge Base was always 15. This operated nearly the same as the default system, and exactly the same as the 18/+6 rule, but increased the potential success of characters for a more high-action feel. This had the additional advantage that rounding off to increments of 5 for some folks may be more intuitive, and makes straight comparison of results between two parties easier–just compare the total result rather than the degree by which one succeeds.

In this printing, we have moved back to expressing the system using the 12 and 18 split, to achieve maximum compatibility at a glance with ***Castles & Crusades***. If you liked the original ***Amazing Adventures*** method of handling ability checks, by all means stick with it. Keeping with that method will not change the game in the slightest!

Finally, if you own one of our older adventures such as ***Temple of the Red God***, which just uses Challenge Class, and wish to use it with this printing of the core rules, simply subtract 15 from any listed CCs to find the CL.

AMAZING CRUSADES!

Amazing Adventures was constructed for maximum compatibility with Troll Lord Games' flagship role playing game, ***Castles & Crusades***. The character classes herein, as well as any and all new "bolt-on" systems, such as the new magic system, psionics, exploding and imploding dice, and generic class abilities, should work seamlessly with the classes and rules in that game. The character class experience charts were created through a careful reverse-engineering of and comparison with the classes in C&C, so game balance should not be an issue. Ability score generation between the two games is slightly different; AA is geared towards ever slightly more powerful heroes out of the gate, but so long as you use the same method for both games, everything should balance out.

It is our hope that by combining C&C with ***Amazing Adventures***, GMs and players can model pulp adventure in the style of H.P. Lovecraft or Robert E. Howard, crafting gritty, high-action sword and sorcery games with just a touch of eldritch horror and madness.

Finally, the ***Castles & Crusades Castle Keeper's Guide*** has an extensive section that digs into the SIEGE engine system, how and why it was developed as it was, and even offers options such as adding *tertiary* attributes to your game. This book is 100% compatible with ***Amazing Adventures*** and is a must-read if you're interested in the core design history of the system.

BOOK SIX: THE ROGUE'S GALLERY

INTRODUCTION

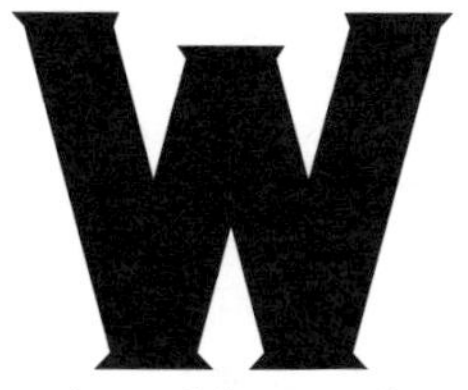

What Pulp game is complete without a collection of rogues, heroes, villains, and other do-gooders and ne'er-do-wells to color the pages of purple prose and high-action text? Here we present a section on secret societies, with guidelines on how to outline and flesh out these groups for inclusion in your game, as well as three sample organizations that are ready to drop in. One of these is an organization that is ideal for player character membership. The second is a "shades of gray" brotherhood who could become either an ally or a foe of your group, and the third is a shadowy conspiracy that trafficks in pure evil and degradation, and could be an untouchable foe to terrorize your heroes time and again.

Following this, we present a collection of pre-generated characters, named villains, and generic thugs that you can use to enhance your game. These characters will be presented in a general format with basic abilities, so that you can quickly adapt them based on the level of character or threat level you need for your game. By rolling hit dice and jotting down the specifics of a few abilities, any character or villain herein should be able to be quickly dropped into your game for instant use. The basic statistics include advanced character customization options; if you choose not to use these in your game, simply drop them and/or replace them with standard class abilities as needed. These abilities will be marked with an asterisk (*) for ease of identification.

We also present a brief write ups on the types of thugs you might encounter when facing a few real-world cults of the day, and a fictional adventuring society, the Brotherhood of William St. John, which you can use to enhance your own game or as a springboard for initial or further adventures for your group.

Finally, we will include a few classic and iconic monsters and animals for your game, in case you get tired of human thugs all the time. Included here are the Shoggoth, Lycanthrope, Mummy, Vampire, and Zombie, and a few animals like apes, snakes, bears, wolves, and great cats. We also include full guidelines on creating your own monsters for use in game.

MORE MONSTERS!

For more monsters to challenge your intrepid investigators, please see the ***Amazing Adventures Manual of Monsters***, which includes well over 100 creatures to terrorize and battle your heroes. In addition, just about any monster from Troll Lord Games' extensive ***Castles and Crusades*** roleplaying game line will work seamlessly with this game!!

SECRET SOCIETIES

The Illuminati. The Hellfire Club. The Skull and Bones. The Mafia. The Yakuza. The Triads. The Order of the Dragon. The Knights Templar. The Freemasons. James Moriarty's League of Crime. All of these names should send a shiver up the spine of any gamer or lover of pulp fiction. Many of them are even shrouded in real world conspiracy theory that gives them a sinister or mysterious air, however true or untrue this may be.

Secret societies are part and parcel of the pulps. Be it an Explorer's Club or Adventuring Society to which the heroes belong, a Mafia, Triad or Yakuza crime syndicate, or the secret New World Order, the power behind the throne represented by such intriguing groups as the Skull and Bones, the Illuminati, the Freemasons or others, secret societies find their way into many pulp adventures.

Creating a secret society for your game is largely a matter of taking the time to sit down and think about the history of the organization, its scope and scale, its resources and goals. Some of these tie into game mechanics, but much of it relies on creating a history and background for your group. This can be as basic as a skeletal outline or as detailed as you like, with reams of paper detailing every important member throughout the society's history. In the end, it comes down to how much time and preparation you want to put into the group (and how much time you have to devote!). Here are a few things to keep in mind when you set about creating a group or society for your pulp game.

DEFINING SECRET SOCIETIES

Not every secret society is completely hidden from view. Indeed, some are very open in terms of their existence, but secretive in the way they operate behind closed doors. Consider the Freemasons, who have open halls and temples all over the world, but who are very secretive as to the contents of their meetings and what happens inside those temples.

Consider a religious cult, like Rev. Jim Jones' Jonestown. Everyone knew that the cult existed, but getting into Jones' inner circle, or even getting frank interviews from members of the cult at the time, was nearly impossible. Newspaper reporters were lied to, escorted within the compound, spied upon and even threatened with violence if they didn't stop digging.

In terms of ***Amazing Adventures***, we are going to define a secret society as any group outside of an established nation, city or town that involves secrecy, clandestine operations, cover-ups, or conspiracies. This is a very broad definition that allows us to include everything from open religious cults to world-spanning clandestine espionage and control agencies. By this definition, the Illuminati, which is perhaps the best-known and most classic secret society of them all, fits just as well as the aforementioned Jamestown cult led by Reverend Jim Jones.

START WITH AN OUTLINE

When answering the questions that follow, use brief sentences or bullet points. Stick to the basic facts and don't try to get too overly detailed with long blocks of prose right off the bat. That will just get you entangled in minutiae and as much as you might be falling in love with the society you're creating or defining, you're not out to write a novel (at least, not at this point). You're trying to define a group that will function as allies or nemeses of your Player Characters, in easy-to-digest terms for your game. You'll need to be able to quickly refer back to your notes on occasion and using bullet points and headings will be of great use when you need to find key information quickly.

After you've got your outline ready to go, then you can start writing prose about the history and adventures throughout time of your secret society. Such text is important as well, because it will help you to find its voice and maintain its flavor. However, if you have to search through long passages of text to find a piece of information you need in the middle of a session, you could lose your players' investment in the game. Bullet points first–you'll be grateful you took this approach later.

ELEMENTS OF THE SECRET SOCIETY

In order to fill out your outline, you'll need to answer a number of questions and bullet-point the details of these answers. Every secret society has ten major elements, which will help to define its role in your world and how it will function within the constraints of your game.

You might be inclined to name your secret society first. This is generally the least important aspect of your group and while it should be at the top of the sheet, you should leave it blank until you've finished defining the society itself. You may discover that the act of writing up the secret society suggests a perfect name; even if you had a name in mind when you started, you might just find a better one while defining the society.

The basic elements of a secret society are:

1. Goals and Intent
2. Reach and Resources
3. Membership Requirements
4. Membership Benefits and Drawbacks
5. Operations and Activities
6. Hierarchy
7. Interior Mobility
8. Degree of Secrecy
9. History
10. Name
11. Expanded Background

Let's take a look at how this all goes together.

STEP ONE: Goals and Intent

The goals of your society should be the very first thing upon which you decide. This will inform everything else. Do they simply want to foster knowledge and invention? Do they want to find lost knowledge? Are they out for adventure and excitement? Are they a nefarious crime syndicate out to control all of the other families in the city, and then branch out? Are they a power broker organization that has had membership from nationwide or world leaders throughout history? Are they the power behind the throne, be it national, regional or worldwide? Are they a religious cult out to raise an ancient, mad god from the depths of the Deeper Dark?

The trick is to define the type of secret society you are creating. Here are some examples.

Fraternal Orders

The most basic type of secret society there is, a fraternal order consists of members who simply come together in common interest. Many adventurer's or explorer's guilds could be considered fraternal brotherhoods. In a fraternal order, members share information about their topic of interest, and support one another whenever they can.

Scholarly Societies

Is the society scholarly in nature? In some cases, the goal of the society involves collecting information, which could

mean infiltrating forbidden stores of knowledge like the Vatican archives, spending a great deal of time investigating ancient mysteries or delving into forgotten tombs in search of knowledge.

Warrior Societies

Is it designed for battle, to combat a general or specific foe? Some secret societies are engaged in open or clandestine war with others. These sorts of societies are violent and feature members with special training, often recruiting from special forces or using mercenaries. To an extent, organized crime syndicates are warrior societies, engaging in clandestine battles with other syndicates for control over territory and criminal activities.

Espionage Societies

Is the society dedicated to espionage, to obtaining and brokering knowledge and secrets? These types of societies can go hand-in-hand with knowledge- and battle-based societies. Real-world "alphabet soup" agencies like the NSA, CIA and such are examples of these types of secret societies. Their stock in trade is the spy game, be it international espionage or domestic counter-terrorism. In many ways, the NSA functions as both a combat- and espionage-related organization. Their goal is to ferret out and combat terrorism on domestic soil through espionage activities and information gathering.

Mystery Cults

Some societies are religious in nature, dedicated to worship of a specific deity or deities, or dedicated to a specific method of worship. These are known as mystery cults, or just cults. The Jamestown cult, The Branch Davidians, the fictional Cult of Cthulhu, Al Qaeda, and even the Manson Family are all examples of religious cults. Each religious cult will have its own goals, though many of them are begun through efforts to prepare for the End of Days, either by getting their members ready or by acting to bring it about.

Guardian Societies

There are societies out there whose duty it is to guard something, be it secret knowledge about a subject–say, the true lineage of Jesus Christ–or the location of a great, lost city in the desert which boasts a library full of forbidden knowledge. Members of these societies may not even have the knowledge they guard; their sworn duty is simply to make sure nobody else gets it.

Control Societies

Control-based societies seek to become the power behind the throne, or preserve such power if they already have it. This could be as small as a group of wealthy individuals who control everything that happens in a rural town, often to the detriment of the citizens, or world-spanning organizations devoted to maintaining a certain level of control and status-quo between world governments or agencies, often steering the world towards a shadowy goal that only their inner circle knows. They are often so fanatical in their operations that they resemble mystery cults, though their means are generally political or social in nature, rather than metaphysical. They want to control and change the world, not get ready for its end.

A secret society may not fall strictly into any one of the above categories, but could be a combination of two or more, or even all of them. You can see how this one simple question can inform a great deal of the description to come. Knowing what your secret society is after and what their overall objective is, will help you to make the right decisions later.

STEP TWO: Reach and Resources

This is one of the most important aspects of your secret society. It tells just about everything about them at a glance. Are they a regional society–a secret lodge that functions as the power base behind a small rural town? Are they an organized crime syndicate in a big city, with some ties to similar syndicates in other areas? Are they a national organization that bestows honors and privileges on members while expecting certain secret concessions in return? Are they a government agency that has secretly struck deals with an alien power? Are they a conspiracy within the government that battles against the insidious alien invasion threat? Or are they a massive, shadowy, international conspiracy that traces their membership and power all the way back to medieval Bavaria?

When you have decided upon the society's reach, you will know what their resources are. Can they provide shelter and safety to members on the run from enemies? Can they provide weapons, equipment and money? Can they get lines of credit or freeze bank accounts? Can they find a fugitive wherever she goes, tracking her to the depths of Antarctica and having someone waiting for her when she gets there? Knowing and defining the resources of the society is important when your player characters either join one or come up against the members of one.

When determining the reach and resources of your group, first define its reach and scope. Is it local, regional, national, or worldwide? Where are its main bases of operation, and how much power does it wield within its scope of influence? Is that power overt, an open secret, or truly hidden from view? Define as much as you can about where the society operates and how far its grasp reaches.

When you have that clarified, it should give you a fairly good idea of what kinds of resources the group can provide. An international clandestine spy organization, for example, will probably have a lot more money, equipment and information to give out than a secret cult operating out of a one-stoplight town in Arkansas. Add a few bullet points describing the

equipment, network, and funding available to members, and any limits thereof.

If you want to add game mechanics to your secret society, here is where to do it. A society may add to the Wealth rating of player characters. It could add access to the benefits of a Generic Class Ability, Background, or Knowledge. Alternately, it could add powerful enemies and adversaries to the mix, or make the PCs into outlaws. The sky is the limit and it's really up to you!

STEP THREE: Membership Requirements

No society or group exists in a vacuum. There are expectations of the members of any organization, and your secret society is no different. Working out the expectations of your secret society is probably one of the most intensive and detailed elements of crafting the group, and involves a number of elements.

Recruitment

This usually starts in how the society recruits. How does one become a member of the secret society? Is it something a character is born into? Can you apply for membership? Are you approached from the shadows after some notable deed? Are you conscripted without choice?

Joining a secret society is bookended by leaving one. Is it possible to leave your secret society, or will you find yourself hunted or watched for the rest of your life? Indeed, in the worst possible scenario, you could be targeted for assassination for leaving the group.

Levels of Membership

Once inside the society, are there levels or circles of membership? Do you start on the outside and gradually work your way to the inner circle, or is it small group dedicated to a singular cause, and everyone in the group knows what it is? Do members know each other or is the society based in cells whose contact is limited, if it exists at all? What does a member need to do to be entrusted with greater responsibilities?

Leaving the Society

Now that you know how members get into and out of your secret society, you can think about what the society expects of its members. Naturally, keeping and guarding the secrets of the society will be the foremost responsibility of any member of any society, but what are the penalties for revealing such secrets? Is it a slap on the wrist, or is it imprisonment or even death?

Secrets and How They Are Kept

What are the secrets that members are expected to keep? To what lengths are members expected to go, to keep and guard these secrets? Being a member of a secret society is often all-encompassing and is rarely something one does lightly.

Member Responsibilities

The different types of secret society explored in step one each have different expectations of their members. For example:

FRATERNAL ORDER: These societies tend to be the most basic type of secret order, with responsibility only to keep the society's secrets, the member receiving brotherhood and aid in times of hardship, in return. Members are expected to always lend support and aid to a brother, and put the society's interests ahead of their own, if necessary.

SCHOLARLY SOCIETIES: Members of these types of society would be expected to leave no stone unturned if it meant finding information related to their society's goals. In some cases, this could be targeted knowledge, like knowledge of a certain ancient religion. Some might be dedicated to recording lost histories, or even chronicling current history in all its forms and facets. In others, members might seek knowledge for knowledge's sake, be it scientific or metaphysical. This type of society could, for example, have members whose job it is to observe and record the activities of the supernatural realm, but never, ever get involved.

WARRIOR SOCIETIES: In warrior societies, members are expected to take every opportunity to battle their sworn enemy, even unto death, but never to reveal evidence of their society's involvement. A society of vampire hunters, for example, out to destroy the undead across the world, may be sworn to combat these unnatural foes wherever they rear their head, but always to cover up evidence of the vampires' existence and their own involvement, for the good of all society.

ESPIONAGE SOCIETIES: These societies expect their members to be experts at covert operations, breaking and entering, surveillance, information gathering, lies, deceit, and even murder and assassination. They generally operate in the service of a larger organization or government, though there could be espionage societies dedicated to obtaining, stealing and brokering knowledge and secrets as well.

MYSTERY CULTS: Members' responsibilities to a religious cult are broad and diverse and may include a devotion to asceticism, a responsibility to bring down societal structures, assault enemy organizations, to summon a dark god to consume the world, or any combination of these. Religious cults tend to be fanatical in their devotion and not only willing, but eager to martyr themselves for the cause. Members are rarely permitted to leave a religious cult lightly, and often have to escape, only to be hunted until the cult is wiped out.

GUARDIAN SOCIETIES: Members of guardian societies have only one duty: to protect the secret they have sworn to guard. To this end, they could be expected to engage in

sabotage, discrediting powerful individuals, or even murder to protect the secret. Often, they are expected to sacrifice their own lives before revealing anything about their group or its activities.

CONTROL SOCIETIES: Membership in these societies involves anything from assassination to infiltration of other agencies, and can very often include elements of all of the above. The shadowy inner circle of these groups demands absolute obedience to the cause, and expects members to put the cause above everything else, even before their own lives.

Knowing what your society's members are going to be expected to do, will help you flesh out the kinds of people that the society attracts and make you better able to whip up an NPC member of the society instantly.

STEP FOUR: Membership Benefits and Drawbacks

This step, in a lot of ways, is a summation of what has come before. What members gain from being a member of the society is tied to the group's resources, reach and goals. However, benefits can go beyond being able to obtain equipment, money and information. Some societies carry with them a degree of prestige or temporal power, like the arrest abilities of an NSA agent. Other societies may carry a certain degree of prestige with them, like membership in a prestigious college fraternity – at the very least, members may have a way to recognize each other and offer support. Make a list of the basic benefits members receive either automatically or upon request, along with limits.

Drawbacks of membership, again, are often tied to membership expectations. The expectation, for example, to commit murder on demand may well be a major drawback for some members. The inability to leave a society once you're in may be another downfall. Are members watched constantly? This can be both an upside and a downfall. After all, the group may be able to protect you if you end up in the fire, but they also know who you're sleeping with and what you had for dinner.

In the end, for a secret society to be successful, the benefits need to outweigh the drawbacks, which can be heavy. Make sure that the members of a society are either fanatical in their devotion to the cause, or get more out of it than they give (at least, so far as surface appearances go). Many societies will give members everything and ask almost nothing until the member is so far indebted to the society that they have no choice but to accept its control.

After all, that mansion in the country and the career as the bestselling novelist of all time, not to mention having the direct ear of Congressman Stevens, is worth a lot, and it can be taken away as easily as it was granted...we gave you everything. Now it's time to give back.

STEP FIVE: Operations and Activities

You may have noticed that we're getting more into bullet points that tie into things we've established before. This is expected and intended. As you move on, you may find that it's easier to answer subsequent questions, knowing what you already know.

The next step is to outline the operations and activities of the group. In some ways this is like further breaking down membership responsibilities. What is a member going to do on an average day or an average mission? What does the group, as a group, do in order to achieve its goals? How does it go about its operations? Does it use exclusively its own agents? Does it have a network of informants? Does it employ mercenary troops? Does it do its own dirty work or are there others that are duped into doing the hard stuff for the group?

No group, no matter how powerful or old, is completely infallible. What are the "tells" of your secret society? What mistakes do they make on occasion that could tip someone off? Do they have a calling card of sorts? Are there secret handshakes, a special lingo, or symbols they use? If a member needs to get in touch, is there an office, or do they pick up a pay phone without dialing, and order a dozen roses to the corner Main and Grant? Are they flashy and grandiose, or do they find overt action crass and distasteful? All of these things go into answering the question of how the society operates.

STEP SIX: Hierarchy

How is the group structured? What levels of command are there, and how many? An organized crime syndicate, for example, might have a boss, who has a limited crew of captains or lieutenants below him. These oversee an army of enforcers and leg breakers, and perhaps people with specialized talents such as bootleggers, assassins and the like. Beneath the enforcers are the soldiers, who do whatever is asked of them, hoping to work their way up the ranks. At the bottom are the "made," those people recently brought into "the family," who get favors and in turn owe favors (which are probably greater than those they received in the first place).

Define the levels of command in your group, along with the amount of knowledge about and control over the group's activities and operations an average member at each level will have. Are there titles for the different strata within the hierarchy, and what are they? For example, is a person a member of a numbered Circle, or does the group use titles similar to a church, such as Priest, Bishop, etc. Some groups may even use family titles—Cousin, Brother, Sister, Uncle, Aunt, Father, Mother, Grandfather, etc.

Define how difficult the members of each level are to access, both by members and by outside forces, and explain why.

Again, keep it simple for quick reference.

STEP SEVEN: Interior Mobility

Moving on from the levels of command, it's time to look at the people within those levels. Is it possible to move from one level to another, and how does this happen? Are there specific benchmarks for movement amongst the hierarchy, or are members promoted and demoted based on great successes and failures, at the discretion of those above them? Aside from prestige, what does one gain from moving upward in the ranks? Certainly there are greater perks, but what are they, and what additional responsibilities go hand-in-hand with those perks?

STEP EIGHT: Degree of Secrecy

To what degree does the group operate in the shadows, and to what degree are they in the light? Earlier we mentioned the Freemasons, which is an openly secret society. Everyone knows who the Freemasons are, and where they are. What not everyone knows is what goes on at their meetings, and if they might be more than they appear to be.

Organized crime syndicates are another open secret group. The Bureau, for example, knows that Lucky Luciano and Al Capone are crime bosses. Unfortunately, the two are so good at covering their tracks that the feds can't get anything on them. Their families range across cities and perhaps even across state boarders through alliances with other crime families, and there's not a lot the feds can do except harass them and hope they make a mistake.

Organizations of this type are **Open Secret Societies.**

The Illuminati, on the other hand, if they exist, is a very secret society. Nobody who isn't a member can point to anyone who is, or even prove that there is such a thing. This is an example of a world-spanning conspiracy that operates entirely in the shadows, their name only known perhaps because of a slip-up at some point in time, or because that's all they want people to know...all the better to add to their power by letting conspiracy theorists build the mystery.

There could actually be secret groups of whom the world is completely unaware, living quietly and totally out of sight. Who knows what their shadowy goals and operations might be like? Organizations like this are called **Shadow Organizations**.

Somewhere between the two are societies like the Skull and Bones. There is a long line of powerful men in existence that we know belonged to this fraternal order, but nobody knows who the group is, where they meet, or what ends they seek to achieve. We know for a fact they exist, and we know who some of the members are. We just don't know what they want or where they might be lurking. These types of groups are **Clandestine Fraternities (or Sororities).**

Define the level of secrecy of your group. Are they an open secret society, a shadow organization, or a clandestine fraternity? To what degree do they maintain their secrecy? After all, a crime family and the Freemasons may both be open secret societies, but the degree of openness is pretty varied between them. Why hasn't the society been exposed? How exactly do they maintain their secrecy? This applies to how they handle both members and witnesses to their activity.

STEP NINE: History

We're getting very close to the end, now. At this point, you have all of the nuts and bolts of your group spelled out. You could run them at the drop of a hat just by referencing a few bullet points and drawing conclusions as to how they apply to the story you're developing.

Now comes the time to add some color, flavor, and back story. Put together a timeline-like history of your group. Keep it to short bullet points like everything else, but include its founding members and date, the reasons for its founding, and a list of benchmark dates, important personages, and notable activities throughout its history. Having this sort of timeline/list will enable you to drop tidbits of information to your players as they work their way up the ranks of a friendly society, or as they investigate and battle a hostile one. Be sure to leave enough open so that you can expand upon what you have, but don't be too vague. After all, these notes are for you, the Game Master, and there's no point hiding information from yourself!

STEP TEN: Name

Now we come to the final step in creating the outline of your society. Choose a name for the group. The name should have significance, and if you are just throwing down a name that you think sounds cool, take the time to give some thought as to *why* the name works for your group. What does it signify? For the most part, names of companies and organizations don't exist in a vacuum and aren't picked out of an *Extraordinary Book of Names.* The group's name will mean something. It could be that the group is named for its members' common occupation, like the Freemasons. It could also be that the group adopted a symbol representative of their ideals, and named themselves after the symbol. A religious cult dedicated to the god Thor, for example, might (and likely would) adopt Mjolnir, Thor's hammer, as their symbol, and may dub themselves "The Brotherhood of Mjolnir," as a result.

If the meaning for the name you choose isn't immediately obvious, make a note of the rationale in case you need to recall it later.

STEP ELEVEN: Flesh It Out

Now you've got the skeleton of your secret society ready to go, preferably with more than a little meat on the bones as well, and perhaps some internal organs to give it life. The only thing left to do is to flesh it out with some expanded background and use it in game! There are two ways to approach this. You can

either start writing the history and story of your secret society in prose, in your spare time, detailing it till your heart's content, or you can let it design itself, concocting elements of the group's history and activities as they become relevant to your game, then writing them down as you do so.

There are advantages to both approaches. The first approach, designing it all from the outline and outside of the game, allows you a great deal of knowledge about the group that you'll be able to use and call on when you need it, challenging your players with a villainous (or even allied) group that you now know intimately. When they ask a question, ideally you'll have the answer already planned out. This gives you a cushion and a fall back point where you won't have to spend as much time thinking on your feet.

The second approach, however, allows you to tailor the society specifically to the way your group approaches the game. Whenever something occurs in your game that could be related to your society, you can figure out how to tie it in, and make a note of it. Your society will then grow and develop organically, alongside the game and players. This can be a fun way to put things together, and you might find yourself as surprised at the twists and turns as your players are.

Which approach you take is entirely up to you. With the skeleton you've put together, you can take your crime syndicate, New World Order group, or Cult of Nyarlathotep anywhere your game wants to go!

SAMPLE SECRET SOCIETIES

Now that we have the guidelines in place to structure an organization, let's look at a few examples that you can drop into your own game and use as you please. These groups range from an adventuring society to which your players can belong, to a guardian society outlined in ***The Heart of Yhtill*** and our first adventure module, ***The Day of the Worm***, to that infamously Satanic brotherhood known as the Hellfire Club.

Please note that the societies below have been entirely fictionalized for use in game, and the author makes no claim or knowledge about the reality or function of any one of them. The Hellfire Clubs were (are?) real-world groups, and the author makes no claim to internal knowledge about their practices, save what has been read in books and online. Their secrets (if any) are still quite safe.

It's also possible that maybe I'm just saying that because I have no choice...

THE BROTHERHOOD OF WILLIAM ST. JOHN

The Brotherhood of William St. John is a fictional explorer's and adventuring guild designed especially for ***Amazing Adventures***. It is hoped that you can use it as a springboard for your game, a group to which your player characters can eventually belong. In the next section, you will find some pre-generated characters who form the core membership of the group. Feel free to use or ignore them in your game, as it suits your needs.

Outline

GOALS AND INTENT: The Brotherhood of William St. John is a fraternal order that also incorporates elements of Scholarly, Warrior, and Espionage societies. It is a philanthropic adventuring guild dedicated to exploration and discovery, and championing justice and the plight of the weak. Members will root out and battle evil wherever it shows its face, and seek to gather, protect and preserve knowledge and information for the good of all mankind.

REACH AND RESOURCES: Nominally, the guild is a wealthy group. However, members come together when needed in more of a "cell" format than as a group *en masse*. Often, any team has only the resources available to the team's wealthiest member. In rare and emergency situations, Mackie Gleeson has been able to provide funding, contacts and personnel to a small degree, but the guild is more of a brotherhood than a paramilitary or espionage group.

MEMBERSHIP REQUIREMENTS: Successful explorers and adventurers are bound to catch the eye of the guild at some point, and will be contacted and offered membership. Despite its name, the Brotherhood allows both men and women into its ranks, so long as prospective members are

judged to be forthright, honorable and stout of heart. Those who seek out the guild will be expected to prove themselves worthy in the field before membership is offered. Mackie Gleeson, the current leader of the guild, makes all formal offers of membership.

There are no formal levels of membership in the guild; members are considered nominal equals, though those with more experience are held in higher regard overall.

Most members will have their own circle of friends and fellow explorers with whom they will consort regularly, and may not know other members very well. Members may identify each other with a series of signs and code words similar to those used by soldiers in the field during wartime. These signs are changed regularly and are distributed to members by Mackie herself.

Any member can choose to leave the guild at any time, simply by announcing their retirement to Mackie. There are no penalties or dangers to doing so, though the guild may occasionally look in on "retired" members to make sure all is well.

Members are expected to battle evil, champion justice and the weak, and search the world for lost and undiscovered knowledge above all other pursuits. It believes that knowledge is to be shared for the good of the world, but has, on occasion, decided as a group to withhold certain arcane secrets dubbed too dangerous for guild to hold. This occurs on a case-by-case basis.

MEMBERSHIP BENEFITS AND DRAWBACKS: Mackie is an exceptionally wealthy woman with a great deal of power behind the scenes and as the granddaughter of William St. John, she is entirely dedicated to the cause. She has contacts and friends all over the world, and can sometimes provide members with aid and assistance in this area. She is also a skilled pilot with her own private plane and if an extraction is needed, may be able to show up to perform the pickup.

On the down side, members don't have unlimited access to supplies and resources. While Mackie is wealthy and dedicated, she doesn't spend blindly and any team of adventurers is expected to be self-reliant, sometimes in the extreme. Members are expected to share any knowledge, contacts, and information they glean with the rest of the guild–the guild does not keep secrets within its ranks. Finally, the expectation to always champion justice and the downtrodden can be a burden at times.

OPERATIONS AND ACTIVITIES: Members of the Brotherhood of William St. John are explorers, adventurers, and though some are flawed in this regard, tend to be heroic to their core. The operations a member might undertake range from exploring South African jungles to root out the secrets of a long-forgotten religion, to attempting to bring down an evil cult that is infiltrating a world government, to stopping a mad scientist from unleashing a plague upon the world. The one thing about which guild members can be certain is that their lives will never be boring.

Since the guild is so loosely organized with such an open mandate, it is vulnerable to infiltration, and there have been one or two times where an enemy has struck a blow against them through gaining access to code words and countersigns. There have also been times when Mackie or another member has played things a little too close to the vest, and injurious situations have resulted. There is certainly a danger in Mackie being the sole keeper of the guild's history and membership roster. That information is vulnerable to loss or theft should something untoward happen to Mackie.

HIERARCHY: The hierarchy within the guild is as informal as its structure. Mackie is the undisputed head of the organization. She funds it and keeps all records and membership rosters. Next to her is Tennessee O'Malley, a well-regarded raider and renowned expert in antiquities. Beyond those two, there are few who have any formal authority in the group; however, the remainder of Mackie's group are often considered her inner circle and most guild members will defer to them when leadership is needed.

INTERIOR MOBILITY: Such a thing as mobility is really not an issue in the guild, where all members are viewed as equals. However, should members render great service directly to Mackie or one of her inner circle, they may find themselves entrusted with specific missions or even working directly with the inner circle itself. This is not an easy thing to accomplish, however; while Mackie welcomes new members into the group, she does not give out personal trust lightly.

DEGREE OF SECRECY: The Brotherhood of William St. John is an open secret guild. It is known amongst the upper crust of society, amongst those downtrodden whose cause it has championed, and well known to its enemies, but it remains something of a legend. While a certain few members might be open about their status, they reveal nothing about the guild itself or its inner workings, on penalty of expulsion from the group. Indeed, should a member reveal information that causes harm to another member or to the guild itself, they may find that they have earned the group's enmity and that their power extends further than the betrayer may once have expected.

While many have heard of the Brotherhood of William St. John, only its members know of their exploits and the group's inner workings. Such an air of mystery gives them an advantage in many situations.

HISTORY:

- **Founded in 1853** by Sir William St. John, renowned British explorer.
- **By 1855**, rendering humanitarian aid all over the world and fighting for the rights of the oppressed wherever they could.

- **In Egypt in 1857**, Sir William ran afoul of a group called the Cult of the Worm, whom he barely defeated with the help of two close allies, Jonathan Trapp and the Lady Sylvia Morningside.
- This group, it turned out, was a splinter group of a much larger organization called the Order of the Black Dragon.
- **1857:** Sir William barely survives his first direct encounter with the Order of the Black Dragon and dedicates their new guild to battling such organizations and gathering lost knowledge to be used for the benefit of all mankind.
- **1858:** guild battles and defeats the Cult of Yig in Brazil. Doctor Serpent is first encountered.
- **1859:** The Order of the Yellow Sign in New York is stopped from summoning a mad god to the world.
- **1862:** The group faces the Blood Sect, a supposed cult of vampires in Hungary
- **1865:** The group defeats the Sisters of the Poison Kiss in Germany. Doctor Serpent is revealed to be in league with the sisters, but escapes capture.
- **1866-1880:** New members enter as older members retire from active service. The guild now has members all over the world.
- **1890:** The guild takes down the worldwide syndicate known as the Brotherhood of Crime. When Doctor Serpent is revealed to be behind the group, an aging Sir William comes out of retirement.
- **1890-1900:** The guild dedicates all of its efforts to tracking down and capturing or killing Doctor Serpent.
- **1901:** Sir William and Doctor Serpent have a final confrontation in the mountains of Tibet. Both are presumed dead following a massive explosion that leveled an ancient temple.
- **1902-1935:** Rumors persist that Sir William and Doctor Serpent survived, and one or both were rejuvenated in the lost city of Shangri-La. The guild continues on, nominally leaderless but under the guidance of the 90-year-old Lady Sylvia.
- **1935:** Sir William's Granddaughter, Mackie Gleeson, comes of age and proves herself an amazing pilot and adventurous spirit. Lady Sylvia chooses Mackie as the new leader of the guild, turning over all of its records and passing away of natural causes soon after.

NAME: The Brotherhood of William St. John

EXPANDED BACKGROUND

The Brotherhood of William St. John is an adventuring guild founded in1853 by the famed British explorer, adventurer and champion of justice and the weak, Sir William St. John. At its founding, Sir William was a 21-year-old wealthy aristocrat who dedicated his life to seeking adventure and excitement. In his travels, Sir William could not help but notice the plight of those the world over who were far worse off than him. Moved by the poverty, downtrodden souls, and victims he saw everywhere he went, Sir William dedicated his life to aiding those less fortunate than himself. At first this aid was delivered in the form of humanitarian donations–food, money, social programs, clothing–but eventually Sir William stumbled onto more than he bargained for.

In Egypt in 1857, Sir William ran afoul of a group called the Cult of the Worm, whom he barely defeated with the help of two close allies, Jonathan Trapp and the Lady Sylvia Morningside.

This group, it turned out, was a splinter group of a much larger organization called the Order of the Black Dragon, whose head was a mysterious villain known only as Doctor Serpent.

Barely surviving his initial encounter with the Black Dragons in 1857, Sir William, who had already been an established athlete, big game hunter and adventurer, took his actions to another level, vowing with his friends to battle evil and darkness both where it publicly reared its head and wherever he could root it out.

Over the next forty-plus years, Sir William grew the guild into a worldwide network of like-minded individuals. It was they who defeated the Cult of Yig in Brazil, the Order of the Yellow Sign in New York City, the Blood Sect in Hungary, The Sisters of the Poison Kiss in Germany, and took down the worldwide syndicate known as the Brotherhood of Crime.

It is said that Sir William defeated dozens of criminal syndicates and secret societies, and eventually went on to establish a worldwide guild of like-minded individuals who would also step up when called to do their duty for God, Country, and humanity. Still, through it all, one adversary kept re-appearing and always eluding their efforts. The crime lord Doctor Serpent seemed ever involved with the conspiracies faced by the group, and Sir William pursued him doggedly.

Sir William and Lady Sylvia eventually married. Sir William retired from active service in 1880, recognizing his advanced age as finally catching up with him, but continued to fund and guide the guild's efforts while focusing time on his family.

In 1890 and against his wife's wishes, Sir William came out of retirement when Doctor Serpent, having vanished long before and believed dead, reappeared. For the next eleven years, Sir William pursued his foe to distraction, determined to rid the world of Doctor Serpent's evil once and for all.

Alas, it happened that age and the years may have been too much for Sir William to bear. Sir William vanished in 1901

in a heroic final battle with his arch-nemesis. It is said that the two perished together in a massive explosion that leveled an ancient ruin in the mountains of Tibet, though there have been whispers ever since that either Sir William, Doctor Serpent, or both survived the explosion and went deep into hiding. It is said that one or both of them discovered the ancient city of Shangri-La, where they regained their youth and vitality and that they may both be at large today.

Regardless, the guild continued on under the guidance of Lady Sylvia, and since its founding, the guild has welcomed adventurers from all over the world who show a unique skills set and determination to uphold the cause of justice, liberty, and the spirit of exploration at the heart of every man's soul. In 1935, the guild came under the guidance of its current leader, one Mackenzie "Mackie" Gleeson, the wealthy New York socialite and ace pilot who many say has picked up where Amelia Earhart left off (and who, some skeptics whisper, will likely suffer the same eventual fate).

Gleeson is also the granddaughter of Sir William and Lady Sylvia, and was passed on the mantle of leadership and all of the guild's records and treasures by Lady Sylvia herself, who died of natural causes soon after doing so, at the astounding age of 103. Some believe that Lady Sylvia imparted secrets about Sir William, Doctor Serpent, and the guild before dying, but Mackie has given no signs of having such knowledge.

THE SOCIETY OF ORMAZD

Another fictional secret society, the Society of Ormazd is featured in our sample adventure, "The Heart of Yhtill," and in its sequel, the adventure module ***The Day of the Worm***.

Outline

GOALS AND INTENT: The sole intent and goal of the Society of Ormazd is to prevent knowledge of the Nameless Black City from falling into the wrong hands. Since nobody can be certain whose hands are the right ones, this goal has spread to protecting the city's secrets at all costs. The Society of Ormazd is a Guardian Society.

REACH AND RESOURCES: The society is a regional society, which has cells and a network of spies and informants across the Middle East. What agents in other cities around the world tend to be ensconced in institutes of learning, where the Society can catch wind of anyone planning an expedition to the Nameless City, but in general, infiltrating the British Museum in London is more difficult than the society's resources allow, and would serve them less well than simply waiting for an offending party to come to where the Society is. By concentrating their forces in the area around the Arabian Desert, the Society keeps a stranglehold on the success of would-be explorers and fortune seekers.

The Society is not wealthy. They are a group of fanatical men and women who pledge their lives to the cause of keeping the Black City secret. They can provide information to their members, and may be able to acquire some weaponry on the black market, such as handguns, rifles and the like, and have safe houses in most cities that are accessed via password, but not much else. They are identified by a tattoo that all wear on their inner forearm depicting the symbol of the Zoroastrian deity Ormazd, bisected by a stylized sword.

RECRUITMENT: Recruitment has always been a problem for the society. Often, it draws its members from amongst those who begin seeking the Black City and come to see the folly of their ways through one method or another. In addition, family members are raised in the society's traditions and when sons and daughters come of age, they are inducted into the group and swear the oath of allegiance and fealty to the ideal, even unto death.

LEVELS OF MEMBERSHIP: Presumably there is an "Inner circle" of sorts that directs the society, but nobody knows who these mysterious figures are. In general, the society operates as a group of largely independent cells who can call upon other cells in time of great need. If an instance arises where the Black City is discovered, the society will mobilize en masse to put down the offending parties and ensure one way or another that the knowledge never reaches humankind in general.

LEAVING THE SOCIETY: There is no leaving the Society of Ormazd. Those who betray the society, or choose to defect from its ranks, become a great threat and at very least will be followed and monitored for the rest of their lives (which could be one way the society ends up with agents outside the Middle East). If the society even gets a whiff of betrayal, the defecting member will be targeted for death.

SECRETS AND HOW THEY ARE KEPT: The society's secrets revolve entirely around the Black City, its location, how to find it, and what horrors and forbidden knowledge lie therein. It is unlikely that any save perhaps the Inner Circle have the full picture. Most members just know that the Black City is located at the heart of the Arabian Desert, in an area called the Empty Space, and is a remnant of an ancient civilization dedicated to the worship of evil, forgotten gods like the Great Old Ones. As such, it is filled with horrors that must never be unleashed upon mankind, and the society is fanatical in its devotion to protecting this knowledge. Members will happily sacrifice their lives to this end.

MEMBER RESPONSIBILITIES: Members have one responsibility, and that is to be ever vigilant against those who would exploit knowledge of the Black City. They are expected to go to any length to stop this knowledge from reaching the world at large, even if it means martyring themselves for the cause. Such efforts could involve sabotage, direct conflict, murder, and espionage to steal back secrets and/or discredit individuals who escape with the secrets of the city.

MEMBERSHIP BENEFITS AND DRAWBACKS: The Society of Ormazd is somewhat unusual in that most members don't choose to be involved, but are conscripted in one way or another. The sole benefit of membership is knowledge. By speaking with other members, challenging society opponents, and general information gathering, a lot of the secrets of the Black City may be there for the taking. In addition, members treat each other like brothers and sisters, being willing to sacrifice their lives for their brethren as well as for the cause. Members of the Society of Ormazd can always count on aid, assistance, and succor from fellow members whatever the situation may be.

On the down side, asking too many questions, pushing too far, or not remaining overwhelmingly loyal to the group could result in danger to the society member, even unto their death.

HIERARCHY: The society is organized in cells which can be anywhere from two to twenty or more members. Each city may have multiple self-contained cells, each with its own subset of overall society knowledge. This ensures that if one cell is compromised, all of the group's secrets are not revealed. Each cell has its own internal hierarchy, but usually consists of a leader, one or more lieutenants, and the rank and file agents.

The rumor within the Society is that there is an Inner Circle who guide the directions of the group overall. The Inner Circle communicates only with the heads of cells, using specialized codes tailored to each individual cell. Nobody knows who they are, how many they are, or where they are located. It is believed, however, that the Inner Circle knows everything about the Black City, and can access its secrets at any time.

No one in the Society of Ormazd can claim to have spoken to, or laid eyes upon, the Inner Circle directly.

INTERIOR MOBILITY: Interior mobility in the society is generally limited to rising in the ranks of an individual cell and/ or building notoriety among other cells. This is accomplished through distinguishing oneself in the field, stopping threats to the group, and demonstrating loyalty and honor overall.

On occasion, the leader or another member of a cell will disappear, and the cell will receive information from the Inner Circle that they have been given special assignments, but nobody can seem to predict how this is accomplished or what these assignments are.

DEGREE OF SECRECY: Absolute. The Society of Ormazd does not want its name, members, organization, or secrets known to anyone. Members are under strict orders never to reveal anything about their society to anyone except those about to die, or those about to be recruited. They move as ghosts through society, having members from all walks of life. Those who discover the society's existence are generally targeted for observation, recruitment, or death. Even the society's informants don't know with whom they deal, and if questioned can only say that they aid members of an elite brotherhood who move like shadows through the world and protect all society from unimaginable darkness.

HISTORY:

- **673 A.D.** – Abdul Alhazred born in Damascus
- **700 A.D.** – Alhazred serves as court poet in the court of a great Caliph, but is mutilated and expelled for turning his eye towards the Caliph's daughter
- **710 A.D**. – Alhazred comes to the library at the Nameless City after wandering the desert for ten years. He claims to have been shown the whole of reality by the wandering mad god Nyarlathotep and is accepted as a scholar at the city.
- **720 A.D.** – A great disaster causes the Nameless City to be swallowed whole by the desert. There are whispers of a curse.
- **730 A.D.** – Alhazred reappears in Damascus as a crazed hermit and begins work on his masterpiece - *Al Azif.*
- **738 A.D.** – Alhazred torn apart by invisible demons in plain view of the city.
- **900 A.D.** – *Al Azif* translated into greek under the title *Necronomicon*.
- **1050 A.D.** – A long suppression campaign by the Church of Rome succeeds in nearly destroying all extant copies of *Al Azif* in all its translations. A very few copies survive.
- **1100 A.D.** – The first explorers seek the Nameless City. Their expedition vanishes without a trace. Whispers begin to circulate that a protector society dedicated to the Zoroastrian deity Ormazd is responsible for their fate.
- **1200 A.D.** – During the Crusades, a group of Knights Templar in the middle of the Empty Space in the Arabian Desert runs afoul of a group of cultists dedicated to the mad deity Hastur, and are aided by a mysterious group of nomads. The Templars, to the man, resign their commissions and vanish into the desert, having joined the Society of Ormazd.
- **1585 A.D.** – John Dee and Francis Bacon race to find the Nameless City following Dee's translation of the *Necronomicon.* The two men are unsuccessful and Bacon later writes that a mysterious group of Arabs thwarted their every effort, but neither man could find any trace of the organization's identity. Dee begins work on the codex that will one day be known as the Voynich Manuscript. The work contains encoded information about the Black

City and the information therein, but Dee leaves no notable cipher for the codex.

- **1600-1900** – A number of excursions into the Arabian Desert meet mysterious and untimely ends at the hands of the Society of Ormazd. Some vanish altogether, some have survivors who refuse to discuss the circumstances of their party even until the day they die. A few are recruited; the rest are terrified into silence.

- **1912** – A mysterious manuscript purported to have been written in cipher by John Dee falls into the hands of Wilfrid Voynich, a member of the Society of Ormazd.

- **1930** – Wilfrid Voynich dies. The manuscript passes into the hands of his widow, Ethel Lillian Voynich. Ethel also inherits membership in the Society of Ormazd.

NAME: The Society of Ormazd

EXPANDED BACKGROUND

No one knows who really founded the Society of Ormazd, or who its shadowy leaders are. What is known amongst its members is that the group traces its lineage back to Abdul Alhazred and the writing of *Al Azif*, the book that would later become known as the *Necronomicon*.

Alhazred was a court poet to a great Caliph in Damascus circa 700 A.D. After a scandal involving the Caliph's daughter, Alhazred had his ears, nose, and manhood cut off and was cast out into the desert to die. However, the mad poet survived by selling his soul to the wandering Great Old One known as Nyarlathotep. The visions granted Alhazred brought him to the degenerate nameless Black City in the heart of the Empty Space, in the Arabian Desert. There Alhazred delved into all manner of black sorceries and dark knowledge. The Great Library in the Black City rivaled that in Alexandria, but was filled with knowledge far more arcane and forbidden.

A great disaster—some say tied to the machinations of the Old One Yig—caused the Nameless City to sink into the desert. All inhabitants were killed, save Alhazred and a circle of three priests. Alhazred fled across the desert, pursued by these priests, who were determined to never again allow the city's secrets to fall into the hands of man.

Somehow, Alhazred eluded the priests and came once again to Damascus, where he vanished from public view, becoming a hermit and working on his magnum opus, the book called *Al Azif*, roughly translated, *The Howling of Demons in the Night*. The book contained extensive treatises on the secrets and mysteries of the Old Ones, and, it was said, instructions on raising the Black City from its sand-covered tomb. It was claimed that an ancient and evil sorcerer sat at the heart of the city, holding in his mummified fist a heart-sized gem dedicated to the Old One Yhtill, patron of the city, and that any sorcerer who possessed this gem would have undreamed of powers drawn from the energy of the Old Ones themselves, at the cost of his sanity.

In 738 A.D., Alhazred was walking down the streets of Damascus, wearing a mask he had adopted to hide his deformed features, when an invisible demon snatched him into the sky and tore him limb from limb. From the shadows, three priests watched in satisfaction.

The three priests worked diligently for the next few decades, recruiting scholars and warriors from the shadows and swearing them to fealty under the fledgling Society of Ormazd. It can only be assumed that when they passed on, they left their legacy to hand-picked successors, though some whisper that the mysterious circle that guides the Society even to this day are the same three priests, their lives extended by means unknown. It is said that philosophers and sorcerers throughout the ages have joined the Society's ranks. If this is the case, then it is possible that Nicholas Flamel himself may have shared with the Three the secrets of the Philosopher's Stone.

Throughout history, the Society has diligently worked to keep knowledge of the city from being revealed to the world at large. They have recruited from such ranks as the Knights Templar, the British army, and scholars from major educational institutions.

In 1585, the noted occultists Sir John Dee and Sir Francis Bacon had a violent competition to become the first one to locate the Black City since its disappearance. The Society stopped the two at every turn, thwarting even their most basic efforts to get into the desert. This coup has gone down in history as the Society's greatest success. Dee, however, discovered a great deal about the city and its whereabouts, and it is said that he drew upon his own translation of the *Necronomicon* and on the information he discovered during his quest, to pen the volume that would later become the Voynich Manuscript, in a secret effort to reveal the Nameless City's location.

Dee failed; however. If he left a cipher for his codex, it has long since been lost, and the manuscript itself passed harmlessly from scholar to scholar throughout the ages, always tracked by the Society. In 1912, the manuscript was recovered by Wilfrid Voynich, a noted revolutionary, antiquarian and scholar, as well as a secret member of the Society of Ormazd. When Voynich passed away in 1930, both the manuscript and his membership in the Society passed to his widow, Ethel, who guards the book to this day.

Things have been quiet for the past several decades for the Society overall, until recently, an American scholar named Martin Seymour gained access to knowledge that no man should ever have seen...

THE HELLFIRE CLUB

(**Note:** Hellfire Clubs are historical fact and have existed at various times throughout history. This "Hellfire Club" society is a careful melding of fact and fiction (more the latter than the former) to create a villainous society that can act as an ongoing foe for ***Amazing Adventures*** characters. In reality, the Phoenix Society still exists to this day at Oxford University, and is a point of pride for the school and the group. No real-world implications or connections with impropriety should be made or assumed insofar as this fictionalized secret society goes.)

GOALS AND INTENT: The Hellfire Club is a control society with elements of a fraternal order. Its goal is control through immorality, corruption, and debauchery. In the end, this is a society that wants to see the world burn, and sit laughing atop its ashes. But through it all, they want control. They want to be the ones who see it go down, and they want to be the instrument of its slow destruction. This society is a powerful agent of chaos and entropy, and they do not brook competition with their goals.

REACH AND RESOURCES: The Hellfire Club is far-reaching and has vast resources available. Their members consist of the movers and shakers in society, powerful men and women in every government all over the world. While they may not have the ability to call down military strikes, they very possibly have "alphabet soup" agents in their pocket, men and women with arrest powers and even, possibly, the ability to call out the S.W.A.T. team on occasion. They prefer, however, to work in the shadows, through corruption. Overt action is not their style. Members can expect funding and contacts at the highest levels of society, and access to all manners of debauched pleasures and fetishes. Sin is the name of the game.

MEMBERSHIP REQUIREMENTS: Members of the Hellfire Club are inducted. First, a potential member of the society does something to get noticed, something which shows promise towards the group's overall goal of corruption, sin, debauchery, and entropy.

At this point, they are observed to ensure that the initial act was not a unique circumstance. If they continue to hold the society's notice, they will be approached and invited to a "party," where they will experience all manner of debauched pleasure. From there, the pit deepens as they descend into ever more lavish and lascivious tortures and pleasures, until they are so far in that there is no escape. At this point, they are formally inducted into the group.

On occasion, a member of the Club will take a fondness to a random young man or woman and take it upon themselves to slowly corrupt and induct the promising young candidate into the Club's circles, gradually breaking down their adherence to societal norms and introducing more debauched ideas one by one until the prospect is hopelessly ensnared.

Membership can also be inherited, passed down from a member to their children, heirs, or other family members, usually either by the member themselves, or through their Will upon their death.

Leaving the society is not possible. Anyone who leaves the Hellfire Club is marked for death, and this death is always a slow, drawn-out, and torturous public spectacle at one of the Club's parties. Bodies of former Club members are rarely found, and more rarely identifiable.

The Hellfire Club practically deals in secrets. They have "dirt" on every single member within the group, and on many people who don't even know the group exists. They use these secrets to slander, blackmail, corrupt and control their power bases all over the world. These secrets are used when needed, and kept through torture, blackmail and murder. Members of the Hellfire Club have in a very real way sold their souls for power and are expected to do anything–even betraying a fellow member–to keep and grow said power.

BOOK SIX:

The only responsibilities of a member of the Hellfire Club revolve around hedonism and control. It is expected that a member will indulge the darkest appetites within, and serve the Club itself–not individual members of the club, but the Club itself. As the power base of the individual grows, so too does the power of the Hellfire Club. Members are kept in line by virtue of the fact that there always seems to be someone with more power, and only the most clever, canny, and debased individuals can rise through its ranks.

MEMBERSHIP BENEFITS AND DRAWBACKS: The biggest benefit to membership in the Hellfire Club is access to the power bases of society. Information is always available to be bought, sold, and granted in return for future favors, and money and power are there for the taking and handing out. Of course, should a member accept a favor from a Brother or Sister, he or she can expect to repay that favor three times over at some future date. In addition, all manners of pleasure are available for the asking, and it is possible to make unbelievable connections among the upper crust of society at the Hellfire Club's orgiastic gatherings.

The drawback of membership is that one is always looking over his or her shoulder. Backstabbing, betrayal, and murder are the order of the day in the Hellfire Club. Its members are fanatically loyal to their goals and cause, and will maim, torture, defame and kill anyone who gets in their way. Only the most ruthless people, those who truly have no conscience, can survive to rise in rank.

OPERATIONS AND ACTIVITIES: The Hellfire club is insidious and omnipresent. They have agents in all walks of life, at every level of society. Their main goal is to build power through knowledge, and to control, corrupt, and eventually disintegrate society so that they can build a new world order based upon sin and debauchery. They believe that anarchy and entropy are the core of humanity's true nature, and seek to expose this rotting core in all of humankind's societal structures.

Members of the Hellfire club revel in debauched glee at their orgiastic gatherings, engaging in Dionysian rites of sensual pleasure and gratification. There are often injuries and deaths at these parties, which are quickly sloughed off as members who weren't worthy of the club. At these parties, every manner of sinful pleasure is available for the asking–or the taking.

HIERARCHY: The group patterns itself after Dante's ***Inferno***. As such, there are nine circles of membership in the Hellfire Club, each corresponding to one of the nine circles of Hell. Circles seven through nine circle have sub-ranks, the name and number of which vary by level. Members are referred to as brothers (or sisters) of their level. For example, members of the first level are referred to as "Brothers of Limbo." A member of the eighth level at the fourth rank might be a Sister of Fraud, Fourth Bolgia. Alternately, the sister might be addressed by a title associated with her level; for example, Sister of Fraud, False Prophet.

At each of the lowest levels (7, 8, and 9) there are limited members per sub-level. There are three members per sub-level at level 7 (for a total of nine members), and one member per sub-level at levels 8 and 9. This means there are ten members total at level 8, and four total at level 9.

Those at the lowest levels (7, 8 and 9) also have the most authority. Those who sit at level nine are known as the Inner Circle, and form the ruling council of the Hellfire Club. There is only one member at level nine for each Round, for a total of four Inner Circle members.

Their word is law, and they gather to establish the missions, goals, and operations of the society. However, they are constantly maneuvering and backstabbing to one-up each other.

The nine levels are:

1. Limbo
2. Lust
3. Gluttony
4. Greed
5. Anger
6. Heresy
7. Violence
   a. Sub-Levels: Three Rings (Outer, Middle, Inner)
   b. Outer Ring: The Violent
   c. Middle Ring: The Suicides
   d. Inner Ring: The Blasphemers
8. Fraud
   a. Sub-Levels: Ten Bolgias
   b. First Bolgia: Panderers or Seducers
   c. Second Bolgia: Flatterers
   d. Third Bolgia: Simoners
   e. Fourth Bolgia: Sorcerers, Astrologers, False Prophets
   f. Fifth Bolgia: Barrators
   g. Sixth Bolgia: Hypocrites
   h. Seventh Bolgia: Thieves
   i. Eighth Bolgia: Evil Counsellors
   j. Ninth Bolgia: Sowers of Discord
   k. Tenth Bolgia: Falsifiers, Alchemists, Counterfeiters, Perjurers, and Impostors
9. Treachery
   a. Sub-Levels: Four Rounds
   b. Round One: Caina
   c. Round Two: Antenora
   d. Round Three: Ptolomea
   e. Round Four: Judecca

INTERIOR MOBILITY: Interior mobility is possible, but only by distinguishing oneself through the obtaining of power and influence in local, state and world affairs, and at the cost of a member at a higher circle. The internal motto of the Hellfire Club is "*Ut unus cadit, alius surget*," or, "As one falls, another shall rise."

DEGREE OF SECRECY: The Hellfire Club is a secret society who likes their name to be known. That is to say, most people in the world have heard of the club, but few know who its members are, where it can be found, or even if it truly exists. The Club thrives on mystery.

HISTORY:

- **1719**: Philip, Duke of Wharton, founds the first Hellfire Club in Great Britain, which is founded as a satire dedicated to making fun of religion and indulging in all manner of activities considered "immoral pleasures" at the time. Members are culled from the upper class, call themselves "devils" and appoint the Devil as the president of the club. Women are admitted as equals in this club.
- **1721:** Duke Wharton's club comes to an end under persecution, as enemies of Philip including Robert Walpole put forth bills against immorality and "horrid impiety." Wharton is removed from Parliament and becomes a Freemason.
- **1730's-1746:** Sir Francis Dashwood and the Earl of Sandwich are members of a Hellfire Club, also comprised of society's elite. This club meets at the George and Vulture Inn, in London and is not known officially as a Hellfire Club until much later.
- **1746:** Dashwood either comes to control of the existing club or establishes a new club, which is ironically dubbed the Order of the Knights of St. Francis. Their motto is "*Fais ce que tu voudras*" (Do what thou wilt). The club at first retains the George and Vulture as its meeting place.
- **1747-1751**: The club changes its name several names, including:
    - o The Brotherhood of St. Francis of Wycombe
    - o The Order of Knights of West Wycombe
    - o The Order of the Friars of St Francis of Wycombe.
- **1748:** Excavation of the Hellfire Caves at West Wycombe begins. These caves, designed according to sexual and pagan themes, complete with a subterranean River Styx, which members had to cross over to get to the meeting place. This final cavern rested directly below a church. All the caves remain to this day. One of the chambers is named "Franklin's Cave," after Benjamin Franklin, who is rumored to have visited the club as a good friend of Dashwood.
- **1751:** The club moves their meetings to Medmenham Abbey and adopts the mantle of the Monks or Friars of Medmenham. The club adopts extreme pagan rituals, honoring such deities as Bacchus and Venus in orgiastic rituals and gatherings held twice a month. Rumors abound of Satanic Black Masses, and of rituals including prostitutes dubbed "Nuns," though there is little evidence of these rituals.
- **1762:** Dashwood obtains a seat in the House of Lords.
- **1763:** Dashwood resigns after pushing a highly unpopular cider tax. Noted club member John Wilkes is driven into exile following the scandalous publication of several blasphemous, libelous and scandalous documents. This exile is likely "arranged" by the Earl of Sandwich, constituting the first noted instance of a Club Member deliberately acting to destroy another.
- **1760-1765:** Several pamphlets are published featuring possibly fictionalized descriptions of club activities, which present club members as lunatics and simpletons. The club is gradually discredited.
- **1766:** Medmenham is finished, its members having been discredited or simply gone their separate ways. In reality, the club simply goes underground, its members gradually adopting a new strategy–to corrupt and bring down the institutions that shackle mankind with morality, what the club views as prudish ideals, and law.
- **1781:** The "Phoenix Society" is established by Dashwood's nephew Joseph Alderson and adopts the motto, " *uno avulso non deficit alter*" (when one is torn away another succeeds). It purports to be continuing Sir Francis' institution, but boasts a very small membership. In reality, the Phoenix Society acts as a public mask to hide the dealings of the true Hellfire Club, which continues underground.
- **1782 – 1888:** The Hellfire Club continues to recruit and draw members from the upper crust of society and cementing its power base across the globe.
- **1888-1891:** Jack the Ripper murders occur in Whitechapel, England. The murders are relegated to the concept of a madman who hated the immorality of Whitechapel prostitutes; in reality, the murders are an effort to silence a group of women who had served as "Nuns" for the Hellfire Club and were believed to be threats to the organization. The identity of the Ripper remains a mystery.
- **1894:** Carl Feigenbaum is arrested in New York City on charges of murder. Some believe Feigenbaum to be the

Ripper. In fact, Feigenbaum is a second-circle Hellfire Club assassin who took over the Ripper's duties between 1891 and 1894, cutting a swath across Europe and the United States before being caught by the authorities and abandoned by the Hellfire Club.

- **1896:** Feigenbaum is executed. By the time of his execution, he has gone utterly mad due to gradual poisoning of his food so that he would not be able to reveal the Club's secrets through testimony.
- **1896 – Present:** The Club's activities appear dormant. There are occasional whispers about clubs devoted to chaos, entropy and hedonistic activities. Sometimes a supposed witness comes forward, only to be silenced, disappear, or die under mysterious circumstances.

NAME: The Hellfire Club

EXPANDED BACKGROUND

The term "Hellfire Club" did not originally refer to an organized worldwide society, but was in reference to a group of so-called "Gentlemen's Clubs" that operated in Great Britain and Ireland in the 18th centuries. The two most prominent of these were the Hellfire Club operated by Philip, Duke of Wharton and Sir Francis Dashwood.

The first Hellfire Club, founded in 1719 by Philip, Duke of Wharton, was dedicated to blasphemy and the satire and ridicule of religion. This was a posh idea in Great Britain at the time, particularly behind closed doors and among the societal elite. The club reveled in its own shock value, even purporting that the Devil himself was the president, and with members addressing each other as devils. At the club's parties, participants would often dress like caricatures of Biblical figures and participate in mock religious rituals. Of interest is that the club accepted women as members and equals within its ranks.

Meetings were sometimes held in public at places like the Greyhound Tavern, but as most taverns of the day did not allow women, more often the meetings were held behind closed doors, in homes or at Wharton's riding club.

As the club flouted its practices more and more, Wharton's political enemies pushed new bills through Parliament which rendered immorality illegal, and the club came to an abrupt end when Wharton was removed from Parliament. He later went on to become a Freemason.

By the 1730's, another lurid gentlemen's club had arisen in London, this one frequented by Sir Francis Dashwood and John Montagu, 4th Earl of Sandwich. Meeting at the George and Vulture Inn, this club would last for nearly twenty years in the public eye before gradually coming to an end, or more accurately, moving underground to secure its power base.

It is believed that the four-person ruling council, in addition to Dashwood and Montagu, included at various times Robert Vansittart, Thomas Potter, Francis Duffield, Edward Thompson, George Bubb Dodington, William Hogarth, John Wilkes and Paul Whitehead.

Membership in this club was believed to be particularly vast, with "visitors" coming from as far away as the American colonies to take part in their gatherings. It was during this time that the club first began to (internally, at least) model itself after Dante's *Inferno.*

Dashwood's club was not initially called the Hellfire Club. It went through several name changes, including the Brotherhood of St. Francis of Wycombe, the Order of Knights of West Wycombe, and the Order of the Friars of St Francis of Wycombe. Finally, after Dashwood had an elaborate series of tunnels created for use of his club, and moved the clubs open meetings to Medmenham Abbey, the club took its final (public) name, the Monks or Friars of Medmenham.

It was under the guidance of Dashwood that the Hellfire Club began to not only expand, but to take on elements of the dark society it was to become. Meetings involved elaborate rituals to ancient pagan gods like Bacchus and Venus, and indulged the basest desires of members, from sensual to sexual to sadistic in nature. Not nearly as enlightened as the original Hellfire Club, Dashwood's group was certainly male-dominated, and women brought into meetings were, by and large, prostitutes who served as the centerpiece of the group's Satanic rites and were referred to as "Nuns" or "Succubi" before being cast out once more, sometimes with financial incentives to keep quiet, sometimes under threat of torture, injury or death.

Publicly, of course, Dashwood and the Earl of Sandwich denied all accusations of impropriety and were careful to leave no evidence of misdeeds. Still, rumors of the club's immoral activities spread throughout London society. Some found the group disgusting; others were desperate to join.

Several factors eventually led to the apparent downfall of Dashwood's society. The first was when Dashwood himself found a seat on the House of Lords and with the title Baron of Le Despencer, thanks to the patronage of the Earl of Bute. Dashwood was forced to resign a year later following his push for a widely unpopular tax on cider.

The next scandal within the society was orchestrated by the Earl of Sandwich, who had developed a serious rivalry with John Wilkes stemming from a prank Wilkes had played on Montagu during a Hellfire Club meeting. As both men sat at in the Inner Circle at the time, Montagu wanted to destroy Wilkes.

As such, Montagu managed to bring to light some of Wilkes' more blasphemous and libelous writings, including some that

appeared to encourage sedition against the king. Wilkes was forced into exile in Paris, where he proceeded to establish his own branch of the Hellfire Club, in secret.

This marked two major milestones in the history of the society: it is the first time that a member betrayed another to this degree, and it is the first time that a new branch of the Club was established, albeit in complete secrecy.

Over the ensuing few years, various scandals and conspiracies both within and without degraded the integrity of Dashwood's club, and it faded from public view. It was assumed that the club had died out; in truth, Dashwood and his friends had scattered across Europe and even to the New World, where the club expanded and grew under the nose of polite society. It had been decided that mystery and secrecy were the way of the future, as club leaders realized the sheer amount of power they could gain through corrupting the masses.

To this end, upon Dashwood's death in 1781, a new "face" of Dashwood's organization was established by his nephew Joseph Alderson. This "Phoenix Society" came into existence in Oxford University and supposedly represented a rise from the ashes of the initial ideals of Dashwood, and served as a perfect deflection of the true activities of the Hellfire Club under the surface. The club even adopted a modified version of the Club's motto: "*uno avulso non deficit alter*" (when one is torn away another succeeds) and claimed this motto referred to the constant renewal of the group through student turnover between under- and upperclassmen.

In truth, the society had adopted the motto, "*Ut unus cadit, alius surget*" (As one falls, another shall rise), which referred to the means by which members moved through its ranks, and the means by which it operated to establish a New World Order of entropy, chaos and absolute freedom through corruption and degradation.

For the next century the Hellfire Club managed to stay largely out of the public eye and became all but forgotten, a ghost in the night. Several major wars were the direct result of the club's work–among them, the French Revolution, the War of 1812, and the American Civil War. None, however, managed to destabilize the world in the way the Club hoped.

By the late 19th Century the Club had grown complacent which led to carelessness. A number of ladies of the night who had been brought in as Nuns for Club rituals were growing dangerous, threatening to form their own rival groups, and even reveal the inner secrets of the Hellfire Club. An assassin was dispatched in London to eliminate this threat. This man became known as Jack the Ripper. Jack was an expert at his task; he was never caught and not even the members of the Hellfire Club know who he was. It is simply known that in 1888 his job began, and in 1891, it was finished and he vanished back into the ranks of the group.

Unfortunately, the threat had extended beyond London, and another assassin was tapped to take care of the same problem which had cropped up in both Germany and the United States. Carl Feigenbaum reveled in his duties, but was more careless than Jack, and was eventually arrested in New York City in 1894. The group saw an opportunity and attempted to plant evidence marking Feigenbaum as the Ripper, but was unsuccessful. Instead, they resorted to using agents within the prison system to slowly poison Feigenbaum's food, driving him mad so that he could not reveal the secrets of the club.

Following this, the Club was shaken out of its complacency and faded back into the shadows, where it remains to this day, quietly and gradually subverting the pillars that hold our law-abiding culture aloft, picking away at the mortar that strengthens them, in fanatical hope that one day, their New World Order will come to fruition.

The Hellfire Club is, in many ways, the incarnation of power and its misuse. Many of their members are untouchables, high-level rulers, aristocrats and lawmakers who live double-lives. If society seems corrupt and irredeemable, that's because the Hellfire Club has made it so. They live little to no evidence or trace of their presence, and are a quiet, insidious, and dangerous force, always operating against the heroes in the shadows of the world's greatest power elite. If they have an Achilles' heel, it is that they are utterly debased, corrupt, and prone to acts of gross immorality, from which they derive their only pleasure. The trick is catching them in these acts.

THE ROGUE'S GALLERY

The non-player characters on the next several pages include some of the current members of note in the Brotherhood of William St. John. They are designed for use as non-player characters in your game with whom the PCs can interact, or as pre-generated characters that your players can use to pick up and go!

These characters have not been designed as starting, first-level characters. This is because should you want to use them as non-player characters, they can be dropped in just as-is to add some color to the game. Remember that in ***Amazing Adventures***, characters are compared by their experience total rather than their level. The characters below should be each assumed to have 25,000 experience points–this has the fortunate effect of giving them comparable levels of experience.

Should you choose to use the characters at a lower level, all you need do is re-roll hit points for the desired level, and check which class abilities are available at the given level. Dropping them all the way back to first level should only take a couple minutes' time at most. Characters like Bucky Newson, The Fox, and Marie Laveau will require a bit more adjustment as Bucky will have fewer gadgets, the Fox fewer mentalism powers, and Marie fewer spells, but that's about it!

MACKENZIE "MACKIE" GLEESON

Aviatrix, wealthy philanthropist, and direct descendant of William St. John, Mackie currently serves as the leader of the Brotherhood of William St. John. A noble, caring, and adventurous soul, she is nonetheless a bit snobbish due to her wealthy upbringing–while she tries her best to uphold the standards of the society (and demands nothing less of her compatriots) she has never known personally the plights of those she seeks to defend, so she sometimes needs to be reminded that she is not better than those of lesser means.

She is particularly fond of Bucky Newson, who acts as the ace mechanic on many of her cars and aircraft, and on whom she looks as a brother, and of the simple but direct Savage Steve McDermott, who serves as a conscience and anchor to the real world. She has a deep and abiding respect and friendship with Tennessee O'Malley, who is a trusted companion in tight spots, and the one person with whom she can be blunt, and who can get away with openly telling her off.

NAME: Mackenzie "Mackie" Gleeson

CLASS/LEVEL: Socialite 5

ALIGNMENT: CG

ABILITIES: Str 9 Dex 18 Con 13 Int 9 Wis 14 Cha 18

PRIMES: Dex, Wis, Cha

AC: 17

COSTUME DESCRIPTION: blouse, leather trousers, boots, bomber jacket, scarf, gloves

HIT DICE: 5d8

HIT POINTS: 32

CLASS ABILITIES: Ace*, charm, connected, embolden, fascinate, demoralize, exhort greatness

FATE POINTS: 8(d8)

BACKGROUNDS*: Philanthropist / Aviator

LANGUAGES/KNOWLEDGES*: English (native)

TRAITS*: Distinctive (Attractive), Polite

GEAR: Colt Detective Special, knife, aviator goggles

APPEARANCE: Long, slightly wavy brown hair, deep brown eyes, round features, a slender but curvaceous physique .

JAMES "BUCKY" NEWSON

Ace mechanic, engineering whiz, and gadgeteer, Bucky is a fearless sort who always has a smile on his lips and a bad tendency to leap before he looks. He's the most swashbuckling of the group in terms of personality, and believes there's no problem that science and technology cannot solve. He looks up to Errol Flynn and tries to emulate his dashing feats of derring-do, and desperately hopes that someday Natalya will be able to introduce him to his swashbuckling idol. He is, to his eternal embarrassment, quite in love with Mackie, but knows that she doesn't look upon him the same way. Still, he gets a bit flustered due to these feelings, which get the better of him all too often. He sees in Tennessee O'Malley a kindred spirit, at least in terms of his outlook on adventuring, but distrusts Marie Laveau, who trafficks in forces that are most certainly not scientific.

NAME: James "Bucky" Newson

CLASS/LEVEL: Gadgeteer 5

ALIGNMENT: NG

ABILITIES: Str 10 Dex 16 Con 13 Int 18 Wis 13 Cha 11

PRIMES: Str, Dex, Int

AC: 16

COSTUME DESCRIPTION: Bomber jacket, short gloves, scarf

HIT DICE: 5d6

HIT POINTS: 25

CLASS ABILITIES: Gadgets, on-the-fly gadgets, jury-rig

FATE POINTS: 10(d8)

GADGET POINTS: 2

BACKGROUNDS*: Engineer, Scientist

LANGUAGES/KNOWLEDGES*: English (Native), French, German, Aircraft Mechanics

TRAITS*: Reckless

GEAR: Tool kit, utility belt, gadgets (See below)

GADGETS: Radium Pistol (2d6+4 damage, +5 to hit, malfunctions on a roll of 1); Electro-sword (2d8+5 damage–1d8+5 of which is electrical–can use as normal sword for 1d8 damage); Perception filter (Lasts for 2d6 rounds before needing a 1-hour recharge; grants +2 AC and +2 to stealth-based checks).

APPEARANCE: Sandy brown hair, mop-style, blue eyes, a broad, angular smile and sharp features.

TENNESSEE O'MALLEY

O'Malley is the consummate adventuring archaeologist with the spirit of a rogue, the heart of a hero, and the ethics of a pure historian. He is cynical, wise cracking, cocky, overconfident, uncouth, and arrogant, but there are few in the world who can be considered more expert in the worlds of archaeology and myth and legend. The one area about which he is humble is that he obtained his PhD from Southwestern University instead of an Ivy League school, such as Harvard or Yale, but he will quickly defend the fact that his PhD is as good as any other when it comes down to brass tacks.

His fast, two-fisted style has gotten him into as many scrapes as it's gotten him out of, and he intends it to stay that way. After all, who wants to die a decrepit old man in a bed? Better to make a name for himself while he can. He's seen a lot in his day, and values the knowledge of Marie Laveau and the instincts and skills of Natalya Abramova, though he has difficulty trusting either of the women, Natalya because of her past and Marie due to the dark forces with which she trafficks. He considers Bucky Newson a trusted friend and companion, and respects the leadership of Mackie Gleeson, with whom he has a deep friendship. He has a quiet bond with Savage Steve, whom O'Malley respects for his simple and direct ways, and while O'Malley may give Steve a hard time, that's his prerogative and nobody else better mess with the gentle giant.

NAME: Tennessee O'Malley

CLASS/LEVEL: Raider 5

ALIGNMENT: CG

ABILITIES: Str 9 Dex 18 Con 9 Int 16 Wis 16 Cha 13

PRIMES: Str, Dex, Int

AC: 17

COSTUME DESCRIPTION: Leather jacket, gloves, fedora, safari gear

HIT DICE: 5d10

HIT POINTS: 41

CLASS ABILITIES: Bonus languages, cryptolinguist, disguise, legend lore, traps, resist elements, two-fisted*, weapon finesse*

FATE POINTS: 9(d8)

BACKGROUNDS*: Academic, classicist

LANGUAGES/KNOWLEDGES*: English (native), Latin, Greek, German, French, Archaeology, History

TRAITS*: Aggressive, Reckless

GEAR: (2) Colt New Service Revolvers (1d12 damage); Tomahawk (1d6 damage); notebook, pen, cigarettes, lighter, knapsack, digging tools, translation codices, string

APPEARANCE: Long, chiseled features, dirty blonde hair, neatly cut and parted, piercing gray eyes.

"SAVAGE" STEVE MCDERMOTT

Savage Steve is a simple sort, a dock worker and brawler who generally prefers the company of his pet Rottweiler Bluto to that of people. He's a gentle giant who, while he loves a good fight, doesn't like to start trouble or hurt people and will avoid it if possible. When troubles come, however, he is more than happy to put an end to them.

Steve sees in the Society a chance to give back something to the world, by protecting those weaker than him, and doing a service to humanity. He has spent his life attempting to atone for the accidental death of his childhood best friend Larry, who died in a horrible accident after Steve dared Larry to climb the walls of an old building, which collapsed mid-climb. When Steve failed to come forward with the truth, another boy was arrested and jailed for the accident. Steve never heard from the boy again, and has ever since carried a deep guilt over the event. This is a secret he doesn't share, but which has defined his sense of right and wrong ever since.

Steve likes Bucky immensely, though he feels protective of the gadgeteer due to Bucky's penchant for taking unnecessary risks. Marie Laveau and Natalya Abramova (The Fox) make him very uncomfortable, but he trusts Mackie with his life and has faith that she would not allow the two into the Society if they didn't have the proper moral outlook and skills to share. As far as Mackie goes, Steve holds himself up as her conscience, in a way—when she needs reminded about the mission of the Society, or that she is not better than those the Society seeks to help, he never hesitates to offer the gentle reminder.

NAME: "Savage" Steve McDermott

CLASS/LEVEL: Pugilist 5

ALIGNMENT: LG

ABILITIES: Str 18 Dex 16 Con 16 Int 9 Wis 13 Cha 9

PRIMES: Str, Dex, Con

AC: 15

COSTUME DESCRIPTION: Dirty t-shirt, worn britches, worker's boots, suspenders

HIT DICE: 5d12

HIT POINTS: 50

CLASS ABILITIES: Animal handling*, down and dirty, tough as nails, unarmed attack, unarmored defense, deflect missiles, fast movement.

FATE POINTS: 10(d8)

BACKGROUNDS*: The Mean Streets, Blue Collar

LANGUAGES/KNOWLEDGES*: English (Native)

TRAITS*: Muscle-bound, uncivilized

GEAR: slingshot (1d8)

APPEARANCE: Bald, thick brown handlebar moustache, brawny, small eyes, not much of a neck.

COMPANION: BLUTO THE ROTTWEILER *(This N dog has vital stats HD 3d8 (16 hp) AC 15 Move 50 ft. Its primary attributes are Physical. It attacks by Bite (+6 to hit; 1d8+3 damage). Its special abilities are scent, trip, track, twilight vision. It knows the tricks attack, come, down, heel, and stay.)*

MARIE LAVEAU

Supposedly the granddaughter of the original Voodoo Queen, Marie Laveau lives in her grandmother's St. Ann's Street home and still operates her mother's Bourbon Street club. She also has a rickety shack in the Bayou, full of shrunken heads and over-the-top voodoo trappings where she meets clients when she wants to make an impression. Here's what people don't know about Marie: she is, in fact, the original Marie Laveau. She made a deal with the Ghedi Loa (Voodoo Spirit) Baron Samedi—also known as Death—in 1881 to remain on this world, when she became uncertain of what awaited her beyond the Pale.

Laveau's youth was restored and she will not age so long as she continues to send Death corrupted souls and send those who have returned from the netherworld screaming back to Hell. Her necromantic skills have served her well in this capacity; unfortunately, she is no longer the powerful sorceress she once was—along with her return to youth, her skills also atrophied, and she has been working for decades to build them back up. The Society has granted her the ability to both re-hone her skills and continue her work for Samedi. Unfortunately, immunity to harm did not come with the eternal youth, and

she tends to be cautious because she doesn't want to get killed before she's sure she has been redeemed.

She respects Mackie very much, and genuinely likes Tennessee. Natalya in some ways seems a kindred spirit, even if her talents are innate and less magical in nature. She gives Steve his distance, since she is wise enough to know his simple mind can't grasp the power she wields. Marie has something of a rivalry with Bucky, who doesn't respect her power, and she in turn has something of a disdain for his reliance on technology.

NOTE: Marie's statistics and spell list below are slightly different and more extensive than that in the "Heart of Yhtill" adventure which follows. This is to facilitate her use as a player character if desired, and the adventure could represent her first introduction to the Society if the GM and players choose or, if the players are running original PCs, a more experienced Marie could facilitate the PCs' induction into the Society. Regardless, the Marie listed here has all of the spells in the adventure scenario, plus a few. It is recommended that the GM treat the spell list in "The Heart of Yhtill" to represent those spells Marie has prepared for the day. Finally, if a PC is already playing Marie, the GM could wait until the proper section in "Heart" to introduce her, or could substitute the Voodoo Queen in that adventure with a different woman–perhaps Marie's own mentor, also still mysteriously alive after far too many years...

A portrait of Marie Laveau can be found on page 91.

NAME: Marie Laveau

CLASS/LEVEL: Arcanist (Wisdom) 5, Socialite 2 (Class and a half)

ALIGNMENT: LN

ABILITIES: Str 9 Dex 13 Con 13 Int 16 Wis 17 Cha 13

PRIMES: Dex, Wis, Cha

AC: 15

COSTUME DESCRIPTION: Ceremonial robes, shawl (scarf), short gloves

HIT DICE: 5d6

HIT POINTS: 30

CLASS ABILITIES: Spellcraft, spells, Charm, Connected, Exalt

FATE POINTS: 10(d8)

MEP: 36

BACKGROUNDS*: Alternative Medicine, High Society, Mean Streets

LANGUAGES/KNOWLEDGES*: English, French, Myth and Legend (Catholic Voodoo)

TRAITS*: Spellgifted (Necromancy/Healing), Specialized (Arcane Knowledge)

GEAR: Browning 1910 (1d8 damage), Ceremonial dagger (1d6), assorted pungent herbs, fetishes, cloth bags, tarot deck, needles, spell components and book of shadows

SPELLS KNOWN: *(0-Level) - Detect Chaos/Evil/Good/Law, Detect Magic, Detect Poison, First Aid, Message, Purify Food/Drink, Prestidigitation (1st-level) – Bless, Command, Cure/Inflict Light Wounds, Detect Undead, Faerie Fire, Invisibility to Undead, Turn Undead (2nd-level) – Aid, Charm Person/Animal, Consecrate/Desecrate, Detect Traps, Lesser Restoration, Speak with Dead.*

SPELLS PER DAY: (0) 6; (1) 5; (2) 3

APPEARANCE: Light-skinned Haitian-Creole mix, piercing black eyes, a serious expression, hauntingly attractive with angular features.

NATALYA "THE FOX" ABRAMOVA

This Russian beauty is an up-and-coming starlet in Hollywood; her face is just beginning to grace the papers and her films just beginning to give her name recognition. What would her adoring public do if they knew that she was also The Fox, a notorious cat burglar wanted for robbing several museums and jewelry merchants throughout the world? Indeed, the very saber and parrying dagger she wields were said to once belong to Nicholas I of Russia; she, of course, liberated it from the New York Metropolitan Museum while it was on temporary exhibit there. Its silver edged blade has served her well against some of the more unnatural foes she's had to face, as have her unique talents–psychic abilities learned from a secretive group of Tibetan monks, which she also keeps well hidden from your adoring public.

So far as the Society knows, Natalya is reformed, and really, she does her best to stay on the right side of the law. It's just that sometimes the thrill of a good burglary is too much to pass up! She gets along with Marie, and likes Steve a lot–his simple-minded ways are refreshing next to the hypocrisy of high society. She respects Mackie as leader of the group, but in many ways Mackie is representative of all Natalya dislikes about the upper class. Bucky is incredibly cute, and Natalya has resolved to one day bed him, but she finds Tennessee too gruff and uncouth for her tastes, though she deeply respects his tenacity and abilities as both a scholar and a warrior.

NAME: Natalya "The Fox" Abramova

CLASS/LEVEL: Mentalist/Hooligan 4

ALIGNMENT: CG

ABILITIES: Str 10 Dex 13 Con 11 Int 16 Wis 13 Cha 18

PRIMES: Dex, Wis, Cha

AC: 17

COSTUME DESCRIPTION: Dark blood-red martial arts uniform, stylized fox mask, gloves, sash, cloak

HIT DICE: 4d6

HIT POINTS: 15

CLASS ABILITIES: Climb, hide, move silently, listen, open lock, sneak attack, pick pocket, traps, meditation, mental resistance, psychic senses, two-fisted*, weapon finesse*

FATE POINTS: 8(d8)

BACKGROUNDS*: The Mean Streets, Hollywood Film Industry

LANGUAGES/KNOWLEDGES*: Russian (native), English, Street Lingo, Locksmith

TRAITS*: Slippery, Quick

GEAR: Saber (1d6+2 damage, silver edged), main gauche (1d6+2 damage silver edged), (2) TT Tokarev pistols (1d10 damage), knapsack, grappling hook, cord/rope, lock picks, glass cutters

APPEARANCE: Slender, athletic build, fiery red hair, crystal blue eyes, soft, round features.

PSIONICS: Obfuscation, Combat Awareness

TITANUS WILLIAMS

A private detective operating out of the low-rent district in The City, Titanus is an African-American who refuses to be kept down by the racism that is rampant in the world. His keen powers of detection and no-nonsense approach have garnered him the grudging respect of many who might otherwise dismiss him out of hand simply due to the color of his skin.

Titanus has made acquaintances, associates, friends, allies, and enemies across the world in his exploits, and has racked up an impressive list of completed cases. His arch-enemy, as he considers it, is Aldus Schwartzhofer, who has defeated the Brotherhood of William St. John, or at the very least escaped capture by them, time and again over the years.

Among the society, Titanus calls every last one of them a friend. He is particularly reverent of Marie Laveau, who he sees as a connection to the "old ways" of his heritage. He likes the gruff approach of Tennessee, finds Bucky exceptionally easy to get along with, and Mackie a strong leader. He likes the simple, straightforward nature of Steve, though he finds his slow-to-comprehend mannerisms frustrating at times. Of the group, he likes Natalya the least; while he finds her charming and certainly quite attractive, he's got her pegged–she's not entirely left her former criminal ways behind, and the day may come when Titanus can no longer turn his head and look the other way.

NAME: Titanus Williams

CLASS/LEVEL: Gumshoe 5

ALIGNMENT: LN

ABILITIES: Str 10 Dex 16 Con 10 Int 16 Wis 16 Cha 13

PRIMES: Dex, Int, Wis

AC: 17

COSTUME DESCRIPTION: Fedora, Three-Piece Suit, Gloves, Trench Coat

HIT DICE: 5d10

HIT POINTS: 30

CLASS ABILITIES: Climb, Cat and Mouse, Hide, Move Silently, Take 'em Down, Deadeye Shot, Face in the Crowd, Adversary

FATE POINTS: 9(d8)

BACKGROUNDS*: The Mean Streets, Prohibition and Bootlegging

LANGUAGES/KNOWLEDGES*: English, Local Personalities, Local Laws

TRAITS*: Abrasive and Cautious

GEAR: .38 Special, Camera, Notebook, Pen, Chalk, Handcuffs, Charcoal

APPEARANCE: Handsome African-American with prominent nose and long face.

VILLAINS

Here we present a named villain to supplement the one featured in the Heart of Yhtill adventure in Book Seven. This non-player character can be used as a shadowy or not-so-shadowy menace for your player characters. In addition, we present a number of generic statistics for various human foes your heroes may face in the course of their adventures.

ALDUS SCHWARTZHOFER

In many ways the Moriarty to Titanus Williams and Tennessee O'Malley's Sherlock Holmes, Schwartzhofer is an archaeologist for hire, but is a selfish mercenary who seeks only to increase his own power and worldly pleasures. He will happily destroy ancient treasures if he can't have them, and would much rather sell treasures to a private collector than to a museum—private collectors pay far more, after all.

As a young teenager, Schwartzhofer's father, a cruel and drunken but brilliant scholar of ancient religions, sent the boy to study with a group of Tibetan mystics, from whom Schwartzhofer learned the skills of a Mentalist. Unfortunately, the boy was expelled after his own cruel tendencies revealed themselves, leaving one of the Mystics severely injured. So it was that Schwartzhofer returned home to his father's beatings until he turned 16, when he murdered his own father and fled Germany for America, where he managed to hide his past and enroll at University.

Schwartzhofer and O'Malley were once great friends, having studied together at Northwestern University. However, with the rise of the Nazi party only a few years ago, their friendship has crumbled and deteriorated as the result of Schwartzhofer's severe betrayal of O'Malley on an archaeological dig to which they were both assigned. When the Nazis came to collect a valuable and ancient Egyptian treasure which O'Malley had intended to go to the British Museum, Schwartzhofer trapped O'Malley in a tomb and absconded with the treasure, kidnapping O'Malley's sidekick, a young Egyptian girl named Nesa, in the process.

O'Malley escaped and tracked Schwartzhofer, only to discover Nesa's murdered body left in O'Malley's own hotel room as a warning to stay away. Enraged, O'Malley tracked Schwartzhofer across Europe, eventually cornering the man in Romania, where they had a pitched battle that left both men shot. Schwartzhofer, however, used his mentalist powers to escape, and the two have been enemies ever since.

NAME: Aldus Schwartzhofer

CLASS/LEVEL: Mentalist/Raider 5

ALIGNMENT: CE

ABILITIES: Str 9 Dex 18 Con 9 Int 16 Wis 16 Cha 13

PRIMES: Dex, Int, Wis

AC: 20

COSTUME DESCRIPTION: Safari gear, trench coat, gloves

HIT DICE: D10/D6

HIT POINTS: 29

CLASS ABILITIES: Bonus languages, cryptolinguist, disguise, legend lore, climb, survival, traps, resist elements, favored weapon, meditation, mental resistance, psychic senses

FATE POINTS: 10(d8)

BACKGROUNDS*: Academic, The Third Reich

LANGUAGES/KNOWLEDGES*: German (Native), English, French, Latin, Greek, Archaeology, Anthropology

TRAITS*: Dishonest, Polite

GEAR: Luger P08 (1d10 damage), dagger (1d6 damage), notebook, pen, cigarettes, lighter, knapsack, digging tools, translation codices, string, survival gear

PSYCHIC POWERS: Obfuscation, Mesmerism, Empathic Transmission, meditation, mental resistance, psychic senses

SAMPLE HUMAN FOES

Here are some quick statistics for various kinds of human foes and non-player characters that your heroes might encounter in the course of their adventures.

How to Read the Stat Blocks

Each of these foes is given a block of quick statistics containing all you need to use them in game. Each block of statistics, or "Stat Block" breaks down as follows; we will break down the "Cultist" stat block below as an example.

1. Character name/type (Example: Cultists)
2. Level, Alignment, Creature Type (Example: 1st-level NE humans)
3. Vital stats including hit dice, hit points, armor class, movement per round. These are fairly self-explanatory. (Example: vital stats HD 1d10 (5 hp each), AC 13, move 30 ft.)
4. Primary Attributes. Note that in general quick-stats use "Physical" or "mental" for Primes. Characters with Physical Primes use CB12 for Str, Dex and Con checks, while Characters with Mental Primes use CB12 for Int,

Wis, and Cha checks. It is rare for human foes to have all stats as prime. If you as the GM choose to do so, you can assign specific Primes for greater detail.

5. Attack types. This is the section that defines any weapon or natural attack damage the characters may have. (Example: They attack by Luger Pistols for 1d10 damage or knives for 1d4 damage.)
6. Special abilities. If the monster or villain has any abilities outside the norm, this is where they would be listed. Include things like spells, psionic powers, class abilities, special vision, etc. (Example: Their special abilities are: those with Physical Primes have hide and move silently, and those with Mental Primes have first-level spells as a Charisma Arcanist: 10 MEP, 0-level; Dancing Lights, Ghost Sound, Influence 1st-level; Command, Obscuring Mist).

Using the Stat Blocks

Monsters and generic villains always have a bonus to hit, saves and ability checks equal to their Hit Dice. Generally, they have no other bonuses; since they effectively have a +1 per level BtH this tends to balance out. GMs can, if they choose, feel free to generate actual ability scores and use class-based BtH progressions for enemies, but this takes extra time and preparation, often too much for characters that are mooks or thugs.

Some stat blocks may list abilities at varying class levels. For example, the Mob Enforcer hides as a 4th level hooligan, but has a submission hold as a 6th-level pugilist. In this case, when rolling for hiding, add +4 to the die roll. When rolling for a submission hold, the bonus is +6.

In general, it is advised to stick to main NPCs or "Named" villains and arch-villains for generation of full character sheets. A compromise between the two would be to simply add an extra -1 to +2 for attacks or saves based on what you feel are the average relevant attributes for a villain of that type. If it helps you to remember, you can add the villain's full "to hit" bonus in the stat block under their attacks or note under special abilities that they get "+x to all ability checks and saves," where "x" is the ability-based bonus.

The Rogue's Gallery

Thule (or Generic) Cultists

Classic Nazi foes–these are cultists who follow the mysterious Thule Society in the inner circle of Nazi Germany. They are fanatically loyal to the cause, and devoted to the idea of the lost continent of Thule as the perfect Aryan Society, which destroyed Atlantis in an effort to rid the world of impurity.

Historically, the Thule Society was a German occultist group based in Munich, which Hitler eventually reorganized into the Nazi party. In many pulp or supernaturally-themed tales, the Society keeps going in secret, run by the high-powered Inner Circle of the Nazi Party, men like Rudolf Hess and Heinrich Himmler (though in real life it is unlikely that Himmler had any involvement with the Thules), who seek to control Hitler and eventually overthrow him to bring about a New Age of purity. They generally worship The Great Old Ones or other dark, Lovecraftian deities. These statistics could also be used to represent any sort of generic cultist who is fanatically devoted to a secret society devoted to a dark, magical purpose and goal.

CULTISTS *(these 1st-level NE humans have vital stats HD 1d10 (5 hp each), AC 13, move 30 ft. Their primary attributes are Physical or Mental. They attack by Luger pistols for 1d10 damage or knives for 1d4 damage. Their special abilities are: those with Physical Primes have hide and move silently, and those with Mental Primes have first-level spells as a Charisma Arcanist: 10 MEP, 0-level; Dancing Lights, Ghost Sound, Influence 1st-level; Command, Obscuring Mist).*

SS Officer

The most vile, elite, and dishonorable men in Hitler's regime, these soldiers are fanatically devoted to the Third Reich. They are racist, brutal, and heartless–true believers in the purity and superiority of the Master Race, and devoted to Hitler's dream of wiping all other races off the face of the Earth. For many Allied soldiers, capturing the sidearm or insignia of an SS was a hotly sought-after trophy, a symbol that they were doing what needed to be done in a world entrenched in the horrors of the Greatest War.

If you are using Thule Cultists in game, there will almost always be at least one SS officer with said cultists, as the SS is tightly interwoven with the Thule Society in such games.

SS OFFICER: *(these 5th-level humans have vital stats HD 5d10 (27 hp each), AC 15, move 30 ft. Their primary attributes are Physical. They attack by Luger or P38 Pistols for 1d10 damage, knives for 1d4 damage, or MP40 submachine gun for 1d12+2 damage. Their special abilities are Charm, Connected, Exalt, Embolden, Fascinate and Demoralize as a 5th-level Socialite).*

Soldier

Axis or Ally, most soldiers have similar statistics. These stats can apply to any military man encountered in a war zone, occupied territory, or wherever else the military may be. Whether it's a Japanese soldier, a Nazi, or an American troop, you can use these statistics to quickly model their game function.

SOLDIER: *(these 3rd-level humans have vital stats HD 3d8 (13 hp each), AC 15, move 30 ft. Their primary attributes are Physical. They attack by rifle for 2d8+4 damage, pistol for 1d8 damage, knife for 1d6 damage, or mounted bayonet for 1d8 damage. Their special abilities are Take 'em Down as a 3rd level Gumshoe, Climb, Hide, Move Silently, Case Target, Lingo (call signs and codes specific to their army) and Listen as a 3rd-level Hooligan. Traps and Survival as a 3rd-level Raider. Embolden as a 3rd-level Socialite.)*

Thuggee Cultist

The origin of the word "Thug," the Thuggee were an organized group of assassins that operated out of India, founded sometime before 1356 (this was their earliest recorded activity, though the writing references the year 1290), they were a deadly secret society and also quite fanatical in their devotion to the Hindu goddess Kali in her aspects of violence, sexuality, and death. Membership was often hereditary, and they preferred the garotte as their means of killing. If a Thuggee succeeds at a successful back attack with a garotte, the victim is caught and each round must make a Constitution test or suffer 1d8 damage. A strength test allows the victim to break free of the garrote. The CL for this test is equal to the Thuggee cultist's hit dice +2.

THUGGEE CULTIST *(these 5th-level NE humans have vital stats HD 5d6 (18 hp each), AC 17, move 30 ft. Their primary attributes are Physical. They attack by Knife pistols for 1d6 damage, sword for 1d8 damage, or garotte (Special). Their special abilities are: Back attack, case target, climb, hide, lingo, listen, move silently, open lock, pick pockets, traps, sneak attack, and garotte).*

Mob Soldier

"Street-level" members of organized crime syndicates, these are the rank and file of such groups as the Mafia, their Jewish and Russian counterparts, and of such mysterious Oriental societies as the Triads and the Yakuza. If your game requires the use of basic thugs and street soldiers, this is the stat block to use.

MOB SOLDIER *(these 2nd-level humans have vital stats HD 2d8 (8 hp each), AC 13, move 30 ft. Their primary attributes are Physical. They attack by Pistol 1d8, Tommy Gun 1d12+2 damage, or knife for 1d4 damage. Their special abilities are Back Attack, Case Target, Hide, Lingo, Listen, Move Silently as a 2nd level Hooligan)*

Mob Enforcer or Lieutenant

A step above your basic soldiers, these are those enforcers that function as captains and lieutenants in organized crime syndicates. Enforcers are the guys trusted by family heads to carry out special missions, assassinations, and intimidation missions. They often have a certain "turf" or geographic region, in which they function as overseers and managers. They are respected and feared by their underlings, but there is generally someone beneath them in the organization plotting to usurp their position. On rare occasions, Mob Enforcers are turned by the Feds, and become informants, contacts or protected witnesses against the Family.

MOB ENFORCER *(these 6th-level humans have vital stats HD 6d8 (27 hp each), AC 15, move 30 ft. Their primary attributes are Physical. They attack by They attack by Pistol 1d8, Tommy Gun 1d12+2 damage, knife for 1d6 damage or unarmed for 1d6 damage. Their special abilities are Back Attack, Case Target, Hide, Lingo, Listen, Move Silently and Sneak Attack as a 4th level Hooligan, Down and Dirty, Unarmed Attack as a 4th-level Pugilist,and Submission Hold as a 6th-level Pugilist)*

Mob Boss

In general, a Mob Boss should be all but untouchable–the head of a Family or organized crime syndicate. These aren't throw-away villains and for the most part, should be created as full NPCs using the guidelines above, or as a full ***Amazing Adventures*** character. Encountering a mob boss should be the eventual goal of an entire campaign, wherein the PCs struggle to climb the ladder to bring down the syndicate–the Mob Boss is their ultimate goal.

However, should you run into a situation where you need to generate stats for a mob boss quickly, as a short-term solution, this stat block is provided for your convenience.

MOB BOSS *(these 12th-level humans have vital stats HD 12d10 (hp 66 each), AC 18, move 30 ft. Their primary attributes are All. They attack by Pistol for 1d8 damage, Tommy Gun for 1d12+2 damage or unarmed for 1d6 damage. Their special abilities are all Gumshoe and Hooligan abilities at 12th level, Down and Dirty, Unarmed Attack as a 4th-level Pugilist, and Submission Hold as a 6th-level Pugilist).*

MONSTERS AND ANIMALS

This bestiary has statistical write-ups of various monsters that may be of use in challenging your group. Following the table listing the monster's game statistics is an explanatory section discussing the monster's tactics, special abilities, etc. For purposes of this game, any enemy or potential enemy of the player characters that does not have a full character background or development is considered a "monster." Non-player characters who have developed personalities, and recurring important villains and adversaries are generally not considered monsters, though they can certainly be built from a monster template herein.

MONSTER CREATION

Eventually, every Game Master comes to the realization that a new monster must be created. The circumstances behind this may differ; one Game Master might simply feel creative and imaginative, and another might need to create something new out of necessity. After many years of gaming, some players may become jaded or complacent, and the inclusion of a new challenge can keep them on their toes. Creating monsters is both fun and challenging, whether it is a hybrid, a genetically enhanced human, or something completely new and altogether terrifying. While creating new monsters, the Game Master should be mindful of a few basic concepts and design elements. After balance and technical concerns, there is no limit to what imagination and creativity can do.

New monsters are tricky. The process involves creating a concept that is plausible, and then mingling balanced abilities with that concept. This is quite challenging by itself, but the Game Master creating a new monster must also determine its appropriate armor class, hit dice, and other technical stats.

Finally, this whole must be coherent to the players. Organizing all of this can be an intimidating process.

When creating monsters, the first concept a Game Master must consider is that of "realism versus fantasy." Does the new monster have a basis in reality as we know it? Does the monster have a fantastic context, with a design concept beyond the ken of "realistic" understanding? Distinguishing between realism and fantasy is important in that it establishes the mood the monster is designed to convey. This mood is often as important as the creature's stats, if not more so, in many game settings. Assembling a haphazard collection of human and animal parts to create a nonsensical creature is more likely to cause a player to spew milk through his or her nose, rather than creating a mood of terror or awe. Even fantastic creatures can have plausibility. Making new monsters plausible for your game setting is conducive to a lasting, positive impact on the game.

When conceiving a monster, consider its ecology. Why does the creature have the physical attributes it has? How does it eat, sleep, and procreate? Does it travel, or is it stationary? In what environment is it found? All of these factors can make even the most fantastic monsters seem real.

A chicken-sized lizard with an elephant-sized head is just not likely to survive its own birth (and your adventure won't survive your players' mirth!). Temper your fantastic ideas with a dash of realism, and the new monster will be far more believable and interesting to both Game Master and player.

After considering these factors, the Game Master must write the description. This portion of monster creation is vital, as it will set the tone for how the monster is perceived at the gaming table. Remember to detail aspects like color, size, shape, and even smell. To add flavor, you might describe its breath and the shape of its eyes, for example. A monster with "yellowed teeth and fetid breath" will have a far greater imaginative impact than a monster that is simply "gray and shaped like a lizard."

After a solid description is completed, the Game Master must

give the creation a life in the context of the game. This is accomplished by creating its vital stats: its hit dice, armor class, attacks, and the like. Consider the level of character that this monster is supposed to challenge, and create statistics based on that sort of challenge. Existing monsters are the best guides. Low level monsters, like fish-men and giant frogs, have few extraordinary skills and are generally fairly weak in combat situations. Monsters like giant eagles and allips are more powerful, and have abilities that are more of a challenge to characters of moderate power. Higher level monsters, such as the vampire, offer useful templates when creating monsters to challenge powerful parties.

When assigning the new monster's stats, use any suitable monster from this book as a template. Give some thought to each statistic based on your concept and description of the monster. Decide how fast the creature should move, its hit dice, armor class, intelligence, and the rest. Give them a great deal of consideration. It is more important, by far, to have creatures that fit the mold of your game than to have creatures that are a mish-mash of abilities thrown together to simply challenge players.

Remember to make monsters interesting and challenging. Good descriptions, reasonable physical attributes, and balanced abilities all play into the monster's conception. Paying careful attention to all of these factors will lead to a more memorable monster.

GAME MECHANICS: The Elements of a Monster

Each completed monster template has a list of statistics, which denote the following:

NO. ENCOUNTERED: The number of creatures normally encountered. In some cases, two listings exist, denoting general encounters, and encounters in the creature's lair. A giant ant, for example, will be found in groups of 10-60 in the wild, but in colonies of 100-1000 in their nest.

SIZE: There are three sizes of monsters: small, medium, and large. Small monsters are anything smaller than a normal adult human; generally anything under 5 feet tall is considered "small." Medium creatures are human-sized, from 5 ft. to 7 ft. in height or length. Large creatures are anything over 7 ft. Where necessary, the average height of the creature is listed in parentheses.

HD: Hit dice. The number and type of dice rolled to determine the monster's hit points. An average value is given in parentheses for quick reference and instant use.

MOVE: The speed at which the creature moves. Some creatures may also have listed climb, flight, or swim speeds.

AC: The creature's armor class. See the Combat section on p. 167 for details.

ATTACKS: The type of normal attacks the creature has, and the damage dealt by each. If attacks are listed as "and," that means the creature has multiple attacks per round. If attacks are listed as "or," the creature has several types of attacks from which to choose.

SPECIAL: Special attacks or abilities such as magical powers, poison, class abilities, etc. are listed here. If a creature's "Special" entry has "SR," this represents the creature's Spell Resistance. See p.180 for more on spell resistance.

SANITY: The sanity loss inflicted by the creature, if the Game Master chooses to use those rules. See "Sanity" in Book Two for more information. The number before the slash indicates Sanity loss from a successful check; the number after the slash indicates loss from a failed check.

SAVES: Like humans, most monsters have three Primes. Unlike humans, monsters' Primes are generally either all three physical (P) attributes (Str, Dex, Con) or all three mental (M) attributes (Int, Wis, Cha). Some extraordinary monsters have all attributes as Prime; these are designated as P, M. Unless otherwise listed, attributes are average, and thus monsters generally roll a d20 and add their hit dice, using 12 as the CB for Primes and 18 as the CB for non-Prime attributes. If a monster's intelligence is listed as high or exceptional, the GM may opt to grant them an extra bonus of +1 to +3, at the GM's discretion.

For Example, A monster with 3d8 HD and M Saves has to make a saving throw against a mind-affecting spell. This would normally be a wisdom save. The monster is assumed to have an average wisdom, providing no bonus or penalty. Thus, the Game Master rolls d20 + 3 (for his 3d8 HD) and uses 12 as the Challenge Base. If the same monster had P saves instead of M, the Game Master would use 18 for the Challenge Base instead.

INT: This is a general assessment of the intellect of the creature. "Animal" denotes the intellect of a lower animal, such as a dog or cat. Even intelligent animals such as apes have animal intelligence, as they have not yet evolved to quite the reasoning power of human beings. "Low" means low human intelligence, probably denoting an Int score of between 6 and 8. "Average" is an average Intelligence score of 9-12, and "High" is any score higher than 12. At the Game Master's option, creatures with intellect other than "Average" may see mental saves or checks based on Intelligence gain bonuses or penalties for the score.

ALIGNMENT: Where the creature falls on the law-chaos-good-evil-neutrality axis.

TYPE: What kind of creature the monster is; animal, construct, magical beast, outsider, undead, etc. Often useful for determining what kinds of spells will affect the creature, or what sorts of general powers it might possess based on its type.

ABERRATION: Aberrations have bizarre anatomy, strange abilities, an alien mindset, or any combination of the three.

ANIMAL: An animal is a non-humanoid creature with a real-world equivalent.

BEAST: A beast is a creature with no real-world equivalent. It is a vertebrate creature with a reasonably normal anatomy and no magical or unusual abilities.

CONSTRUCT: A construct is an animated object or artificially constructed creature.

DRAGON: A dragon is a reptilian creature, usually winged, with magical or unusual abilities.

ELEMENTAL: An elemental is an entity composed of one of the four classical elements: air, earth, fire, or water.

FEY: Fey are creatures with supernatural abilities and connections to natural forces and/or places.

GIANT: Giants are large-sized humanoid creatures of great strength and bulk.

HUMANOID: A humanoid is a medium-sized creature that is anthropomorphic: they have two arms, two legs, one head, and a human-like torso.

MAGICAL BEAST: Magical beasts are similar to beasts but can have intelligence of inferior or better. Magical beasts typically have supernatural or extraordinary abilities.

MONSTROUS HUMANOID: These are humanoid creatures with monstrous or animalistic features, occasionally possessing supernatural abilities.

OOZE: An ooze is an amorphous or mutable creature.

EXTRAPLANAR: An extraplanar creature is a non-elemental that originates from another dimension, reality, or plane.

PLANT: This type encompasses all plants and plant-like creatures.

SHAPECHANGER: This type of creature has a stable body but can assume other forms.

VERMIN: This type includes insects, arachnids, other arthropods, worms, and similar invertebrates.

UNDEAD: Undead are once-living creatures animated by spiritual or supernatural forces. Undead are immune to all mind-affecting effects (charms, compulsions, etc.) and to poison, sleep effects, paralysis, stunning, disease, and death effects.

XP: The experience value of the creature, expressed in a base value plus a number of XP per hit point of the creature. Thus, a creature listed as 7+1 gives 7 XP, plus 1 per hit point. If the creature had 5 hit points, it would give a total of 12 XP. As with the HD field, an average value is listed in parentheses for quick reference.

ASSIGNING MONSTER EXPERIENCE POINTS

Use the table below to determine an experience point value for your new monster, with the following guidelines.

EXPERIENCE PER HIT POINT: A monster's hit point total influences the amount of experience it confers. To calculate this, simply multiply the number of hit points by the hit dice of the creature, and divide by 2. For example, a 5 (d10) HD creature has an average of 25 hit points. The base is 160 experience points plus 5 experience points per hit point. 125 extra experience points would be awarded for this creature, for a total of 285.

SPECIAL: There are three categories of special abilities, designated in the chart by the Roman numerals I, II and III. A given monster's total experience value increases by the amount of special abilities it has. Special ability experience is added to the base experience for the monster. For example, Skagg (4HD) has four attacks per round, a category I ability. So its base experience points are increased by 40 points (for a total of 120) plus 4 per hit point.

SPECIAL I: This category includes three or more attacks per round, spell use of 1st-3rd level (or equivalent spell-like abilities), and unique abilities such as tracking, hiding, or back attacks.

SPECIAL II: This category includes 5 or more attacks per round, damage of 4d6 or more for a single attack, spell use of 4th-7th level or equivalent, and extraordinary powers like invisibility or etherealness.

SPECIAL III: This category includes death attacks, petrification attacks, and spell use of 8th level and higher (or equivalent).

TABLE: MONSTER EXPERIENCE POINTS

HD	Base	Per HP	I	II	III
1	5	1	2	4	5
2	10	2	5	7	10
3	20	3	10	15	20
4	40	4	20	30	40
5	80	5	40	60	80
6	120	6	60	90	120
7	180	7	90	135	180
8	250	8	125	200	250
9	400	9	200	300	400
10	600	10	300	450	600

CHANGING MONSTERS

Never, as a Game Master, feel betrothed or chained to the monster statistics as written. After all, some monsters have become so familiar to players as to be trite, and mixing up their abilities and vulnerabilities can take a tried and true monster and make it terrifying again.

Consider the basic vampire. The statistics here are well-known to players, many of whom may hear "vampire" and give a yawn, having grown used to the tragic or even (gag) "sparkly" variety of these creatures. But what if the vampires in your game are immune to crosses, garlic, and stakes through the heart, and can only be hurt by silver—or worse, gold? What if they are all powerful Mentalists with the full psychic abilities of a 15th-level Psionic? Let's also not forget that many have genius-level intelligence. Suddenly, all your players know about vampires is that they drink blood and live forever.

Suddenly, vampires are pretty damn scary again.

LIST OF MONSTERS AND ANIMALS

APE , GREAT

NO. ENCOUNTERED: Solitary, Family of 4-16
SIZE: Medium
HD: 3d8 (12 hp)
MOVE: 30 ft., 30 ft. (climb)
AC: 14
ATTACKS: 2 Claw (1d3), Bite (1d6)
SPECIAL: Rend, Twilight Vision
SANITY: None
SAVES: P
INT: Animal
ALIGNMENT: Neutral
TYPE: Animal
XP: 30+3 (66)

The great apes live in large family groups in tropical forests. For every four apes there is one bull and one infant. Ape family groups are strictly hierarchical, and they are led by the strongest bull ape. If anything should happen to him, the next strongest bull replaces him. The bull ape is generally very aggressive, territorial, and protective. Gigantopithecus is a member of the Great Ape family that is thought to have been extinct for the last 300,000 years. Given the rarity of these creatures, however, they are far more solitary than their more common great ape cousins, though every so often a giganto might be found as the bull of a great ape tribe.

COMBAT: Apes almost always try to avoid conflict, but if the family is threatened, the bull leads all the males to attack, while females defend the younger apes. Giganto apes are generally slightly more aggressive due to their great size and might challenge a group of adventurers to make an opportunity for its chosen family to escape, or just because it feels ornery. Like great apes, gigantos are intelligent, and will flee if combat goes badly.

REND: The ape is able to rend for 2d4 points of extra damage if both claws hit. The giganto ape is able to rend for 2d6 points of extra damage if both claws hit.

BEAR, BLACK OR BROWN (GRIZZLY)

BLACK

NO. ENCOUNTERED: 1-4
SIZE: Medium
HD: 3d8 (12 hp)
MOVE: 40 ft.
AC: 13
ATTACKS: 2 Claw (1d6), Bite (1d8)
SPECIAL: Hug
SANITY: None
SAVES: P
INT: Animal
ALIGNMENT: Neutral
TYPE: Animal
XP: 40+3 (76)

BROWN (GRIZZLY)

NO. ENCOUNTERED: 1-6
SIZE: Large
HD: 6d8 (24 hp)
MOVE: 40 ft.
AC: 15
ATTACKS: 2 Claw (1d8), Bite (1d12)
SPECIAL: Hug
SANITY: None
SAVES: P
INT: Animal
ALIGNMENT: Neutral
TYPE: Animal
XP: 280+6 (424)

Bears are omnivorous creatures that inhabit most temperate or arctic climes. The male bear is almost always solitary. If more than one is encountered, the group consists of a mother and one to three cubs. Once a year black and brown bears gather along the banks of rivers feeding on salmon as they swim upstream to spawn. Bears generally try to avoid contact with humans or like creatures. Brown bears dwell in cold, forested environments, and are encountered in families of up to six members. Much like their kin the black bear, they travel in small family groups. Brown bears are particularly strong, aggressive, and very hard to kill.

The cave bear is a prehistoric bear of monstrous size. They stand up to 14 feet tall on their hind quarters and can weigh several tons. These creatures are rare, living in mountainous environments far from civilization. They live together in groups of up to four members. The cave bear is very territorial and fears nothing. They attack any creature they perceive as a threat or a meal.

COMBAT: Bears are not generally aggressive, but if a bear feels threatened, it will attack by rushing an opponent, attempting to knock it over and grasp it in its huge claws. Once pinned, the bear bites at the victim's head and face until it is satisfied that creature is immobilized or dead. Cave bears always drag their victims back to their lairs and eat them.

HUG: The bear is able to hug an opponent in a vice-like grip. If both of the bear's claw attacks are successful in a single round, the bear's foe must make a strength save or be caught in the bear's crushing hug. The victim can attempt to break free of the hug during subsequent rounds by making

additional strength saves. The bear can bite a hugged victim automatically each round.

BLOODRAGE: A cave bear can continue attacking until it is reduced to -10 hit points, at which point it dies. Once the bear is reduced to negative hit points, it gains a +2 bonus to all attack and damage rolls.

CAT, GREAT

NO. ENCOUNTERED: 1-6	**SANITY:** None
SIZE: Large	**SAVES:** P
HD: 5d8+5 (25 hp)	**INT:** Animal
MOVE: 40 ft.	**ALIGNMENT:** Neutral
AC: 14	**TYPE:** Animal
ATTACKS: 2 Claw (1d4); Bite (1d10)	**XP:** 180+5 (205)
SPECIAL: Rake, Twilight Vision	

Great predatory cats can be found the world over, from temperate to tropical climates, forests, mountains, jungles, and savannas. Some are solitary creatures while some move in Prides. Some are aggressive hunters while others are quite timid.

COMBAT: Great cats stalk their prey using the cover of the jungle for camouflage. They almost always begin an attack by springing on their prey from concealment, and biting and raking viciously in an attempt to make a quick kill. Once it has incapacitated its prey, a tiger will drag it into the foliage to be devoured.

RAKE: If a great cat successfully bites, it can make two rake attacks with its hind legs. Each attack gains an additional +3 bonus to hit and inflicts 1d4+2 damage.

CROCODILE (ALLIGATOR)

NO. ENCOUNTERED: 4-36	**SAVES:** P
SIZE: Medium	**SANITY:** None
HD: 3d8 (12 hp)	**INT:** Animal
MOVE: 20 ft., 30 ft. (swim)	**ALIGNMENT:** Neutral
AC: 15	**TYPE:** Animal
ATTACKS: Bite (2d4), Tail Slap (1d12)	**XP:** 30+3 (66 hp)
SPECIAL: Roll, Twilight Vision	

Crocodiles dwell in swamps, marshes or river banks, often gathering in groups of 4 to 36. They are stealthy and hunt almost any prey. They live in large communities and tend to feed together. If one attacks a target, it is shortly joined by any others in the area. Alligators typically measure 8 to 15 feet in length and weigh 500 to 1,200 lbs.; crocodiles are slightly larger, and measure from 10 to 20 feet and weigh 1,000 to 2,000 lbs.

COMBAT: Crocodiles stalk their prey by approaching slowly under water. They blend perfectly with their environment and almost always surprise an opponent. They attack with a sudden lunge, grab their victims, pull them into the water and attempt to drown them.

ROLL: After a successful bite attack, the victim must succeed at a strength save or be dragged underwater and held by the crocodile. The crocodile spins itself and the prey in a barrel roll as they sink together, making escape difficult. On subsequent rounds, the reptile deals bite damage to the victim automatically. The victim is incapacitated in 2-5 rounds unless the crocodile is slain. This ability may only be used in water, and only against an opponent up to double the size of the crocodile. At times, monstrous crocodiles and alligators are encountered, measuring up to 30 feet and weighing 2 tons. These creatures are always large, have 7d8 hit dice (28 hp), an armor class of 17, and bite for 2d8 points of damage.

HUMAN (Generic, Thug, or Cultist)

These statistics represent a general representation of human adversaries and cover everything from pygmy jungle-dwellers to Australian aborigines to Bedouin warriors, generic street thugs, police, F.B.I. agents, Chicago gangsters, or whatever you like. Any so-called "mook" the characters encounter could be represented by this entry.

NO. ENCOUNTERED: 1-1,000+	**SANITY:** None
SIZE: Medium	**SAVES:** P or M (Choose one)
HD: Variable, or 1d6 (4 hp)	**INT:** Average
MOVE: 30 ft.	**ALIGNMENT:** Chaotic Neutral
AC: 13	**TYPE:** Humanoid
ATTACKS: by weapon or firearms	**XP:** 7+1 (11) or by HD.
SPECIAL: Spells, Tracking, Survival, Climb, Hide, Move Silently	

COMBAT: Humans attack by weapons, generally in modernized societies using firearms or knives and small swords dealing 1d6 damage, or using bows or spears (also dealing 1d6) possibly tipped with paralytic poison in primitive societies.

CLASS ABILITIES: Most mooks possess one or more of the following class abilities: Tracking (generic; see Book 2), Survival (Raider), Climb (Hooligan), Hide (Hooligan), Move Silently (Hooligan). For purposes of using these abilities, treat physical attributes as Prime and the number of hit dice the mook has as its level equivalency.

SPELLS: Shamans or cultists may have some spellcasting ability as a Wisdom or Charisma-based arcanist.

SPECIAL: Mooks can be made tougher simply by adding extra hit dice, increasing base XP value to double the previous level, rounded to the nearest five, plus the number of hit dice per hit point. Thus, a 2 HD mook is worth 15+2, a 3 HD mook is worth 30+3, a 4 HD mook 60+4, etc.

LYCANTHROPE, WEREWOLF

NO. ENCOUNTERED: 3-18
SIZE: Medium
HD: 4d8 (16 hp)
MOVE: 30 ft., 50 ft. (as wolf)
AC: 16
ATTACKS: Bite (2d4)
SANITY: 1d6/1d8
SAVES: P
INT: Average
ALIGNMENT: Varies as human, chaotic evil in wolf form
TYPE: Humanoid
XP: 120+4 (184)
SPECIAL: Curse of Lycanthropy, Wolf Empathy, Trip, Alternate Form, Twilight Vision, Protect

Werewolves are thoroughly tainted by evil, and in animal form, they are among the most wicked of creatures. Their animal form are massive, far larger than a typical wolf. They dwell in dark forests and prowl only at night. Werewolves are very protective of their domains, and of each other, rallying to any howl of distress. These creatures always hunt in packs of 3 to 18.

COMBAT: Werewolves are cunning hunters. They will utilize pack tactics and harassing techniques before closing in for a kill. They are cunning, and very dangerous, but will flee in the face of capable opposition.

TRIP: A werewolf can attempt to drag an opponent to the ground when it makes a successful bite. The opponent is allowed a dexterity save to resist being pulled to the ground. Opponents pulled down in this manner automatically act last in the next round.

CURSE OF LYCANTHROPY: The wounds inflicted by a lycanthrope are infected with a magical pathogen that will eventually cause the victim to be transformed into a lycanthrope. The form assumed will be the same as the lycanthrope that inflicted the wound. At the end of any combat encounter with a lycanthrope, human combatants that were damaged by the beast must make constitution saves at a penalty equal to 1/2 the amount of damage that the beast inflicted. This penalty is assigned on an individual basis – a character that suffers more damage from a lycanthrope has a larger penalty. If this save is failed, the victim will become a lycanthrope in 28 days. Over that period, the victim will notice changes in mentality, strange traces of fur in his bedroll, an appetite for raw meat, or other symptoms. If a cure disease spell is applied before the 28th day, the lycanthropy is prevented. After the 28th day, nothing can reverse the disease short of a wish.

ALTERNATE FORM: A werewolf's normal form is that of a human being. The lycanthrope can choose to assume wolf form once per day, and every 28 days, during the three days of the full moon, the lycanthrope is forced to change into wolf form at night. It retains the following abilities in human form: alternate form and twilight vision. Werewolves are immune to polymorph attacks or effects unless they wish to be affected.

PROTECT: A werewolf that sees a wolf or another werewolf taking damage becomes incensed and protective. This instinct provides the werewolf with a +2 bonus on all attack and damage rolls. This bonus only applies if at least 2 werewolves are in combat, and one sees another suffer damage.

WOLF EMPATHY: Wolves empathize and enjoy the company of werewolves. Werewolves can telepathically communicate with any wolf within 1 mile. In addition, the werewolf can summon 1d6 wolf to its location if the wolf are within 1 mile. The wolves will begin to arrive 2d6 turns later.

LYCANTHROPY

Lycanthropy is a supernatural disease that afflicts only humankind. It is the cause and creator of were-beasts, transforming its unwilling victims between human and animal forms. There are many classifications of lycanthropes, but the most commonly encountered are the dreaded werewolves. Though these creatures can be of any alignment while in human form, they are very aggressive in animal form, assuming a different consciousness of sorts. It is not unusual for a lycanthrope to be unable to distinguish between friend and enemy when in animal form.

Lycanthropes are very susceptible to silver weapons, taking double damage whenever they are hit by any weapon made of silver. Weapons that are specially coated with a layer of silver affect lycanthropes as well – this vulnerability is not to solid silver alone.

HUMAN FORM: A lycanthrope in its human form should be created as an NPC. They are able to be any class, level or alignment. Lycanthropes retain individual powers in human form, as listed. Player characters who contract Lycanthropy can still be played, though they will lose control of their character, becoming an evil NPC in the hands of the Game Master whenever the transformation into lycanthropic form is upon them.

MUMMY

LESSER

NO. ENC: 1-4
SIZE: Medium
HD: 7d12 (42 hp)
MOVE: 20 ft.
AC: 20
ATTACKS: Slam (1d12)
SANITY: 1d6/1d8
SAVES: P
INT: Low
ALIGN: Lawful Evil
TYPE: Undead
XP: 720+7 (1,014)
SPECIAL: Despair, Mummy Rot, Darkvision 60 ft., Fire Vulnerability, Subject to Raising

GREATER

NO. ENC: 1
SIZE: Medium
HD: 8d12 (48 hp)
MOVE: 30 ft.
AC: 21
ATTACKS: Slam (1d12) or by weapon
SANITY: 1d8/1d10
SAVES: P, M
INT: High
ALIGN: Any Evil
TYPE: Undead
XP: 825+8 (1,209)
SPECIAL: Despair, Mummy Rot, Darkvision 60 ft., Fire Vulnerability, Subject to Raising, Magic

A mummy is an undead creature usually wrapped in divine bandages and urged to existence through prayer and ceremony. Mummies are bound to their tombs and are encountered in their vicinity, which is most commonly the deserts of Egypt, though mummies have been encountered in Central and South America and in arctic, desert, and

jungle climes the world over, where conditions are right for preservation of the body. Any creature that defiles or loots the tomb of a mummy is doomed to face the mummy's wrath. Their connection with the artifacts of life and the resting places of the dead are tremendous, and they punish grave looters with unmediated violence. The process required to create a mummy gives the creature powerful protections against physical damage. However, the most terrifying aspect of a mummy is not its ability to withstand damage or doggedly pursue its quarry, but its lingering effects upon those that managed to escape. The touch of a mummy instills a disease that causes a victim's body to slowly wilting and rotting away into a useless mass of pulpy flesh. These creatures are often created in pairs, but the most unholy sanctums can be guarded by up to eight.

COMBAT: Mummies enter combat without fear. Mummies of the lesser variety do not take prisoners, and do not bargain or communicate. They batter their foes until victorious, or the mummies themselves are destroyed. Greater mummies, on the other hand, are masterful tacticians, plotters and schemers and may employ all manner of tricks, traps, and henchmen in the furthering of their plans and schemes. Sleep and charm spells, as well as poison and paralysis, have no affect on mummies. They can only be hit and damaged by magical weapons.

DESPAIR: The mere sight of a mummy causes an opponent to become unnerved, shaken and repulsed. This affect is identical to the spell fear. In addition, an additional wisdom save is required by all opponents. If the save fails, that victim is

paralyzed by the mummy's presence, and remains so for 1d4 rounds. Humans gain a +2 bonus to resist this effect. There is safety and security in numbers, however. All individuals in a group will gain a +1 bonus if group members outnumber mummies present by at least 6 to 1. This bonus is cumulative to the bonus given to humans. For example, if two mummies are present, 12 group members are required to gain a +1 bonus, giving humans a total of +3.

MUMMY ROT: A victim stricken by this horrible affliction contracts a dreadful disease that resists natural methods of healing. Only the spell cure disease can remove Mummy Rot. Each time a victim is struck by a mummy, a successful constitution save is required to resist the mummy's scabrous touch. Failure indicates that the creature has been afflicted with the Rot, and no further saves are allowed. While afflicted with Mummy Rot, magical spells and effects that restore hit points do not function on the victim. Methods of natural healing, including regeneration, are 10 times slower. In addition, a victim of Mummy Rot loses two points of charisma each month, permanently, culminating in the victim's death 1d6 months after exposure and contraction.

SUBJECT TO RAISING: A mummy targeted by a raise dead spell must succeed at a physical save or be restored from undeath. Most will be transformed into a human of 7th level, but a mummy will typically assume the class it had in life. However, the corruption of undeath lingers, and these individuals will almost always retain the lawful evil alignment. Greater Mummies may make a Wisdom save against raising.

SPELL CASTING: Greater mummies are intelligent, often the remains of deceased priests or leaders. These creatures always have the abilities of at least an eighth-level Arcanist, generally with spells from the Wisdom or Charisma list. Some may be as high as twentieth level; for higher level arcanist-mummies, the Game Master should increase hit points (and experience) proportionally, granting 6 additional hit points per arcanist level above eighth.

SHOGGOTH

NO. ENCOUNTERED: 1
SIZE: Large
HD: 17 (d10)
MOVE: 20 ft. (n/a)
AC: 20
ATTACKS: 12 Tentacles (1d12), Bite (5d10; special, see below)
SANITY: 1d6/1d12
SAVES: P
INT: High
ALIGNMENT: Neutral Evil
TYPE: Magical Beast
XP: 11700+17
SPECIAL: Constrict, Swallow Whole, Poison, Darkvision 60 ft., Twilight Vision, Sanity-Blasting Visage

A shoggoth is a black, fetid, fleshy mass of tentacles, eyes, and hundreds of tooth-filled mouths. It is a creature from Beyond the Pale, existing in the spaces between worlds, those shadowy realms known to arcanists as The Deeper Dark. It is only one of a species of similar creatures, who can be summoned by evil arcanists to work their dark will, wreaking havoc and destruction wherever it appears.

COMBAT: the shoggoth lashes out at anyone and everything in range, without apparent rhyme or reason. It will grapple with its tentacles, squeezing and dragging its poisoned victim towards its gaping, toothy maw, where it simply eats people alive. The creature is massive, at least 20 feet in diameter, with writhing tentacles that reach a further forty feet.

SANITY-BLASTING VISAGE: All who see the creature must make a Wisdom save or spend a Fate Point to avoid being knocked unconscious for 1d4 rounds from the sanity-blasting visage of the thing. GMs should inform players who fail their save that they can spend a Fate Point to avoid this...fate.

CONSTRICT: If a shoggoth strikes with 2 or more tentacles, it wraps them around the victim, and begins to crush and strangle it. On the following round, the victim is allowed an attempt to break free with a strength save. Failure means that the character is constricted and cannot move, save to attack with a small weapon (already in hand) at a –4 penalty. Each round that the victim remains constricted, it automatically suffers 3d4 points of damage. A victim can attempt another save every round. However, a shoggoth can wrap additional tentacles around a constricted victim. A shoggoth can automatically strike a constricted creature with additional tentacles, inflicting tentacle damage as well as constricting damage. The victim's saving throws are penalized, in these cases, by –1 for each constricting tentacle beyond the first. A tentacle can be severed by directly attacking it. Tentacles have 20 hit points and an armor class of 20. If a shoggoth suffers damage to more than 3 of its tentacles while holding a victim, it slams its victim against the ground for 6d6 damage.

BITE: The shoggoth may only bite its victim if it pulls the victim to its mouth, having snared it with 2 or more tentacles and begun constriction.

SWALLOW WHOLE: When a shoggoth makes a bite attack, and the roll is a natural 19 or better, the victim must succeed at a dexterity save at a -10 penalty to avoid being swallowed whole. Once swallowed, the victim enters the worm's crushing, acidic digestive system. Each round spent inside the worm causes 1d20 + 10 points of damage, and 10 points of acid damage. A victim can attempt to cut its way out of the beast by using a light slashing weapon to deal 30 points of damage to the creature (armor class 17). If a victim manages to cut free of the monster, peristalsis and other muscular actions close the hole, and other swallowed victims must cut their own way out.

POISON: Any creature struck by the shoggoth's stinger suffers 2-24 points of damage. A successful constitution save reduces this damage by half.

SKELETON

NO. ENCOUNTERED: 1-10
SIZE: Medium
HD: 1d12 (7 hp)
MOVE: 30 ft.
AC: 13
ATTACKS: Weapon
SPECIAL: Undead
SANITY: 1d6/1d8
SAVES: P
INT: None
ALIGNMENT: Neutral
TYPE: Undead (Common)
XP: 10+1 (17)

Skeletons are the animated remains of dead creatures. Their bodies are little more than bone and sinew held together by vile sorcery. They move with a slow gait, but sometimes have the strength to wield weapons and wear armor. Skeletons are mindless, but are aware of living things and always attack them. They are often encountered under the command of an evil arcanist.

COMBAT: Skeletons attack silently and with a very frightening intensity, killing anything living in their path. Because of their boney nature, any slashing or piercing weapons do half damage, while blunt weapons do normal damage.

SNAKE

	CONSTRICTOR, GIANT	VENOMOUS
NO. ENC:	1	1
SIZE:	Large	Small
HD:	6d8 (12 hp)	1d4 (2 hp)
MOVE:	30 ft., 30 ft. (climb), 30 ft. (swim)	20 ft., 20 ft. (climb), 20 ft. (swim)
AC:	15	13
ATTACKS:	Bite (1d4), Coil (2d6)	Bite (poison only)
SPECIAL	Constrict	Poison
SANITY:	None	None
SAVES:	P	P
INT:	Animal	Animal
ALIGN:	Neutral	Neutral
TYPE:	Animal	Animal
XP:	210+6 (282)	9+1 (11)

There are many species of snakes, venomous and non-venomous. They are found in most warm and temperate climates, and have adapted to most terrain. They are shy creatures that generally avoid contact with larger animals. They will strike if cornered or threatened. Only the giant constrictor actively hunts man-sized prey.

COMBAT: Snakes usually avoid combat altogether unless they feel extremely threatened. Giant constrictors are exceptions. They will lay in wait, perfectly still, shrouded in foliage until prey passes underneath them. Then, they will drop onto the victim, wrapping their coils around it, and squeezing it mightily until it dies. Then, the snake will unhinge its jaw and slowly swallow the victim whole.

POISON: Venomous snakes can deliver a wide variety of poisons of varying toxicities, effects, and onset times. These range from the relatively mild bite of the copper head to the very potent bite of the king cobra. To determine the potency of the snake bite roll on the table below. Someone bitten by a venomous snake must make a constitution save. A successful save halves the listed damage for first round effects and there are no effects in the following rounds. A failed save on the first round delivers the damage indicated below and the character becomes ill, suffering a -1 to all physical attribute checks and a -1 to hit and damage for ten minutes. First round effects always occur immediately.

Ten turns, or 10 minutes after the initial bite, another constitution save must be made to avoid the further effects of the poison. A successful save indicates the poison has been fought off. A failed save causes the onset of the effects listed below and the character must make daily saves thereafter until the poison is successfully fought off or runs its course–or the character dies.

Type	First Save	Second Save	Duration
1-2	1d2	1d2, double effects of illness	1 week
3	1d4	1d4, triple effects of illness	1 week
4	1d6	1d6, quadruple effects of illness	1-2 weeks
5	1d8	1d8, incapacitated	1-4 weeks
6	1d10	Death in 2-8 rounds	not long

A failed save indicates that the effects listed continue for another day. Additionally, the character loses 1 point of constitution. The same process is followed for each successive day until the character successfully saves and fights off the poison. For every five points of constitution lost, one point is lost permanently. Should a character's constitution ever reach zero, it is dead.

CONSTRICTION: A successful attack by the snake can lead to a constriction attack. In the round following the successful attack, the victim must make a strength save. If this save fails, the victim is constricted by the snake for either 1d6 or 2d6 (depending on the snake's size) points of damage per round. A victim can make addition strength saves every round to escape constriction, but escape becomes more difficult as the snake tightens its grip. Strength saves to escape therefore suffer a -2 cumulative penalty for each round after the first that the victim is constricted.

VAMPIRE

NO. ENCOUNTERED: 1
SIZE: Medium
HD: 8d12 (48 hp)
MOVE: 40 ft., 60 ft. (fly), 20 ft. (climb)
AC: 20
ATTACKS: Slam (1d6)
SANITY: 1d8/1d10
SAVES: M, P
INT: Average to Genius
ALIGNMENT: Chaotic Evil
TYPE: Undead (Unique)
XP: 1885+8 (2269)
SPECIAL: Blood Drain, Children of the Night, Dominate, Create Spawn, Energy Drain, Alternate Form, Gaseous Form, Entourage, Electrical Resistance (half), Spider Climb

Vampires are legendary undead predators, feared and reviled by all. Formerly human, these foul creatures have become completely corrupted, lurking in a state between life and death, and requiring warm, fresh blood for sustenance. They prowl at night, through decrepit city streets, seeking healthy but unsuspecting victims. Unlike other undead, vampires are not ghastly or decayed in appearance. To most observers, they appear quite normal, and some are rather attractive. They often have pale skin that takes on a less pallid tone after they feed. All vampires must retreat to the safety of their lairs as the sun rises, as sunlight is fatal to them. They tend to make abandoned crypts and tombs their homes. They are vulnerable when resting during the day, sleeping in coffins and sarcophagi, and therefore rely on remote, avoided locations in which to lair. Up to four vampires may share a single location. However foreboding their chosen shelter, they always choose a place that is relatively close to cities and settlements. This provides them with easy access to a food supply.

Vampires are very intelligent, even if not very smart in life, and will not overfeed in a particular location. This helps prevent discovery and allows the hunting ground to be used for a longer period of time. Vampires are freakishly strong. This innate toughness enables them to turn aside mundane weaponry and they are susceptible only to silver, piercing weapons made entirely of wood, holy water and artifacts, and garlic.

COMBAT: Vampires are aggressive, but not foolhardy, when stalking prey. They stalk targets traveling alone, weak stragglers, drunkards, and other vulnerable targets. They are not favorably disposed to prolonged combats, as they realize dangers to them despite their own great power. To avoid battle, they will try to mentally dominate other creatures. If that fails, and they are pressed, they will call their nocturnal allies to aid them in the fight. If a battle goes poorly for them, they will change shape and flee.

BLOOD DRAIN: If a vampire successfully strikes an opponent with its fists (slam), the target must succeed at a strength save or be held in the vampire's grip. If the save fails, a vampire will use its great strength to bring the victim to its mouth, where it will bite it and begin to drain it of blood. This attack automatically inflicts 1d4 points of damage per round. For each point drained from a victim, a vampire will heal one hit point. If a vampire is able to drain a victim of 36 hit points in this way, it is satiated, and will release its grip. A victim of this bite does not experience pain; instead, they become euphoric during the process, and some may become addicted to it. Once a victim is bitten, it will not struggle to escape the vampire's clutches. A vampire must use this ability every few weeks, or it will die.

ENERGY DRAIN: Along with the blood drain, living creatures hit by a vampire's bite attack instantly lose one level or hit die. Thereafter, for every round that the vampire is able to continue feeding, the victim loses one level or hit die until the creature has perished. This loss is permanent

unless reversed with a restoration spell or a wish. Vampires can choose not to drain energy, or to do so more slowly so as to prolong their feeding on a given subject.

CHILDREN OF THE NIGHT: Vampires are able to summon other night-time predators, having a special bond with these creatures. A vampire can summon a swarm of bats, rats, or 3d6 wolves. They can summon only once per day, but success is guaranteed. Summoned creatures will arrive 2d4 rounds after being called by the vampire. The summoned creatures obey the vampire without reservation, and remain until killed or released.

DOMINATE: The intense gaze of a vampire is intoxicating, as overwhelming feelings of both fear and lust cross the victim's mind. A creature that looks into a vampire's eyes must make a charisma save at a -2 penalty. Failure results in the victim suffering the effects of a permanent duration charm person spell. However, a person charmed in this manner will defend the vampire at all costs, even against former allies.

CREATE SPAWN: If a vampire chooses, it can drain the blood or energy of a human victim in such a way as to bring the deceased into unlife as a vampire spawn. This spawn is under the control of the slaying vampire. This ability is not automatic, but must be consciously used. An affected human loses all abilities, and gains the statistics of a vampire spawn (see below).

VAMPIRE SPAWN: These are essentially half-power vampires with 4 hit dice, 30 ft. movement, and only the following special abilities: Blood Drain, Children of the Night, Dominate, Energy Drain, Alternate Form, and Electrical Resistance (Half). If a Vampire is killed, all of its spawn immediately become full vampires.

ALTERNATE FORM: Any vampire can assume the form of a large canine, of any non-magical or natural breed or species,

and remain in that form indefinitely. A vampire can also assume the form of a large bat, and can remain in that form indefinitely. A vampire in either form retains all special qualities, but loses its special attacks. True seeing and other effects will not reveal a vampire in either of these forms, and these forms cannot be dispelled. However, a vampire killed in either form will become gaseous (see below). Vampires are immune to polymorph attacks unless the vampire wishes to be affected.

GASEOUS FORM: A vampire can assume the form of a thick cloud, at will, as the spell gaseous form. If a vampire in any form other than gaseous is reduced to 0 hit points, it automatically assumes the gaseous state and retreats to its lair. There, it will heal and prepare for another attack.

SPIDER CLIMB: Vampires are endowed with the supernatural ability to adhere to and climb any surface.

VAMPIRE VULNERABILITIES: Vampires retreat from garlic, reflective surfaces, or holy symbols of good deities. These objects cause vampires to recoil, and deal 1d4 damage per touch from a holy item or through contact with garlic. Fear of these items causes a vampire to delay any attack by 1d4 rounds while it tries to find a way to maneuver around the offending object. When exposed to true daylight, a vampire is rendered powerless and unable to move or attack. It will begin to smolder, and after 6 rounds of exposure, a vampire will burst into flame and burn to ashes. This permanently destroys the vampire. If a vampire is ever immersed in running water, a vampire's flesh is rapidly degraded, killing it permanently in 3 rounds. Each round of immersion causes the vampire to lose one-third of its hit points. A stake driven through the heart of a vampire will kill it as long as the stake remains in place. If it is removed, the vampire awakens and functions normally. To permanently kill a staked vampire, its head must be removed, its mouth filled with holy wafers, and then the entire corpse must be buried in consecrated ground.

ENTOURAGE: A vampire may be encountered with up to 6 vampire spawn.

SPECIAL: Vampires always have the abilities of a socialite and/or raider of the same level as the vampire has hit dice. By adding the abilities of other classes and/or increasing the creature's hit dice, a vampire can become an exceptionally formidable recurring foe for a group of pulp adventurers.

WOLF

NO. ENCOUNTERED: 4-24
SIZE: Small-Medium
HD: 2d8 (9 hp)
MOVE: 50 ft.
AC: 13
ATTACKS: Bite (1d6)
SANITY: None
SAVES: P
INT: Animal
ALIGNMENT: Neutral
TYPE: Animal
XP: 10+2 (28)
SPECIAL: Trip, Scent, Twilight Vision, Track

Wolves range in size from small to medium. They are ferocious predators and often hunt in packs. They will bring down any prey they sense is weak or alone. There is always a dominate male and female in wolf packs. At times worgs or winter wolves lead large packs of wolves. They are found in many environments. Wolves have a superior sense of smell and can use it to track prey with a Wisdom check. For purposes of scent tracking only, treat Wisdom as a Prime attribute.

COMBAT: Wolves always attack in groups. Usually one or two distract their prey while two or three others bite its feet and legs, trying to bring it down. If the prey falls the whole of the pack falls upon it, often feeding before the prey is wholly dead.

ZOMBIE

NO. ENCOUNTERED: 1-10
SIZE: Medium
HD: 2d8 (8)
MOVE: 20 ft.
AC: 12
SANITY: 1d6/1d8
SAVES: P
INT: None
ALIGNMENT: Neutral Evil
TYPE: Undead (Common)
ATTACKS: Slam (1d8) or grapple and bite (1d6 + 1d4/round–see special) or by weapon
SPECIAL: Slow, Feed, Create Spawn (only certain varieties)
XP: 15+1 (23) or 25+1 (33) (species that can create spawn)

Zombies are undead humanoids, reanimated corpses that stalk the earth with little purpose or reason. They typically appear as shambling, rotting bodies, complete with ragged clothes and rusted mail. They are unable to use complicated weapons like guns, cast spells, or even communicate, though they can use rudimentary clubs, blades, and other primitive stabbing and bashing weapons. They possess only a vague instinct to gather in groups, find living creatures, and kill them. They are shambling and slow, but have a powerful attack. A zombie is mindless, fearless, and only seeks to kill and devour living flesh.

SLOW: A zombie never gains initiative and always acts last in any given round.

FEED: Following a successful grapple check, a zombie bites its victim for 1d6 damage. Thereafter, every round the grapple is maintained, the zombie automatically deals another 1d4 damage from chewing on the flesh of its victim. A victim may break the grapple with an opposed Strength check.

CREATE SPAWN: In some campaigns, zombies may be able to infect others with their bite, slowly turning the infected into zombies. In such a case, the victim bitten must make a constitution save at -2 or be infected. Infected victims will lose 1d4 points of strength and constitution each day until one of the two abilities reaches 0, at which point the victim dies, rising within 1d4 minutes as a new zombie unless the body is destroyed (often through decapitation or other destruction of the head)

BOOK SEVEN: THE HEART OF YHTILL

A complete adventure for 3-5 first-level characters

QUICK SYNOPSIS

Amanda Seymour approaches the group seeking help in solving her husband's mysterious disappearance. Martin Seymour vanished during the night after working late in his study a week ago. She found him missing in the morning and he has not been seen since. There is evidence that Martin was engaged in much research - lots of cryptic references and what appears to be several attempts to crack a code of some kind.

The truth is that Martin has become possessed by Abd Al-Hazred and is making for the Black City of Irem in the Arabian Desert, for some nefarious purpose the PCs do not yet know. The PCs must pursue Martin to Irem and beneath it, and stop the Mad Arab from acquiring the ancient and powerful Heart of Yhtill.

CUT SCENE

Amanda was having a dream. A nice dream, about beaches and Mai Tais. There were bikinis and sun involved, and Amanda had the body she'd had when she was 18. Martin looked like an athlete, and to Amanda's knowledge, Martin never looked like an athlete in his life. In Amanda's dream, life was good.

Then something changed. Dark clouds rolled in, a vortex of blacks and grays intershot with flashes of yellow, red, green, and colors she had never imagined, let alone was able to identify. Out of the dark vortex, a face emerged, Arabic, but not Arabic, the nose and ears cut off so that the face was a leering skull with leathery skin, grinning at her. It swooped down on her and Martin, and she felt ecstasy and agony unlike anything she'd ever imagined.

When the darkness passed, Martin was gone. Everyone was gone, except Amanda, and the writhing masses of tentacles, flesh, and reproductive organs all around her. First she was terrified, then sick, then utterly calm, accepting of her fate, welcoming it.

Amanda sat up in bed, breathing heavily. Her bedclothes looked as though they'd been left out in a storm; she didn't realize a person could sweat that much.

"What a strange dream," she muttered, then turned to Martin...who wasn't there.

Amanda shuddered and squinted into the darkness. Sure enough, a thin beam of light leaked out from beneath the door of Martin's study. She threw on a robe and approached the door.

"Martin? Martin, you promised you'd be to bed soon. It's nearly 3 AM."

She raised her hand to knock, and at her first gentle tap the door swung open with the creak of hinges long overdue for oiling. She padded in and looked around. Martin was nowhere to be seen. His room was a shambles, filled with notes and scribblings, most of which looked like nonsensical gibberish. Amanda couldn't make heads or tails of any of it.

A quick peek out the window confirmed her worst fears.

Martin's car was gone.

ACT ONE

Act one begins with a murder most foul. As our heroes mingle at the Club Cayman, a posh Caribbean-themed nightclub in the heart of New York, minor chaos erupts when a woman screams and her companion sinks to the floor, holding his neck. By the time the heroes get to him, he's quite dead. Checking over the body reveals what appears to be a small needle or dart in his neck. His lips are blue and his complexion ashen.

Questioning the crowd doesn't reveal much, though a CC 20 Charisma check will garner several witnesses who saw a waiter with what appeared to be an odd-looking tube or reed, make haste through the kitchen doors just before the woman screamed.

As for the woman, she's an absolute knockout, with blonde hair, crystal blue eyes, full, pomegranate-red lips, and long, curvaceous legs that begin with delicate ankles, and just don't quit. Even shaken and upset as she is, this is a Stella whose glance can still melt a Jake's heart. Her name is Amanda Seymour, and the dead man was her brother, Jimmy Diamond. Any Gumshoes in the group can make an Intelligence Check with a CC of 18 to recognize the name as a relatively new player in the city's social scene; Amanda recently through a string of "fortunate" investments became a member of the nouveau-riche set. She's been quietly investigated over the suddenness of her success, but nothing untoward was discovered and the investigation dropped. Amanda insists that she has no idea why anyone would want to kill her husband; he went out of his way never to get on anyone's bad side, figuring it was better to be liked all around than to have a few powerful friends and lots of enemies. She seems very sincere.

> **AMANDA SEYMOUR** *(This third-level CN Socialite/first-level Arcanist has vital stats HD 3d8+1d6 (20 hp), AC 15 (evening clothes, long gloves, scarf), move 30 feet. her primary attributes are Dex 15, Wis 14, and Cha 18. She attacks with a small dagger for 1d4 damage or a 2-shot derringer for 1d8 damage (BtH +2). Her special abilities are Charm Person, Connected, Exalt, and Embolden)*

(Amanda won't show the arcanist aspect of her persona till much later, as she knows it is incriminating. When she

does reveal herself in Act 4, she has 9 MEP and knows the following spells: 0-level – Ghost Sound, Influence, Mage Hand, Prestidigitation. 1st level – Command, Daze, Hypnotism. She wears a special ring that hides her aura, to keep psychics and other Arcanists from detecting her magical abilities).

As this is a very posh club, the police arrive on the scene quickly, and the characters likely find themselves unable to approach the body or Amanda, who is being questioned by the cops (though a gumshoe currently in the police force or FBI won't have this problem). Things take a turn for the worse very quickly, however, when poor old Jimmy Diamond jumps up and bites a cop, after stabbing him in the throat with the needle that killed Jimmy! The cop falls over, dead, his throat wound gushing blood onto the floor.

Chaos erupts and a circle clears around Jimmy. Not long after that (and before the characters can react), the cop also gets up, his head hanging at an awkward angle from the bite wound in his throat. Both men are frothing at the mouth and look completely feral...as well as quite dead. At this point the characters should roll for initiative before the zombies start eating people. Assume that the characters, being the elite heroes of their world, react to the situation 1d4 rounds (6-24 seconds) before the police do.

> **ZOMBIES** *(these undead monsters have vital stats HD 2d8 (8 hp each), AC 12, move 20 ft. Their primary attributes are physical. They attack by slam for 1d8 damage or bite for 1d6 damage, following a successful grapple check. Their special abilities are slow and feed, dealing 1d4 per round following a bite until the grapple is broken or the zombie killed).*

Nobody else turns into a zombie, even if the zombies manage to kill any more bystanders. This should lead the PC's to believe that it was, in fact, something on the needle that created the undead killing machines. GM's may wish to give the characters a Wisdom check to note that Jimmy stabbed the cop with the needle before biting him, if the PC's don't figure it out on their own. If any arcanists or characters with medical or chemistry backgrounds want to get blood samples or anything else, try and roll with them. Give them an opportunity to do so, just as long as they're not stupidly obvious or blatant about it.

Eventually the police will want to clear the scene, and the PC's will be asked to leave after giving a statement.

ACT TWO

RUNDOWN

The PCs get a visit from a frightened Amanda Seymour, whose husband has been missing for a week. Their investigations yield a mysterious connection to the lost city of Irem, where the mad Arab Abdul Al-Hazred gained much of his forbidden knowledge. A visit from Nyarlathotep makes the PCs uneasy, as his visits tend to do.

ACTION

Visions of the Mad Arab

Sometime that night, any characters with psychic abilities (arcanists or mentalists) who make an appropriate ability check share a psychic vision: a man, slender and gaunt, looking like he might once have been attractive, but now is malnourished and obsessed, pours over a collection of ancient books, scribbling feverishly in one of a thousand notebooks on his desk. The vision shifts; Amanda Seymour tosses and turns in her bed, in the throes of a nightmare. The vision returns to the man, muttering in strange tongues as he reads and translates.

Suddenly, a vortex opens in the office. Papers blow everywhere, and the vision is shot with bursts of red, yellow, green, and purple lights, as well as lights in colors our psychic heroes have never seen before. A man—at least, it seems to be a man—steps forth from the portal and into the light. The man is Arabic, and yet somehow not Arabic. He wears a head wrap and the robes of a nomad, and sports a thick black beard, but his nose and ears have been cut off, leaving him to resemble a skeleton with skin. He approaches the man, puts his hand on the man's shoulder, grins, and says, "It is time, Martin. The Fire awaits."

Perhaps most horrifying is that the man speaks Arabic, but the characters understand him clearly even if they do not. If they do, in fact, speak Arabic, they will know he is speaking Arabic, but will hear him in English (or whatever their native language is).

Then, the two men merge into one, the Arab vanishing into the body of Martin, who hastily collects a couple sheets of paper, throws on his coat, and walks out into the night.

The vision ends, and the characters wake up. It's roughly 3 am.

A New Client

The next morning, the PCs are at work as per normal, when Amanda Seymour approaches them. She wants the characters to find her husband Martin, who has been missing for a week. She simply woke up one night to find Martin's office a mess, and his car gone. She suspects that there are other forces at work who also want her husband, and that the attack last night was directed at her.

The police claim to be looking into where Martin might have gone. But she doesn't feel they're taking his disappearance very seriously, and is well aware that if he's left the country the police can't do anything about it. She has approached the PCs because of their response to the situation last night; she is clearly paranoid and doesn't trust the police or feds at all. She wants the PCs to find out where he's gone and what happened. She is willing to give any information she can, and will allow the PCs to come to her house to investigate.

Amanda's Information: Martin had been feverishly working on some new "pet project" of his lately, something about the key to translating some ancient historical text or another.

Amanda, who considers herself little more than a trophy wife, had little interest in her husband's passion for amateur archaeology and ancient religions, so she doesn't know anything about the exact nature of his studies. She will say, however, that recently he'd become more and more obsessive, ranting and raving about "the key" and how the secrets to the universe were his for the unlocking. Once she'd suggested he take a break and get away from the work for awhile, and he went mad, accusing her of working for "them," and threatening her life if she ever interfered again (she doesn't know who "they" are). A combination of love and real fear of the madness behind his eyes kept her quiet, living in terror, until the night he vanished.

Visiting the Scene: The Seymours live on a posh estate, approximately 25 minutes south of the city. The 2-story house has a great hall, 6 bedrooms, 3 baths (one of which is a powder room on the ground floor), a smoking room (Martin's office), a parlor, a library, a fairly large kitchen, a dining room, and a living room.

The house looks largely undisturbed. The office and library, however, are a shambles. Not the kind of shambles you'd expect from someone ransacking the place. No, this is the shambles of a man so obsessed with his work he's been going quietly insane for months. There are stacks of papers everywhere: newspapers old and new, archaeological and religious journals, notebooks, you name it. It could take months to go through everything here.

With a successful Intelligence or Wisdom Ability check (CL 2 for Int, CL 4 for Wis), however, there is something of value on the desk: The degree of success reveals what information the PCs find in the mess. Basically for every 3 the character rolls over the required target, he gains one degree of success.

1 **SUCCESS:** Three photographic prints from some sort of manuscript, untranslatable, in a script that looks like some sort of proto-Arabic.

2 **SUCCESSES:** Next to that is a notebook with an impression on it, as though someone had written on the sheet above it and pressed down hard. A rubbing might reveal the writing. If this is attempted (A Dexterity Ability check is required to do it without smoothing out the indentations), the PCs can make out a few words: Irem, Nameless City, Nug and Yeb, Empty Space, and a phrase that repeats several times: The Heart of Yhtill, .

3 **SUCCESSES:** Half-buried under the piles of notes is a small, leather-bound journal that has what appears to be a partially-finished cipher for the photographed pages on the desk! It would take a real expert in ancient languages and ciphers months to complete the translation.

POLICE CONTACTS: Doubtless the PCs will call their police contacts (if any) to exchange notes and alert the authorities that Mrs. Seymour has hired them. The police will be curious as to why they're on the case, but will share the information that has just come in: It looks like Martin purchased a one-way ticket by airship to Saudi Arabia (if they ask for specifics, it's the city of At Taif). The police have found no evidence of foul play, and given that Martin is out of the country, they have no legal recourse to follow up on his disappearance, save to keep an eye out for his return.

The PCs know now that Martin was working on some sort of translation and is after the Heart of Yhtill, and that he is on his way to the Middle East. But that's a very thin thread to try and follow.

MYSTICAL CONTACTS: Calling any mystical contacts can yield positive results. If the Party doesn't have any mystical contacts, Amanda can provide one: Martin was a personal friend of one Marie Laveau, the daughter of the Voodoo Queen of New Orleans herself. It seems that Ms. Laveau has some rare books under lock and key, among these a copy of the John Dee translation of the Necronomicon, considered to be the most accurate translation of Wormius' Latin edition in existence. Amanda is more than willing to front the cost of a plane ticket and set them up in a nice hotel. She will also cable ahead to inform Ms. Laveau that the PCs are coming. When the characters are ready to return to New York, they have only to cable Amanda and she'll send approval for funds for a ticket home.

Voodoo Land

The Party land at their destination with no troubles and as soon as they check into their hotel, they can obtain transport to Laveau's cottage deep in the bayou. Marie is something of a mercenary and will provide services to whoever pays for them, but truthfully proclaims to have no love for Nazis.

If the Party have brought with them the dart-fetish used to create the zombies in our opening scene, she recognizes the fetish as being in her style and theorizes a scopolamine derivative was used, but denies (again, truthfully) having anything to do with it. Though she knows how, she doesn't engage in what she calls "black juju." If properly motivated, however (money helps, as does proper displays of deference and etiquette; she can be talked into helping given her distaste for Nazis), she will admit that she has had many a student who may have put it together. When she was taking on students, many were eventually dismissed for having no respect for the old ways; these merely wanted power, without the requisite respect for the loa that comes with that power. As much as it disgusts her, it's not outside the realm of possibility that some may have fallen in with a mystical Nazi cult known as the Thule Society. The Thules are obsessed with furthering the esoteric knowledge that drives the Nazis, and seek to use any and all mystical secrets they can get their hands on, to ensure that the Third Reich lasts for a thousand years.

She doesn't know Amanda Seymour personally, but was a friend of Martin's. If they mention Amanda Diamond, Marie

says she doesn't know an Amanda Diamond. She once knew a young lady named Alice Diamond, a young urchin Marie took care of on occasion, and to whom Marie taught a few basic tricks, but that poor Alice got lost and drowned in the bayou ten years ago. They dragged her body out, Marie says, half-eaten by gators. She then gets choked up by the memory, and can't go on. She will tell the PCs where Alice's grave is, if they want, and should they investigate, they will discover Marie is telling the truth. There are newspaper clippings and a death certificate in the archives, and a grave right in Lafayette Cemetery.

As the PCs talk to Marie in her bayou cottage, a ruckus sounds outside and the group find themselves under attack! Looking out the windows reveals one zombie for each Party Member (and one for Marie) and three robed figures with guns, who seem to be directing the zombies. The robed figures are Thule Cultists, out to kill Marie so that she doesn't share information with anyone else (like our heroes); these men will not fight to the death: the spell caster will use obscuring mist to provide cover for himself and his cohorts to escape into the bayou.

The zombies use the same stats as those in Act One.

THULE CULTISTS *(these 1st-level NE humans have vital stats HD 1d10 (5 hp each), AC 13, move 30 ft. Their primary attributes are Physical (one has mental). They attack by Luger pistols for 1d10 damage or knives for 1d4 damage. Their special abilities are: those with Physical Primes have hide and move silently, and the one with Mental Primes has first-level spells as a Charisma arcanist:10 MEP, 0-level; Dancing Lights, Ghost Sound, Influence 1st-level; Command, Obscuring Mist).*

MARIE LAVEAU *(this 5th-level LN Wisdom-based arcanist has vital stats HD 5d6 (18 hp), AC 13 (ceremonial robes and Dex 15), move 30 ft. Her primary attributes are Dex 15, Wis 18, Cha 16. She attacks by spell or dagger dealing 1d4 damage (BtH +1). Her special abilities are MEP 35, 0-level: Detect Chaos/Evil/Good/Law, Detect Magic, Detect Poison, First Aid, Purify Food/Drink, Prestidigitation; 1st-level: Bless, Cure Light Wounds, Detect Undead, Faerie Fire, Invisibility to Undead; 2nd-level: Aid, Charm Person/Animal, Speak with Dead)*

If the Party thinks to ask her, or you as GM decide to volunteer Marie's ability to speak with the dead, the cultists know very little. They are low-level followers of the Thule cult and associated with the Nazi party in Germany; all are initiate members of the SS. They were ordered to kill Marie Laveau and anyone with whom she was talking, so she didn't give away her secrets to anyone else. They know of the Heart of Yhtill and the scopolamine derivative, but don't know where the heart is now, nor do they know who is behind the processing of scopolamine for the Germans. They do know there's a Nazi plan in place to produce undead soldiers under the direct control of the SS and that, for now, the scopolamine simply creates mindless killing machines.

Regardless, Marie will be grateful to the PCs for saving her, and can in gratitude provide each of them a gris gris similar to a Native American medicine bag which when used will grant them the effects of a Bless spell (+1 to hit, +1 to save vs. fear for 50 minutes), but will only work once. To use the gris gris, the character must squeeze the bag to inhale the pungent fumes that cloud forth, then wear it for the duration of the spell (activation requires one action). She wishes them good fortune, and tells them that the loa go with them. If they need her services in the future, they need only call upon her. She is also willing to let them remain to study the Necronomicon as long as they like, but will of course not allow the book to leave her care.

The Necronomicon includes a few references to the Black City, which seems to be located at the heart of the Arabian Desert, somewhere near the northern border of Yemen. It is described as appearing only infrequently, rising up from beneath the sand, and is supposed to contain vast treasures and secrets, among them a great jewel called the Heart of Yhtill. This jewel is located in a temple beneath a great library, the Library of Ashurbanipal, at the heart of the city. This library is supposed to hold within it the secrets of the Old Ones, and the means to use the jewel to gain power over life and death, but most disturbing is a prophecy that the Great Unnameable Chaos at the center of the universe can be awakened by using the jewel, and his awakening would unleash a cohesive thought of entropy that could tear apart all of reality.

It would appear that Martin is seeking the Heart in the Arabian desert...and walking into a mystical trap of epic proportions.

Another Fine Mess

When the PCs return to their hotel, they find their rooms a shambles. They've been torn apart, rifled through, and generally vandalized. There is a note in scribbled handwriting on one of their pillows, which appears to have been written in blood (it has; chicken's blood). The handwriting is shaky block printing, as though a right-handed person wrote it left-handed. It reads: "You cannot stop us. The descendents of Thule will rise again, and the weapon of God will destroy all of their enemies!"

If the PCs alert the police, they'll be asked to stay in town while the police investigate; any gumshoe, hooligan, or anyone with any sort of contacts in the police or FBI would know this. However, gumshoes in the party can cut through this red tape with a basic Charisma check (CC 15), allowing the PCs to head home with contact information left behind. Of course the feds will get involved; Thule is popping up all over the East Coast, and if it's moving inland that's a real problem. They suspect it's connected with the Nazis, somehow, and that it's the beginning of a secret invasion force for Germany. J. Edgar Hoover is extremely concerned.

If there are trust issues between the PCs and the authorities, don't hesitate to remind them that in this era, unless they have a criminal background, past, or associations, people tend to trust the government and authorities. The FBI are,

in the eyes of the public, unequivocally the “Good Guys.” These particular agents, however, know nothing of the Heart of Yhtill or of Thule beyond the fact that they suspect it is a cult affiliated with the Nazis.

When the PCs wire or phone Amanda to come home, she arranges transportation immediately. She can’t imagine Martin being involved with the Thules, but has no doubt that they’ve become aware of his research, especially given the multiple attacks, now. She suggests that she arrange transport for the group to Saudi Arabia, if they don’t bring it up themselves. If they want to back out, she is now adamant that they follow through, even willing to double her monetary offer. What if the Nazis get hold of this gem? At very least it’s got to be worth a fortune, and could fund a lot of military and covert research. She doesn’t have any military connections, and who is going to believe a raving socialite, or for that matter anyone who calls the military with a wild story about zombies and Nazi cultists and magical jewels?

And let’s be real: if the PCs want to back out, the players aren’t very pulp, are they?

Finally, if the PCs mention Alice Diamond to Amanda, she denies any knowledge of the girl’s existence. She will, however, mention that it seems too convenient to be a coincidence and suggest the PCs keep their eyes and ears open, because if she has some long-lost relative who is involved in this, she’d like to know who it is and why.

ACT THREE

RUNDOWN

The PCs head to Saudi Arabia on the trail of Martin Seymour, where they encounter The Society of Ormazd, a group of nomads sworn to protect the secrets of Irem, lest the evils contained therein be unleashed upon the world.

ACTION

The PCs catch a flight to At-Taif, south of Mecca. This portion of the episode mostly revolves around their efforts to find the Nameless City, which is entirely motivated by the PCs’s actions.

If the PCs simply start asking people about Abd Al-Hazred, Irem, The Nameless City, or anything else they find in the Necronomicon, the response will be cold at best. Mostly, the locals will kiss their Ta’wiz talismans and turn their backs, muttering prayers to Allah. Such open queries will definitely lead to a confrontation with the Society of Ormazd (see below).

However, with appropriate Charisma checks (determine CL and CC based on the tact and tactics used by the players) they can learn that Martin has caused some trouble at a temple in Mecca. People are reporting frightening supernatural events occurring in the north of the city.

If the group charters a vehicle and goes north to investigate, they can discover that Martin walked into the great temple at Mecca, announced that the Old Ones were returning, cut off his nose and ears, stabbed several people, then lifted off the floor and flew out through a hole in the ceiling! Anyone who participated in the study of the Necronomicon can make an Intelligence check at CC 16 to realize that Martin is emulating Abd Al-Hazred, who had his nose and ears cut off before being castrated by an angry sultan after Al-Hazred violated the sultan’s daughter. Martin may simply be mad, but given the things they’ve witnessed, it’s not outside the realm of possibility that the man has been possessed by the spirit of the Mad Arab.

The Society of Ormazd

Outside the temple, the group is attacked in an alley by a group of men who have the holy symbol of the Zoroastrian god Ormazd tattooed on their bodies. Use stats for Thule Cultists to represent these guys, though they are not the same and indeed are staunch enemies of Thule. The exception to the stat block is that Society of Ormazd cultists are CG instead of NE. Taking one alive is difficult, as the agents all wear poisoned rings and have false tooth caps with cyanide capsules in them. Suicide devices. Still, it should not be impossible, especially if the PCs don’t have anyone with them who can speak with the dead. One of the society, realizing that the PCs may not be evil, might even allow himself to be captured and questioned before committing suicide. Or he may choose not to die, after all, and may simply give the PCs the information they need before rejoining his compatriots. In fact, this could be a great opportunity for the PCs to gain allies that they might sorely need later, if they have someone with strong social skills amongst them.

If they don’t manage to get one alive for questioning, this might be a time to call upon Marie Laveau’s assistance once more.

If the PCs can capture a prisoner or summon the spirit of one of the men back, their captive can inform them that they are members of a group called the Society of Ormazd, whose sacred duty it is to protect the location of the Black City. Even the members of the Society don’t know exactly how to find the city, but it is rumored that if one follows the rising sun into the center of the desert for two weeks, the city will appear behind them in the last rays of dusk. The Society swear their lives to protecting the secret from the world, and none can claim to ever have entered the accursed place. Hidden within the city, the captive reveals, is a gem called the Eye of Ashurbanipal, or the Heart of Yhtill. The captive surmises that perhaps if Al-Hazred gets the gem, he can resurrect himself, but warns that there is a legendary and horrific guardian at the temple that will devour those who try to remove the gem from the priest Xuthltan, who is cursed to hold it in his dead fist for all eternity.

The prisoner then reveals that the PCs are not the only ones who seek the city. A large group of German soldiers, all

wearing the dual lightning bolt symbol and some mystically inclined, have also arrived and are looking for Martin and the city. The race is on.

TROUBLESHOOTING NOTE: If the PCs find themselves at a dead end, unable to question the Ormazd agents, give them a chance to make a basic Intelligence or Wisdom check to remember that there was a strange, out-of-context passage in the Necronomicon referring to "A fortnight's journey toward the rising desert sun, the goal achieved by turning away at twilight's last stroke."

ACT FOUR

RUNDOWN

The PCs race against the Nazis to the Black City, where they face down with Martin, possessed by the Mad Arab Abdul Al-Hazred, who has come to Irem to retrieve the Heart of Yhtill. While in the Black City, they must do battle with the guardian of the Heart, unleashed when someone tries to take the jewel from the hand of the King.

ACTION

From here, it is likely the PCs will acquire camels, horses, or a jeep and try to head into the desert to follow the instructions given by their prisoner. If they do this, wing it, keeping in mind the difficulties of surviving in the desert. There are all manner of demons, ghouls, and creatures to plague the PCs, as well as the Thule Society (and potentially the Society of Ormazd, depending on how the party handled themselves) who will certainly seek to stop them from finding Irem. See Book Five for inspiration regarding monsters with which to harass the heroes.

Here the GM is encouraged to wing it, allowing the adventure to go on as long as he likes, checking for random (or even not-so-random) monster encounters at least once every other day over the course of the two weeks. The most likely encounters will be ghuls, spirits, nomads, and cultists, as well as desert animals like snakes, jackals, and other predators. To keep players on their toes, the GM is encouraged to portray ghouls as wild, but canny and intelligent creatures who use pack hunting tactics and can employ rudimentary technology such as ranged weapons. Ghuls use the entry for "Ghouls," but instead of being rotting undead, are diseased, mutated degenerates who were once humans that turned to cannibalism in the service of their master, who they know only as the Dark Man. They are more likely to aid Al-Hazred than the PCs, but could potentially be "bought" with trinkets or meat.

What if the party, traveling through a ravine, is set upon by a band of ghouls, which they manage to escape through hook or crook, and later find themselves attacked by Thule cultists? Leading the cultists back to the ravine where the ghouls await a new meal would certainly be a clever tactic by the party.

However you decide to handle the journey through the desert, it is suggested that it become a wild chase, with the Party fleeing from a group of SS officers and Thule Cultists. At the end of two weeks of this, just as twilight approaches, the party find themselves at a standoff, hidden behind a small dune while the Thule cultists take shelter behind another. Suddenly, after perhaps a few rounds of ranged combat, the ground begins to quake and sand blows over the field, blinding all within. Turning to look back to the west, the PCs see the spires of a great pillared city that appears to be built entirely of obsidian, that has risen straight out of the sand from beneath the desert. A successful Wisdom check (CC 17) reveals a lone man, without ears or nose, who leaps out of a dune where he had apparently been partially buried to run wildly into the ruins. He's out of rifle range, and the only way to stop him is to give chase and find him within the city.

There's little time to debate; the Nazis have also seen the city rise and are racing for the gates. The group leaps on their horses and races for the city. Once they make the gates, they bob and weave through alleyways, searching for any building where they might find the gem they seek. How you handle this again, is up to you. These types of scenarios are best played fast-and-loose rather than scripted. Eventually, however, a Wisdom check will spot Martin–possessed by Al-Hazred–making a run for a cyclopean building at the far end of the city. The group can give chase just as the Nazis close in.

With bullets whizzing by their heads, the group makes the library. The place is vast, at least three storeys, the second and third forming octagonal balconies surrounding the first, so that the high, spired ceiling can be seen if one looks straight up (a dizzying experience). The floor and balconies, of course, are covered with several inches of sand, but air vents in the walls have allowed much of it to drain when the city rose. The codices and scrolls in this place are a treasure trove of ancient, arcane knowledge that probably rivals the legendary Library at Alexandria. The black walls are polished to a high, mirrored sheen, which would cause sunlight that filtered in through the windows at each level to reflect back and forth throughout the place, casting more than enough illumination by which one could read. Now, however, the windows are shuttered, and the only light comes in through the front door. It still reflects, however, casting a dim and shadowy illumination throughout the place.

Martin dashes for the front, where he pulls a book and a ramp drops down. As the ramp descends, there is a near-blinding flash of light and the sound of multiple fires springing to life. Descending, the party can see that there are torches in sconces along the walls, each with a metallic back plate and a shard of flint attached to a rod and chain which pulls up when the ramp descends, causing a spark that lights each torch in succession.

The ramp descends for at least sixty feet, leading to a massive underground temple, square in shape and measuring forty

feet to a side. The place is the very definition of all that the party would consider sacrilegious, full of ancient symbols, twisted statues of demonic tentacle horrors, and invocations to evil and diabolic gods with names like Shub-Niggurath, Yig, Nug, and Yeb. Even now, thousands of years after the city had sunk beneath the desert, the stench of old death and rotted blood still hangs thick in the air. At the far end, behind an altar, a mummified figure sits upon a throne, clutching a fist-sized glowing yellow diamond: the Heart of Yhtill. Martin races for the Heart, and just before the PCs catch the man, a gunshot rings out and a female voice yells, "Stop right there!"

The Cast turn to see about twenty to thirty SS officers (Thule cultists), guns trained on the group. The leader of the SS group, veiled and clad in a traditional sari, orders the PCs surrounded and gloats over their inevitable victory, calling the gem a "great prize" for the fuehrer. She then steps forward and removes her veil to reveal that she is Amanda Seymour, and her real name is Alice Diamond. She used the power the Voodoo Queen gave her to rise to the status of a wealthy socialite, but wanted more. She knew Laveau would never teach her the true secrets to power, so she faked her death, murdering another young girl who bore a superficial resemblance to her, and absconded north. She has sold her people out to the Nazis in exchange for great power. When her husband stumbled upon the secret of the gem, she manipulated him into this little quest. When the PCs interfered with her zombie experiment at the club, she knew they had to be either removed or used.

At gunpoint, she commands Martin/Al-Hazred to take the gem and bring it to him. The horrifically mutilated man gives a grotesque grin and moves to the altar.

More gunfire. The Ormazd society has followed the PCs, and the place erupts in chaos. Martin reaches for the gem. The PCs are surrounded by Thule cultists and don't have time to get there to stop him. There's no way to predict how the next few rounds of combat will go, but if anything happens that causes the gem to be removed from Xuthltan's fist, the temple quakes, and the walls split open, and a horrific tentacled thing emerges, wreaking havoc amongst the combatants, many of whom pass out in sheer horror. The creature is the Temple Guardian – a shoggoth. It is a black, fetid, fleshy mass of tentacles, eyes, and hundreds of tooth-filled mouth, whose entire existence is dedicated to ensuring that nobody removes the Heart of Yhtill. The PCs must each make a Wisdom save to avoid being knocked unconscious from the sanity-blasting visage of the thing.

THE TEMPLE GUARDIAN *(Shoggoth) (this 5th-level NE monster has vital stats HD 17d10 (94 hp), AC 20, move 20 ft. Its saves are P. It attacks by 12 Tentacles (1d12), Bite (5d10 plus swallow whole). Its special abilities are Constrict, Swallow Whole, Poison, Darkvision 60 ft., Twilight Vision, Sanity-Blasting Visage)*

This creature is beyond the ken of the PCs to battle, and they'll know it. Their only chance is to find a weakness or attempt to flee, with or without the gem, though anyone who picks up the Heart will find themselves the sole target of the creature's ire. Still, simply cutting and running means the SS or Al-Hazred might actually get the accursed thing. The Nazis and the Ormazd agents open fire on the creature, with little effect.

A successful Wisdom check allows a PC to realize that the creature seems to be actively avoiding contact with the gem; if someone grabs it, the creature kills the person, but is careful not to draw them into its mouths until the gem falls to the floor, even going so far as to smack the body off the floor to knock the thing free. If a PC hurls, kicks, or otherwise forces the gem into one of the creature's mouths, it lets out a horrid scream and explodes in a blinding flash of light and ichor, and the temple begins to violently shake. The PCs will realize, in their horror, that the city is once again sinking! Alternately, if the PCs don't figure out that the gem is the secret to killing the monster, Amanda could grab it as the creature drags her to its mouth and try to use it against the monster. She can't harness its power, of course, but she might be dragged in with it. Or that might be just the clue the PCs need, when the creature hurls her away to knock the jewel loose. In any case, there should be a suitably grotesque and/or inconclusive "death" for Amanda Seymour. Perhaps she's the creature's last victim, dragged into its mouth just as it explodes, or is buried in an avalanche of debris as the city sinks.

They barely have time to notice that the Ormazd Society has emerged victorious in the battle against the Thules as they dash for the city gates. They and seven members of the Ormazd Society can make it out before the city is once again swallowed by the Desert, though you may want to throw in a few Dexterity saves to avoid falling blocks and other pitfalls as they attempt to make it to freedom.

DENOUEMENT

The PCs emerge from the city along with seven surviving agents of the Society of Ormazd, their goal hopefully achieved, and possibly with the Heart of Yhtill in hand. The Society realizes that the party are not threats, and are not evil, and if the party agrees to let (or help) the Society bury the Heart deep in the sand, and forever keep the secret of the Black City, they will be named brothers in the Society, and allowed to go their own way. They may return to civilization, having completed their first heroic adventure.

Of course, somehow or another, Alice Diamond has survived this little disaster, and she'll eventually be back, with a vengeance. After all, every set of heroes need an archenemy, a nemesis who becomes a thorn in their side, the heel of their greatest victories, and the hammer of their greatest defeats. Alice and the Thules are set up to fulfill this function, if this scenario is used to begin a campaign. Of course, you're free to have this be a one-shot to get things going and devise your own villains, cults, and other adversaries, too. In the end, so long as you're enjoying the high-flying, two-fisted action, go with it!

CHARACTER REFERENCE SHEET

CHARACTER NAME

PLAYER NAME

CLASS

LEVEL

ALIGNMENT

TRAITS	BENEFITS	DRAWBACKS

BONUSES AND MODIFIERS

COSTUME MOD	DEX MOD	OTHER AC MODS	CON BONUS	OTHER HP MODS

AC	HD	BTH	HIT POINTS

COSTUME DESCRIPTION

WEALTH MOD

FATE POINTS

ABILITY SCORES

ATTRIBUTES

SAVING THROWS

P		SCORE	CATEGORY	MOD	TN
o	STR STRENGTH		Paralysis & Constriction		
o	DEX DEXTERITY		Breath Weapon & Traps		
o	CON CONSTITUTION		Disease, Energy Drain, & Poison		
o	INT INTELLIGENCE		Arcane Magic & Illusion		
o	WIS WISDOM		Confusion, Divine Magic, Gaze Attack, Petrification, Polymorph		
o	CHA CHARISMA		Death Attack, Charm, & Fear		

ATTRIBUTE CHECK = d20 + MOD + lvl. ≥ CC

CLASS ABILITIES, LANGUAGES, BACKGROUNDS AND KNOWLEDGE SKILLS

WEAPON/GADGET	BTH	DAMAGE	NOTES

WEAPONS

TO HIT = D20 + MOD + BtH + misc. ≥ AC

WEAPON IN HAND

POSSESSIONS

ITEM	LOCATION	WT

ITEM	LOCATION	WT

ITEM	LOCATION	WT

EXPERIENCE POINTS

Next Level Goal:

MONEY/ASSETS

PSIONICS

BASIC	ADVANCED

AMMUNITION

SPELLS

LEVEL	SPELLS/ DAY	BONUS SPELLS	SPELLS KNOWN
0			
1st			
2nd			
3rd			
4th			
5th			
6th			
7th			
8th			
9th			

MEP/GADGET POINTS

GADGETS, SPELLS, & POWERS

FEATURES

HEIGHT **SEX** **HAIR**

WEIGHT **AGE** **EYES**

DESCRIPTION

Last Will and Testament: I, the undersigned, do hereby make the following requests, to be executed in the event of my untimely demise: